The Little Book
of
Business Wisdom

The Little Book

of

Business Wisdom

*Rules of Success from More Than
50 Business Legends*

Edited by

Peter Krass

JOHN WILEY & SONS, INC.

NEW YORK · CHICHESTER · WEINHEIM · BRISBANE · SINGAPORE · TORONTO

ISBN 978-1-118-19863-6

Printed in the United States of America.

10 9 8 7 6 5 4 3

Contents

PART VIII: **Maxims for Life**

Introduction

Imagine if past and present business legends such as Andrew Carnegie, Michael Dell, John D. Rockefeller, and Jack Welch were your personal drill sergeants, guiding you through your business paces. Imagine them marching before you, shouting short, pithy, and poignant commands to challenge you and to build you up. After all, a drill sergeant's purpose is not only to teach survival, but to conquer the enemy—however the enemy might manifest itself. Of course, I use the term *enemy* loosely. For us, it might be substituted for a megalomaniac boss, an unhappy customer, a daunting corporate ladder, a roller-coaster stock market, or even self-delusion, among endless other possibilities. But the real question is: What would the drill sergeant's commands be? Fortunately, many moguls and gurus have distilled their philosophies into hard-hitting lists of maxims—the ultimate commandments—and I have collected them here in *The Little Book of Business Wisdom*.

Sure, you could read a 750-page monster book on how to manage your career or your business, but perhaps those should be left to the academicians and their students with time to kill. The legends in this book deliver their formulas for success unencumbered by complicated jargon and fancy words—as

Lee Iacocca writes for his rule No. 3: "Say it in English and keep it short."

Some of the rules you'll discover are philosophical in nature, such as Iacocca's. Some are anecdotal: Michael Dell writes, "Swing for hits, not home runs: Business is like baseball. Go for the highest batting average rather than trying to hit a home run every time. If your competitor is batting .300, you want to bat .350 or .400." Or consider Peter Lynch's last rule on buying stocks: "Invest at least as much time and effort in choosing a new stock as you would in choosing a new refrigerator." Still other rules are very concrete: John D. Rockefeller writes, "Study diligently your capital requirements, and fortify yourself fully to cover possible setbacks, because you can absolutely count on meeting setbacks."

As you can imagine, these legendary business figures come from very different backgrounds and have very different priorities, which are reflected in their particular list. The differences—the topics and the attitudes are all over the place—are what make them both entertaining and instructive to read. *USA Today* founder Al Neuharth expounds on how to avoid burnout and stay fit, declaring, "Eat only when you're hungry; drink only when you're thirsty; sleep only when you're tired; screw only when you're horny." Holiday Inn's founder Kemmons Wilson opens his list with a slightly more prudent, but wry statement: "Work only a half a day; it makes no difference which half—it can be either the first 12 hours or the last 12 hours."

Certainly, some legends address the same topics, and if they happen to concur on a particular issue, we should take note because it is most likely essential to success. Take Andrew Carnegie and P. T. Barnum, one the king of steel, the other of entertainment. Carnegie writes, "And here is the prime condition for success, the great secret: concentrate your energy, thought, and capital exclusively upon the business in which you are engaged." Barnum also states unequivocally: "Don't scatter your powers." Others contradict each other. Advertising genius David Ogilvy admires well-organized people, writing, "The Duke of Wellington never went home until he had finished *all* the work on his desk." Newspaper magnate E. W. Scripps counters, "Never do anything today that you can put off till tomorrow." Hey, whatever works best.

Comparing and contrasting the business gurus with the executives in the trenches is another worthwhile exercise. You'll discover, for example, that Dale Carnegie, who penned the huge best-seller, *How to Win Friends and Influence People*, takes a far more subtle approach to criticizing others than does Dave Thomas, founder of Wendy's. Carnegie writes, "Call attention to people's mistakes indirectly," and "Let the other person save face." Whereas Thomas writes with a tougher tone, "Make 'em feel guilty when they do nothing," and "Don't put up with excuses." Although the authors have different viewpoints, an important point to recognize is that they have very definite opinions and maxims, which they *do not compromise*.

Returning to Iacocca, he concludes his list by stating, "When all is said and done, management is a code of values and judgments. And that's why, in the end, you have to be yourself." It is a fitting message to heed before you indulge: In the heat of the battle, don't try to follow every command these drill sergeants have barked out—take what's best for you without compromising your own beliefs.

PART I

Management Principles

Lee Iacocca

1924–

*B*orn *and raised in a working-class neighborhood of Allen-town, Pennsylvania, Lee Iacocca never left his tough up-bringing behind—his street smarts aided his rise to the top of Ford and Chrysler. He first stepped into the limelight in April of 1964 when he made the covers of both* Time *and* Newsweek *for his introduction of the immensely popular Ford Mustang. His celebrity status carried him to the presidency of the company in 1970, but then a fickle Henry Ford II, grandson of the legend, fired him in 1978. Iacocca, who developed a rigid management philosophy to survive good times and bad, was immediately tapped to head a virtually bankrupt Chrysler. The company's woes were ultimately turned around by the antithesis of the Mus-tang—the groundbreaking, hugely popular minivan.*

My Little Commandments of Management

1. **Hire the Best.** Nothing will make a CEO look better than a talented management team. When I'm asked about how I turned Chrysler around, I always make the point that I didn't do it by myself—a lot of smart, dedicated people did it. Actually, since according to *Time* magazine my ego is as

big as all outdoors, I should probably take credit for having done all of it by myself.

2. **Get Your Priorities Straight and Keep a Hot List of What You're Trying to Do.** No matter how complex a business is, and ours is pretty complex, I believe you should be able to write down your top priorities on a single sheet of 8½-by-11 paper. It's always amazed me to see how many companies, even small ones, devote hours of effort and literally tons of paper to detailed plans of what they want the company to do over time. There are a lot of different names for them—Long Range Strategic Plans, Ten-Year Business Plans, Five-Year Profit Plans, and so forth. I guess if you've got a big staff and lots of extra time on your hands, it's not going to hurt you. But I've never seen a long-range business plan that couldn't be boiled down to a single page of priorities.

3. **Say It in English and Keep It Short.** Everyone has seen examples of bureaucratic double talk in written communication. You know what I mean—a long-winded document that takes the reader through two dozen options and alternatives and ends up with any one of six or seven different conclusions. Most of us associate this phenomenon with government bureaucracies. But take my word for it, a lot of double talk exists in corporations as well.

There are three factors behind the mumbo jumbo. First, the almost uncontrollable desire to tell all you know on any given subject. Second, the love of adjectives and adverbs over nouns and verbs. And third, the desire to impress your audience with your depth of vocabulary. I once read a fifteen-page paper that was tough to understand. I called in the author and asked him to explain what was in the tome he had written. He did it in two minutes flat. He identified what we were doing wrong, what we could do to fix it, and what he recommended. When he finished I asked him why he didn't write that in the paper the way he'd just said it to me. He didn't have an answer. All he said was: "I was taught that way." And he was an M.B.A. to boot.

Write the way you talk. If you don't talk that way, don't write that way.

4. **Never Forget the Line Makes the Money.** The political maneuvering between staff and line organizations is a wasteful and costly exercise. Every chief executive has got to come to grips with how he parcels out authority and accountability between these two groups. So I have a single axiom that helps me remember how to manage these often conflicting organizations. When the chips are down, it's the line organization that makes the money; the staff doesn't make a dime. I view the role of the staff as primarily to help the CEO do his job and to act as a catalyst to the line. If you really want to get a line group motivated, just float up a "staff idea" with the right amount of "Why didn't you guys think of that?"

5. **Lay Out the Size of the Playing Field.** I'm a strong believer in letting line operations "operate"—delegating to good people and then letting them do the job. But, you might ask, if the key managers are running the business, what's left for the CEO to do?

> ## Savvy Leadership
> To help save an almost bankrupt Chrysler, Iacocca cut his salary to $1 as part of an austerity program. This also showed that he meant business when he told union officials, "Hey, boys, I've got a shotgun at your head. I've got thousands of jobs available at seventeen bucks an hour. I've got none at twenty."

I think a big part of my job is what I call "defining the envelope," or setting the limits within which line management can operate on a relatively freewheeling basis. It's similar to a parent telling a child: "Play in the backyard but don't go past the gate and don't climb over the fence and don't invite anyone over." The child has the run of the yard, but the parent has prescribed limits on where he can go and what he can do.

As a CEO, I set limits. I set limits on the total amount of capital that can be spent—but not necessarily on how to spend it. I set limits on the number of executives I want on the payroll—but not who they are. I set limits on the amount of R & D spending I'm willing to support—but not the projects that are funded. And I establish the company priorities, which represent the limits or parameters that set the direction of the whole line effort.

6. **Keep Some Mavericks Around.** All CEOs should worry about getting fed a single point of view: that is, a party line that has been filtered, refiltered, homogenized, pasteurized, and synthesized—what we call "cooking the pudding." Without differences in viewpoint, and openness to constructive expression of these differences, a corporation can be led into a lot of bad decisions. There is a real risk in telling the CEO only what he wants to hear and never having any disagreements in his presence.

To guard against this risk, I've always tried to keep some smart people around me who are contrarians, who for whatever reason will not accept very much at face value and are not impressed by the rationale that something is being done in a certain way because it's always been done that way.

7. **Stay in Business During Alterations.** A lot of CEO surveys indicate that long-range planning and strategic planning are seen as among the most important responsibilities for a CEO. I'm not going to argue with that, but I've always felt that making sure you're maximizing earnings today is also a key responsibility. It's easy, I think, for an organization to get mesmerized by long-range plans. On paper, at least, they're neat and squared-off—and always work.

8. **Remember the Fundamentals.** I have always been a fan of Vince Lombardi, the late great leader of the Green Bay Packers. Although his teams had a fairly versatile offensive game, at least for that period of time, their real strength lay in their adherence to the fundamentals of playing solid football: blocking and tackling, good play execution, and mental discipline. They weren't the fanciest football team of their day, but to watch them run a power sweep with the linemen pulling out and blocking was to see a thing of beauty. It was also a devastatingly effective offensive weapon.

When all is said and done, management is a code of values and judgments. And that's why, in the end, you have to be yourself.

Which brings me to the best rule of management: Pick a style that you're comfortable with and stick with it. You can have role models, but don't try to be somebody else. Be yourself, stay natural and dammit, smile once in a while!

Bill Gates
1955–

*T*oday's richest man in the world and software mogul was in eighth grade when he encountered his first computer; he's also a college dropout. After two years at Harvard, where he enjoyed playing poker over going to classes, Bill Gates dropped out in 1975 to start Microsoft with his high school buddy, Paul Allen. Their first project was writing software for a home-brew computer, and their first big coup was winning the contract in 1980 to develop an operating system for IBM's personal computer. They then expanded rapidly into word processing and spreadsheet software, going public in 1986. After a bout with cancer, Allen left the company and today Gates is chairman. Although the company lost an antitrust case brought against them, Gates remains an aggressive visionary who devoutly believes in the power of digital tools.

New Rules for the Age of Information

To make digital information flow an intrinsic part of your company, here are twelve key steps:

For *knowledge work:*

1. Insist that communication flow through the organization over e-mail so that you can act on news with reflexlike speed.

2. Study sales data online to find patterns and share insights easily. Understand overall trends and personalize service for individual customers.
3. Use PCs for business analysis, and shift knowledge workers into high-level thinking work about products, services, and profitability.
4. Use digital tools to create cross-departmental virtual teams that can share knowledge and build on each other's ideas in real time, worldwide. Use digital systems to capture corporate history for use by anyone.
5. Convert every paper process to a digital process, eliminating administrative bottlenecks and freeing knowledge workers for more important tasks.

For *business operations:*

> ### Savvy Leadership
> Twice a year, Gates would personally visit archrival WordPerfect's best customers, seeking to understand why they chose WordPerfect over Microsoft's Word.

6. Use digital tools to eliminate single-task jobs or change them into value-added jobs that use the skills of a knowledge worker.
7. Create a digital feedback loop to improve the efficiency of physical processes and improve the quality of the products and services created. Every employee should be able to easily track all the key metrics.
8. Use digital systems to route customer complaints immediately to the people who can improve a product or service.
9. Use digital communications to redefine the nature of your business and the boundaries around your business. Become larger and more substantial or smaller and more intimate as the customer situation warrants.

For *commerce:*

10. Trade information for time. Decrease cycle time by using digital transactions with all suppliers and partners, and transform every business process into just-in-time delivery.

11. Use digital delivery of sales and service to eliminate the middleman from customer transactions. If you're a middleman, use digital tools to add value to transactions.

12. Use digital tools to help customers solve problems for themselves, and reserve personal contact to respond to complex, high-value customer needs.

Smart Habits

While en route to an unfamiliar place, Gates voraciously reads books and magazine articles about it—the material is often recommended by local managers—and then asks plenty of follow-up questions once he is there. While in India, he discovered that there were 14 distinct languages and realized Microsoft's products had to be much more localized, ultimately fueling sales.

Managing Unhappy Customers

I recommend the following approach to integrating customer complaints and wish lists into product and service development:

1. Focus on your most unhappy customers.
2. Use technology to gather rich information on their unhappy experiences with your product and to find out what they want you to put into the product.

3. Use technology to drive the news to the right people in a hurry.

If you do these three things, you'll turn those draining, bad news experiences into an exhilarating process of improving your product or service. Unhappy customers are always a concern. They're also your greatest opportunity.

Michael S. Dell

1965–

*M*ichael Dell's direct business model, which involves selling customized products directly to the consumer and keeping inventory to a minimum, has revolutionized the way in which companies do business as they attempt to emulate Dell's success. Dell Computer's stock was up more than 3,000 percent in the 1990s—not bad for a college dropout. His mother was a stockbroker and his father an orthodontist, who wanted their son to become a doctor. Although he enrolled at the University of Texas as a premed student, computers were Dell's first love, and in his first semester in 1983 he started buying old computers and upgrading them for resale. That next summer he sold $180,000 worth and never returned to school. Dell took the company public in 1988 and maintains a competitive edge by infusing his company with a sense of urgency.

The Competitive Edge

- Think about the customer, not the competition: Competitors represent your industry's past, as, over the years, collective habits become ingrained. Customers are your future, representing new opportunities, ideas, and avenues for growth.

- Work to maintain a healthy sense of urgency and crisis: This doesn't mean that you want to fabricate deadlines or keep people so stressed that they quickly burn out. Set the bar slightly higher than you normally would, so that your people can achieve aggressive goals by working smarter.
- Turn your competition's greatest strength into a weakness: Much as every great athlete has an Achilles' heel, so, too, do all great companies. Study the competition's "game": Exploit its weakness by exposing its greatest strength.
- Be opportunistic, but also be fast: Look to find opportunity, especially when it isn't readily apparent. Focusing on the customer doesn't mean that you should ignore the competition. If something that your competition did or didn't do provided you with an opportunity today, would you recognize it and be able to act on it immediately? Today a competitive win can be decided literally one day at a time. You have to act fast, be ready, then be ready to change—fast.

> ### Savvy Leadership
> To make sure that all employees became Internet-literate, Dell had posters hung in all high-traffic areas of their buildings. On the poster was Michael Dell, posing as Uncle Sam, with the caption, "Michael wants YOU to know the Net!"

- Swing for hits, not home runs: Business is like baseball. Go for the highest batting average rather than trying to hit a home run every time. If your competitor is batting .300, you want to bat .350 or .400. No one's batting 1.000, so you can't worry about it. What you want to focus on is being the best as often as you can. Because there's no such thing as a grand slam product or technology that lasts forever, your competitive edge must come from strategic execution, and from gaining knowledge, studying the economics of your business, and ensuring the flow of information throughout your organization.

- Be the hunter, not the hunted: Success is a dangerous thing, as we are at once invincible and vulnerable. Always strive to keep your team focused on growing the business and on winning and acquiring new business. Even though your company may be leading the market, you never want your people to act as though you are. That leads to complacency, and complacency kills. Encourage people to think, "This is good. This worked. Now how can we take what we've proven and use it to win new business?" There's a big difference between asking that and asking, "How can we defend our existing accounts?"

Charles B. Wang

1944–

C harles Wang, born in China, is cofounder, chairman, and CEO of the world's third largest independent software maker, Computer Associates International (CA). After the Chinese Communist revolution in 1949, Wang and his family fled to the United States. They found themselves in a Queens, New York, housing project. Wang attended Queens College, where he earned degrees in both mathematics and physics. When the time came to choose a profession, Wang settled on becoming a computer programmer; he concluded that because there were so many help-wanted ads for them, this was a growing industry. When the company for which he was working decided to sell its software division in 1975, he and friend Russell Artzt went for it. Wang, who strives to be in sync with technology and wants his company to match up with the best, took CA public in 1981 and has used the proceeds to gobble up some 60 other companies.

Sync or Swim: Seven Steps to Being the Best

1. **Benchmark to determine the world standard.** Some organization has to be the best, why not yours? Find the world champion in every process—technical and otherwise—that

you measure. Do the benchmarks to determine how your performance compares. Recalibrate your goals accordingly.

2. **Map your processes.** Break activities down into processes. Identify the inefficiencies. Reinvent. For each step, ask whether customers, if given a choice, would pay for it.

3. **Get your people focused on external reality.** The issues are customers and competitors. Define a clear vision that creates a sense of urgency. Insist that people accept responsibility for their own behavior.

4. **Start with the hardest part.** Distinguish what needs to be done from how hard it is to do it. The most difficult steps are generally the most important. Model the attitude that if something really needs to be done, the difficulty of doing it is irrelevant.

5. **Set the goals high and then double them.** Your people will rise to the challenge if you support them properly. Set the goal but don't tell them how to do it. Their ideas will be better than yours. If people fail to reach the goal, don't punish them, adjust your support.

6. **Let go and watch.** You can't do it alone so kick back and enjoy.

Outrageous Promotion

Early on in building his business, Wang would pick 20 pages from the Yellow Pages, drink three cups of coffee, and cold-call every potential customer before going to the bathroom.

Savvy Leadership

Wang banned the use of e-mail from 10:00 A.M. until noon and from 2:00 P.M. until 4:00 P.M. to force face-to-face interaction among his people.

7. **Wave laurels; don't rest on them.** When you're on top of the mountain, it's natural to want to relax. Take a minute and enjoy the view. But hang on. It's windy up there. You won't have privacy for long. Your competitors — benchmarks in hand — are within hailing distance.

John Erik Jonsson

1901–1995

*J*ohn Jonsson, the son of Swedish immigrants, cofounded the electronics giant Texas Instruments (TI) and served as mayor of Dallas from 1964 to 1971. Originally, he was from New Jersey, where his father owned a cigar and candy shop. While studying engineering at Rensselaer Polytechnic Institute, he repaired radios at night to make money. Jonsson went to work for the Aluminum Company of America in 1922 and then was recruited in 1930 to manage a laboratory of Geophysical Service, Inc., which was based in Dallas and developed seismographic instruments for finding oil and gas. Eventually, Jonsson and a partner bought the company, and in 1951, the company's name was changed to TI. A master strategist, he believed in programming *every function in the company, based on proven management principles.*

Management Principles

1. We write down and try to see that as many people in our organization as possible understand the basic objectives of TI. We re-examine and restate these objectives regularly to meet changing needs and changing times.

2. To achieve sound growth, we believe that we must have a well-conceived and well-executed planning program aimed toward the achievement of TI objectives. Our basic objectives are long-range. When planning begins, it may be necessary to think only of the short-range, but as soon afterward as possible, we must lengthen the range and broaden the scope of all our plans.

3. We must organize to implement our plans fully. The scope of the organizing job should be comprehensive enough to include adequate handling and dovetailing of all functions requisite to execution of the plans. Such functions as research and development, its staffing, and its laboratories should be carefully organized and programmed. Similarly, our financial programming must be early and comprehensive enough to permit proper sequential staging of individual steps, since the sequence may be as important as the individual steps themselves.

> ### Savvy Leadership
> In evaluating an acquisition or merger opportunity, evaluate your people's capabilities to pull it off. To manage growth successfully, Jonsson passed up good opportunities because he didn't think he had the right people.

4. As part of the planning program, our management personnel requirements through all levels should be considered far ahead of actual needs, so that the balanced procurement of required individuals can sometimes be achieved as much as several years in advance.

5. Keep flexible, keep current. Change our plans whenever circumstances require. Plans are not axiomatic of themselves, and a planning program whose original premises are wrong

or obsolete may be worse than none. Re-examine regularly the what, when, where, why, and how of all plans.

6. Since our growth pattern includes diversified product lines or services for a variety of markets, decentralized product divisions are the best organizational answer for us.

7. Each new product division we create must be as completely and capably staffed as the parent from which it sprang. All product divisions should be as complete in function and as autonomous as possible and should operate within the over-all limits established by central management.

8. Our central management staff must be strong and, in addition to performing general management duties and the usual specialization and service assistance to product divisions, should have the prime responsibility for formalizing the policies and procedures within whose framework the entire organization must function. This staff should take as one of its special responsibilities our purely long-term and over-all planning.

9. It is our purpose not to waste energy in research and development, or in manufacturing or marketing a product line to which we are unwilling to devote the time and money necessary for success. Especially in product lines obtained by mergers and acquisitions, accomplishment of the desired objectives will be harder, slower, and often more expensive than with those developed internally.

10. Timing is of the essence in everything we undertake. A research and development program or an entry into new markets that comes too early or late can defeat the original intent. The vital importance of timing can be seen directly in financing, for example, since it is reflected immediately in terms and rates.

11. Our performance as a company will be limited only by the quality of our people.

I should like to amplify this last point, since it is the most important of all. We have discussed products and services and delineated some management principles we believe to be sound. However, little has been said about the men and women on whose efforts our hopes of future success are based. We have tried to surround ourselves with people of quality and ability who can be integrated into a powerful team moving toward common, clearly defined and understood goals. Because we have faith and confidence in the capabilities of our people, we have set our targets high. And these difficult challenges have always sparked their creativeness and will to succeed. While we have attempted to make rewards as directly proportional to accomplishment as possible, the personnel of Texas Instruments have shown a loyalty and willingness to produce beyond reasonable expectations. This, together with the understanding support of customers and stockholders, has provided those of us in TI's top management with a challenge of our own. We must try to grow with our company, to develop a statesmanship in business management worthy of the confidence and respect of all.

Harold S. Geneen

1910–1997

*H*arold Geneen is regarded as one of the most brilliant busi-
nesspeople to lead a multinational conglomerate. Born in
Britain, he and his family moved to the United States when he
was less than a year old. After a stint as a page on Wall Street, he
pursued an accounting career and went through a number of
finance jobs (and companies). Geneen was hired as an executive
vice president of Raytheon in 1956 and was given the mission to
turn the ailing company around, which he did. When he was
recruited for ITT's presidency in 1959, he inherited a stodgy
telecommunications company. Geneen, however, transformed it
into a powerhouse that included 150 affiliated companies operating in 57 countries. Although he was managing a complex
organization, his precepts were as simple as: Avoid pretensions
and ego trips.

Succeeding in a Business Career

Some time ago, speaking at the Wharton School of Business
Administration, I was asked how one should go about succeeding in a business career. I told the students that one should move
around and gain experience in his or her early years and then
settle down to a chosen career at age thirty or thirty-five. That
would give a person a career of some thirty or thirty-five years. In

that time, the top management of a company is likely to turn over three or four times. So there would always be room for a good manager. All a young person had to do was to pick his or her job and start working toward it. As I said about *all* management, including the management of one's life: Decide what it is you want to do, and start doing it.

If I were to amend that answer today and try to sum up what I have come to believe over a long career in business, I would put forth these personal precepts on how to manage:

- You must play by the rules, going through the channels of the company structure, taking no shortcuts; but you don't have to *think* by the rules. It would be a great mistake to confine your imagination to the way things have always been done. In fact, it would consign you to the mediocrity of the marketplace.
- Avoid all pretensions. Doing things for "show" will backfire on you and turn the whole flavor of your enterprise rancid. Avoid ego trips, office politics, and acting a part that is not really you.
- Remember: Facts from paper are not the same as facts from people. The reliability of the person giving you the facts is as important as the facts themselves. Keep in mind that facts are seldom facts, but what people think are facts, heavily tinged with assumptions.
- You must find out everything essential by yourself. As a manager, you are entitled to a straight answer to a straight question, and you will usually get it when your question is right. The right question comes from many sources and must be assembled in your own head, perhaps for the first time.
- The good guys in your organization want you to ask the right question, because they can and want to answer it. Then you can all move forward together.

- Only the phonies will squirm when confronted by questions that go straight to the heart of the matter, and it is your job as a manager to recognize the phonies and to get rid of them. The good guys will expect it of you.
- No one is going to tell you the answer or solution to any problem in advance of your questioning. It is the nature of organization and the interaction of the hierarchy that usually stop a bright man from breaking the code of getting along with his peers.

Smart Habits

Whether you are a CEO or low-level manager, Geneen warns that you must screen your actions for personal prejudice and vanity; for example, if you start worrying about the view from your office or whom you sit next to in a meeting, it's time to evaluate your ego.

- When you are the man or woman in charge, you and only you must make the decisions, particularly the close ones. That's what you are being paid for, whether you head a task force, a department, or a whole company. Your decisions should be based upon the facts of the situation. The facts are the authority. Because you are in charge, *you* are entitled to be right or wrong, but it must be you. Your commands will be honored and respected, but they must be *your* commands. You are not entitled to announce decisions or give commands by proxy, by allowing someone else to speak for you.

PART II

~

Leadership Secrets

T. Boone Pickens

1928–

T. Boone Pickens built the largest independently owned oil and gas company in the United States, Mesa Petroleum; and yet Pickens recalls that in the fourth grade he was so shy, the girl next to him had to read his homework out loud when he was chosen by the teacher. After studying geology at Oklahoma State, he took a job with Phillips Petroleum in 1951 as an oil well–site geologist. It was not long before he became disillusioned with the company's bureaucracy and quit at the age of 26, even though he had a wife, two young children, and a third on the way. Pickens lived out of his station wagon as he drove around Texas prospecting choice land to drill and raising the financing to do it. In 1956, with two partners and $2,500, Pickens founded Mesa Petroleum and became a maverick leader, who thrived on risk and took on the big oil companies.

The Art of Leadership

- Master the art of leadership. A wise woman, retired U.S. Navy Admiral Grace Hopper, expressed my philosophy succinctly when she said, "You don't manage people. You manage things. You *lead* people." She was right. The important part of being a leader is what goes on inside your own mind—what you do to yourself, not what you do to others. Part of leadership is taking risks and building confidence in yourself. You have to serve many apprenticeships throughout your life. Show me somebody who won't serve an apprenticeship, and I'll show you somebody who won't go very far. At Mesa, people who are good, strong players find their apprenticeships to be surprisingly short.

- Concentrate on the goals, not the size of the organization. You can't measure a place by size unless it's a football stadium. At Mesa, we work short-handed. That way people have a greater opportunity to advance and less time for office politics.

- Forget about age, which means giving the young people a chance. I have a bias toward youth, but I also think that youth is a state of mind. You can be old at 30 or young at 70. I am interested in whether a person can do the job. Mesa personnel know this well, and it is a great boost for morale. The average age of all Mesa employees is 36.

- Keep things informal. Talking is the natural way to do business. Writing is great for keeping records and pinning down details, but talk generates ideas. Great things come from our luncheon meetings, which consist of a sandwich, a cup of soup, and a good idea or two. No martinis.

- Keep communication lines open. Communication is crucial—not the formal stuff, but frequent conversation among the people who make the decisions. My people know that they can talk to me, no matter how busy I am. So when it's time to make a decision I'm ready, with no need for lengthy presentations. Communication means no surprises. I hate surprises.

- Play by the rules. This applies not only outside the company, but inside too. I'm disturbed by what I've seen in the last several years, with people being asked to take early retirement in their 50s while the C.E.O. stays on past the mandatory retirement age of 65. Are any of us so valuable that we should be exempt from the rules?

- Hire the best. I choose people for their intelligence, attitude, and enthusiasm—people who can do a job better than I can. I never load myself so that people under me aren't challenged. But if you aren't a worker, you won't make it with me. The same goes for people who are not comfortable in a fast-moving operation, who want more time to think or maybe procrastinate. My advice to our people is: If you aren't happy, leave. As for people who drink on the job, steal, or carry on an interoffice relationship, I'll fire them on the spot.

> ### *Smart Habits*
> Never set psychological limits for yourself, Pickens advises; for example, don't set a particular job level, salary amount, or net worth as a satisfactory career goal. Although you may change your mind later, that original goal, while only in your mind, can become as great a barrier as a real roadblock.

- Keep fit. Physical fitness is an essential part of the best-run companies—and that includes C.E.O.s. I never had a weight problem because I did things in moderation. But I gradually got out of shape, which is easy to do in your late 30s or early 40s. In 1972 I began to work out. I jogged and took up racquetball seriously. All those things you hear about being in shape are true: I felt better. My stamina improved and so did my powers of concentration. I was getting a lot more done each day and still had energy to burn.

Keeping fit has economic as well as spiritual and psychological benefits. In 1979 Mesa built a first-class athletic facility equipped as well as any commercial health center. About three-quarters of Mesa's employees, me included, participate in the fitness program. The Fitness Center saves Mesa more than $200,000 in insurance claims annually. Our records show that employees who exercise regularly average $173 in medical bills a year, whereas it costs $434 for inactive employees. Exercisers average 27 hours of sick leave per year; non-exercisers, 44 hours.

- Finally, enjoy it. We may work hard, but there are no stomachaches. We laugh a lot. If we screw up, then we all screwed up. We move quickly, which often creates an advantage. Some companies operate on a two-, five-, or ten-year plan. At Mesa, we're a different company every two years.

John F. Welch, Jr.

1935–

*B*ack in 1973, Jack Welch boldly stated on his employee
evaluation that his long-range goal was to be CEO.
Welch, whose father was a train conductor, grew up in blue-
collar Salem, Massachusetts. After studying at the University of
Massachusetts and at the University of Illinois, where he earned
a Ph.D. in chemical engineering, he joined General Electric
(GE) as a junior engineer. However, he quit just over a year
later in 1961, because he couldn't stand the bureaucracy. Fortunately, his boss convinced him to stay. Twenty years later he
did, indeed, take over as CEO of GE. Welch, who has a defini-
tive philosophy for corporate revolution, was quickly dubbed
"Neutron Jack" by Newsweek magazine as he reengineered the
company, either eliminating or divesting one-third of the company's workforce (170,000 jobs) over the next five years.

Leading a Revolution

- You've got to be prepared for massive resistance. Incremen-
tal change doesn't work well in the type of transformation
GE has gone through. If your change isn't big enough, revolutionary enough, the bureaucracy can beat you.
- You've got to be hard to be soft. You have to demonstrate the
ability to make the hard, tough decisions—closing plants,

divesting, delayering—if you want to have any credibility when you try to promote soft values.

- Every organization needs values, but a lean organization needs them even more. When you strip away the support systems of staffs and layers, people have to change their habits and expectations, or else the stress will just overwhelm them.

Savvy Leadership

To inspire and motivate the troops, Welch spontaneously sends a handwritten note to those in need of encouragement, whether they be direct reports or hourly workers. He faxes the note directly to them and then puts the original in the mail.

- You've got to be out in front of crowds, repeating yourself over and over again, never changing your message no matter how much it bores you.

- You need an overarching message, something big but simple and understandable. Whatever it is—*we're going to be No. 1 or No. 2*, or *fix/close/sell, or boundaryless*—every idea you present must be something you could get across easily at a cocktail party with strangers.

- The three most important things you need to measure in a business are customer satisfaction, employee satisfaction, and cash flow.

GE Values Guide on Wallet-Size Card

GE employees are required to carry the GE Values Guide on a wallet-size card.

GE Leaders . . . Always with Unyielding Integrity:

- Have a Passion for Excellence and Hate Bureaucracy
- Are Open to Ideas from Anywhere . . . and Committed to Work-Out
- Live Quality . . . and Drive Cost and Speed for Competitive Advantage
- Have the Self-Confidence to Involve Everyone and Behave in a Boundaryless Fashion
- Create a Clear, Simple, Reality-Based Vision . . . and Communicate It to All Constituencies
- Have Enormous Energy and the Ability to Energize Others
- Stretch . . . Set Aggressive Goals . . . Reward Progress . . . Yet Understand Accountability and Commitment
- See Change as Opportunity . . . Not Threat
- Have Global Brains . . . and Build Diverse and Global Teams

Robert Townsend

1920–

*R*obert Townsend, *author of the best-selling* Up the Organization, *has always promoted employee independence. The Townsend family was imbued with a rebellious spirit; an American ancestor was a revolutionary spy who worked against the British. After earning an English literature degree at Princeton University, Townsend also served in the military during World War II. In 1948, he joined Hertz American Express International and became senior vice president of the investment and international banking operations for American Express. While there, he observed how the cash-rich company could afford to make mistakes; he later incorporated many of those no-no's into his leadership philosophy. In 1962, he left to become president and chairman of Avis, Inc.*

No-No's

Reserved parking spaces. If you're so bloody important, you better be first one in the office. Besides, you'll meet a nice class of people in the employees' parking lot.

Special-quality stationery for the boss and his elite.

Muzak, except in the areas where the work is only suitable for mental defectives.

Bells and buzzers (even telephones can be made to signal with lights).

Company shrinks. Unless it's really optional, and the shrink reports only to the patient, and suitable precautions have been taken to make sure the personnel department can't tap into the data.

Outside directorships and trusteeships for the chief executive. Give up all those non-jobs. You can't even run your own company, dummy.

Company plane. It's just a variation of the company-paid golf club, and the big office with three secretaries. Another line drawn through the company between the Brahmins and the untouchables. And the plane's always in Palm Beach, Augusta, Aspen, or Las Vegas when the business needs it. Best thing about it: if it has only one pilot, someday he'll get ptomaine with a whole load of "top" management aboard . . .

Manager's Monthly. Or any other time-consuming report imposed on the troops by "top" management. It's a joke because it consumes ten pounds of energy to produce each ounce of misunderstanding.

Except in poker, bridge, and similar play-period activities, **don't con anybody.**

Not your wife
Not your children
Not your employees
Not your customers
Not your stockholders
Not your boss
Not your associates

Not your suppliers
Not your regulatory authorities
Not even your competitors

Don't con yourself either.
Social relations within the firm. Okay with your peers. But
not with people who report to you. You'll inevitably see
more of the ones you like—and they may not be the best
performers. Your own performance depends on your ability to be just. Don't make it any tougher than it is.

Hiring. To keep an organization
young and fit, don't hire anyone until everybody's so over-
worked they'll be glad to
see the newcomer no matter
where he sits.

> ### Savvy Leadership
> To blur the us-them line between
> headquarters and the front lines,
> Townsend forced all HQ man-
> agers to go to car rental school,
> and then to wear Avis's red rental
> uniforms to honor the frontline
> counter workers.

Trade associations—as a chance
to fix prices, and allocate
customers and markets with
your friendly competitors.
Antitrust laws are different: you're not innocent until
proven guilty. If all your customers are north of Main Street
and all your competitor's customers are south of Main
Street, you're both guilty by inference. And nobody has to
prove the two of you ever communicated in any way. Treble
damages. Jail. So watch it, bubele.

Conventions. The public relations dream: much money,
time, and energy signifying nothing. The best way is to
ignore them. The next best way is to send one line man
(rotate the assignment like kitchen police). On his
return, ask him to make a thirty-second all-inclusive oral

report to the weekly staff meeting covering everything of significance that he heard, saw, and learned. The worst way is to give your P.R. department a blank check and tell them to make a big splash.

House organs. Spend the money making stockholders out of your employees and then sending them (along with the other stockholders) honest reports on how the company's really doing: good and bad. Reading a house organ is like going down in warm maple syrup for the third time.

> ### Smart Habits
> Townsend, who preached against the delegation of grunt work, did not have a personal secretary and answered his own phone.

Greed. To increase our share of the market a few years ago, I was on the verge of approving the start-up of a new subsidiary—which would compete with our bread-and-butter business—at discount prices. To verify my own brilliance I tried the idea out on a tall, rangy regional vice-president named Stepnowski. After hearing the plan described in some detail, he sank the whole project with one sentence: "I don't know what *you* call it, but we Polacks call that 'pissing in the soup.' "

Office Party, How Not to Do the Annual

1. *Start it at 5 p.m. instead of noon, so the company doesn't lose any man-hours.*
2. *Invite spouses so bosses and their secretaries don't enjoy dancing together.*

(Continued)

3. *Make sure the top brass either doesn't show or puts in a token appearance—underscoring the difference between them and the rest of us playful, indolent darkies.*

4. *Invite clients and suppliers to help reinforce their contempt for your company.*

5. *Skimp on the setting. A third-rate roadhouse is always good.*

6. *Cut corners on the food and booze. Two-day-old hors d'oeuvres left over from a wedding, a tray of Manhattans, and a mystery punch ought to do it.*

7. *Save money on the music. Better than a phonograph is a tin-eared accordionist whose idea of a new number is "I Could Have Danced All Night."*

8. *Kill two birds by combining it with the annual quarter-century-club party. Then all your employees can see living examples (you should excuse the expression) of what twenty-five years in your outfit will do to what were once healthy human beings.*

9. *Better yet, turn the whole thing over to the head of the personnel department and tell him to use his best judgment.*

John H. Patterson

1844–1922

*C*onsidered the father of modern salesmanship, John Patterson was a great communicator and motivator who founded the National Cash Register Company (NCR). After attending Dartmouth College, he eventually went to work managing a coal yard and a company store for the employees. The store was always in the red because the cashiers were skimming, and it was then that Patterson decided to give a new contraption a try—Ritty's Incorruptible Cashier, which tabulated sales. He bought two registers in 1882, and in 1884 he decided to buy the entire company, changing the name to NCR. His sales innovations included establishing an equitable sales quota system, codifying sales talk, and producing one of the first sales manuals that surely included his principles for communicating.

Principles for Idea-Conveying

If I should reduce my principles of idea-conveying to a creed, it would run something in this fashion:

1. The nerves from the eyes to the brain are many times larger than those from the ears to the brain. Therefore,

when possible to *use a picture* instead of words, use one and make the words mere connectives for the pictures.

2. Confine the attention to the exact subject by drawing outlines and putting in the divisions; then we make certain that we are all talking about the same thing.

Extreme Measures

Patterson was known to throw away everything in his executives' desks, including personal items, to make them start afresh.

---

3. Aim for dramatic effects either in speaking or writing—study them out beforehand. This holds the attention.

4. Red is the best color to attract and hold attention, therefore use plenty of it.

5. Few words—short sentences—small words—big ideas.

6. Tell why as well as how.

7. Do not be afraid of big type and do not put too much on a page.

8. Do not crowd ideas in speaking or writing. No advertisement is big enough for two ideas.

9. Before you try to convince anyone else, make sure that you are convinced, and if you cannot convince yourself, drop the subject. Do not try to "put over anything."

10. Tell the truth.

John D. Rockefeller

1839–1937

*R*ockefeller's father was to have said, "I cheat my boys every chance I get. I want to make 'em sharp." Clearly, Rockefeller had a sharp eye for deal making; fortunately, though, he later turned to philanthropy and gave away more than $500 million. In 1859, Rockefeller and a partner opened a commission house in Cleveland, the same year that oil was discovered in western Pennsylvania. Crude oil and related products were soon bought and sold by Rockefeller, and he quickly grasped the importance of oil refining. With his brother, William, and two other partners, he founded the Standard Oil Company in 1870. By the 1880s, Rockefeller, who relied on patience, courage, and good old common sense, controlled over 90 percent of the U.S. oil refinery business (and was eventually declared in violation of The Sherman Anti-Trust Act).

The American Businessman

- The man who starts out simply with the idea of getting rich won't succeed; you must have a larger ambition.
- Sometimes I feel that we Americans think we can find a short road to success, and it may appear that often this feat is accomplished; but the real efficiency in work comes from knowing your facts and building upon that sure foundation.

- It takes infinite patience and courage to compel men to have confidence in you. I believe I have both of these qualities, and I also believe that they are the secrets of my success.
- There is no mystery in business success. The great industrial leaders have told again and again the plain and obvious fact that there can be no permanent success without fair dealing that leads to widespread confidence in the man himself, and that is the real capital we all prize and work for.
- It is not always the easiest of tasks to induce strong, forceful men to agree. It has always been our policy to hear patiently and discuss frankly until the last shred of evidence is on the table, before trying to reach a conclusion and to decide finally upon a course of action.
- Look ahead. It is surprising how many bright business men go into important undertakings with little or no study of the controlling conditions they risk their all upon.
- As I began my business life as a bookkeeper, I learned to have great respect for figures and facts, no matter how small they were.
- It is to be remembered that oftimes, the most difficult competition comes, not from the strong, the intelligent, the conservative competitor, but from the man who is holding on by the eyelids and is ignorant of his costs, and anyway, he's got to "keep running or bust."

Smart Habits

After a spirited conversation, whether with ally or enemy, Rockefeller would repeat to himself over and over the important points made by others. He disciplined himself to be a great listener to retain important information for later use. Each night he would also talk out loud to his pillow, reviewing the day's events and voicing his concerns.

- Study diligently your capital requirements, and fortify yourself fully to cover possible set-backs, because you can absolutely count on meeting set-backs. Be sure that you are not deceiving yourself at any time about actual conditions.
- Good old-fashioned common sense has always been a mighty rare commodity.

J. C. Penney

1875–1971

J. C. Penney's first business venture as a butcher failed because he refused to supply meat to hotels that sold liquor. In 1902 he started working for a dry goods store in Kemmerer, Wyoming, and was eventually allowed to buy into one-third of the business. Eight years later, he had opened 13 stores of his own, calling them the Golden Rule Stores. The name of the stores was changed to JCPenney in 1913, and Penney, whose winning formula was built on hard work and honesty, was operating 175 stores in 1917. The rapid growth was achieved by requiring the store managers to own 33 percent of their store, an early form of franchising, along with Penney's most ingenious revolution of creating a central warehouse and corresponding inventory control system to increase buying power and reduce costs.

Six Principles for Winning

Preparation Wins. A man must know all about his business. He must know a little more than any other man knows. As a rule we achieve what we prepare for.

Hard Work Wins. The only kind of luck that any man is justified in banking on is hard work, which is made up of sacrifice, persistent effort, and dogged determination. Growth is never by mere chance. The success we build will be the achievement of our united efforts.

Honesty Wins. This must be not only the kind of honesty that keeps a man's fingers out of his neighbor's till, but the finer honesty that will not allow a man to give less than his best, the kind of honesty that makes him count not his hours but his duties and opportunities, and constantly urges him to increase his efficiency.

Confidence in Men Wins. I have found my most successful associates by giving men responsibility, by making them feel that I relied upon them; and those who have proved to be unworthy have only caused the others, who far outnumbered them, to stand in a clearer light. This principle, at least in a measure, is responsible for the success of our mercantile organization. Use good business judgment, of course. Do not throw away common sense, but believe in yourself, and trust your fellows.

> ### Savvy Leadership
>
> When interviewing prospective hires, Penney made the job sound as unattractive as possible to see if they flinched, to determine who was timid and who was not. On the other hand, if an interviewee jumped at the chance too eagerly, they were also scratched from the list.

The Spirit Wins. One of the wisest men who ever lived said, "The letter killeth, the spirit giveth life." Every enterprise I have been interested in demonstrates this fact. It is the spirit of the individuals comprising any organization, the spirit of the pioneers in any enterprise or endeavor—that spirit of men and women who are at the foundation of such organizations and enterprises—which will solve problems, conquer difficulties, and achieve individual and collective successes.

Extreme Measures

Penney, whose stores were called the Golden Rule Stores before being renamed after himself, did not permit his employees to drink or to smoke.

A *Practical Application of the Golden Rule Wins*. As enunciated by the Master Teacher on the hillsides of Judea nearly two thousand years ago, the golden rule runs, "Therefore all things whatsoever ye would that men should do to you, do ye even so to them; for this is the law and the prophets."

PART III

~

Qualities for Personal Advancement

David Ogilvy

1911–

*B*orn and raised in Scotland, advertising genius David Ogilvy recalled, "When I was six, he [his father] required that I should drink a glass of raw blood every day." Early in his career, Ogilvy bounced through several jobs, including that of a chef and a stove salesman. Eventually, he went to work doing research for a London advertising agency, and then he emigrated to America in search of adventure. Ogilvy found work with Dr. George Gallup, creator of the Gallup Poll. When World War II broke out, he used his position with Gallup to gather information and to advise the British Government on American opinions. It was not until after a stint as a farmer in Amish country that, in 1952, Ogilvy finally founded Ogilvy & Mather. In the wild world of advertising, Ogilvy discovered that finding the right people was essential to his success.

Qualities I Admire

1. I admire people who work hard, who bite the bullet. I dislike passengers who don't pull their weight in the boat. It is more fun to be overworked than to be underworked. There is an economic factor built into hard work. The harder you work, the fewer employees we need, and the

more profit we make. The more profit we make, the more money becomes available for all of us.

2. I admire people with first-class brains, because you cannot run a great advertising agency without brainy people. But brains are not enough unless they are combined with *intellectual honesty*.

3. I have an inviolable rule against employing nepots and spouses, because they breed politics. Whenever two of our people get married, one of them must depart—preferably the female, to look after her baby.

Savvy Leadership

Do not summon subordinates to your office, Ogilvy advised, because it scares them. Go to their office; it puts them at ease and makes you more visible throughout the organization.

4. I admire people who work with gusto. If you don't enjoy what you are doing, I beg you to find another job. Remember the Scottish proverb, "Be happy while you're living, for you're a long time dead."

5. I despise toadies who suck up to their bosses; they are generally the same people who bully their subordinates.

6. I admire self-confident professionals, the craftsmen who do their jobs with superlative excellence. They always seem to respect the expertise of their colleagues. They don't poach.

7. I admire people who hire subordinates who are good enough to succeed them. I pity people who are so insecure that they feel compelled to hire inferiors as their subordinates.

8. I admire people who build up their subordinates, because this is the only way we can promote from within the ranks.

I detest having to go outside to fill important jobs, and I look forward to the day when that will never be necessary.

9. I admire people with gentle manners who treat other people as human beings. I abhor quarrelsome people. I abhor people who wage paper-warfare. The best way to keep the peace is to be candid. Remember Blake:

> I was angry with my friend;
> I told my wrath, my wrath did end.
> I was angry with my foe;
> I told it not, my wrath did grow.

10. I admire well-organized people who deliver their work on time. The Duke of Wellington never went home until he had finished *all* the work on his desk.

What I Expect of Myself

Having told my staff what I expect of them, I then tell them what I expect of myself:

1. I try to be fair and to be firm, to make unpopular decisions without cowardice, to create an atmosphere of stability, and to listen more than I talk.
2. I try to sustain the momentum of the agency—its ferment, its vitality, its forward thrust.
3. I try to build the agency by landing new accounts. (At this point the upturned faces in my audience look like baby birds waiting for the father bird to feed them.)

(Continued)

4. I try to win the confidence of our clients at their highest level.
5. I try to make sufficient profits to keep you all from penury in old age.
6. I plan our policies far into the future.
7. I try to recruit people of the highest quality at all levels, to build the hottest staff in the agency business.
8. I try to get the best out of every man and woman in the agency.

Andrew Carnegie

1835–1919

S cottish-born Andrew Carnegie immigrated to the United States in 1848 and, in the classic rags-to-riches story, became the king of steel. His first job was in a textile factory earning $1.20 a week. At 16, he became a telegraph operator for the Pennsylvania Railroad, where his boss showed him the ropes of business and investing. Carnegie struck out on his own in 1865, selling bonds, building bridges, and managing an iron ore foundry; then, in 1873 he started to focus on steel. Unfortunately, the Homestead Steel Worker's strike of 1892, in which 10 men were killed and scores were injured, has left a black mark on his legacy. On the other hand, Carnegie was considered a saint for giving more than $325 million to public causes.

The Road to Business Success

- The rising man must do something exceptional, and beyond the range of his special department. HE MUST ATTRACT ATTENTION.
- Always break orders to save owners. There never was a great character who did not sometimes smash the routine regulations and make new ones for himself.

- Boss your boss just as soon as you can; try it on early. There is nothing he will like so well if he is the right kind of boss; if he is not, he is not the man for you to remain with—leave him whenever you can, even at a present sacrafice, and find one capable of discerning genius.

- There is always a boom in brains, cultivate that crop, for if you grow any amount of that commodity, here is your best market and you cannot overstock it, and the more brains you have to sell, the higher price you can exact.

- And here is the prime condition for success, the great secret: concentrate your energy, thought, and capital exclusively upon the business in which you are engaged. . . . I tell you "put all your eggs in one basket, and then watch that basket."

Outrageous Promotion

With great hoopla, Carnegie named his first steel plant after his most important customer—Edgar Thomson, president of the Pennsylvania Railroad.

Savvy Leadership

According to one of Carnegie's lieutenants, the steel king advised that you should never "blame your men for little, trivial faults. If you do, you will dishearten them." If criticism was necessary, Carnegie never did so in front of others.

John H. Johnson
1918–

*J*ohn *Johnson, founder of* Negro Digest, Ebony, *and* Fash-
*ion Fair Cosmetics, among many other ventures, is the most
powerful African-American businessperson in the United
States. Not bad, considering his father was killed when Johnson
was just a child and he then grew up in poverty. To inspire himself as a young man, he made a habit of reading Dale
Carnegie's* How to Win Friends and Influence People *in high
school. In 1942, he founded* Negro Digest *by putting his
mother's furniture up as collateral for a $500 loan; in 1945, he
founded* Ebony *magazine, the cornerstone of his empire. In
breaking through racial barriers to attract advertising from
white-owned companies, Johnson often had less than five minutes to say his piece.*

How to Sell Anything in Five Minutes or Less

Whether I had five or thirty-five minutes, I always based my
presentation on three tried-and-tested rules:

1. Grab the client's attention in the first two or three seconds
   with a fact or an emotional statement that hits him where
   he lives or does business.

2. Find the vulnerable spot. Everybody has something that will make him or her move or say yes. It may have nothing in the world to do with his or her business life. It may be a dream or a hope or a commitment to a person or a thing. Selling is finding the vulnerable point and pushing the yes button.

> ### Smart Habits
> To inspire a positive mental attitude, Johnson would lock himself in his office and say the word *success* over and over.

A remarkable example of this was reported by William Grayson, who discovered that a powerful advertising executive was a fan of Roy Campanella, the great Brooklyn Dodgers catcher. The executive and his son virtually lived in the old Ebbets Field and virtually worshipped the home-plate ground Campanella walked on.

> ### Extreme Measures
> Early on as an entrepreneur, Johnson so feared failure that he fired an employee merely for suggesting that Johnson might fail.

Grayson, who lived down the street from Campanella, asked the baseball star to autograph one of his home-run balls to the boy. The ball carried not only Campanella's name but the date he hit the home run. By coincidence, the advertising executive and his son had been in Ebbets Field on the day Campanella hit the home run. That sold the account. Nothing—neither statistics nor pretty graphs nor hundreds of telephone calls—was as powerful as an unexpectedly powerful gift to a loved one.

3. Find and emphasize common ground. You and the client may disagree on many things. You may like Jesse Jackson and he or she may dislike Jesse Jackson. You're not there to

talk about what divides you. You're there to emphasize the values, hopes, and aspirations that bind you together. Successful selling is a matter of finding common ground, no matter how narrow it might be, on which you and your client can stand together.

Jo Foxworth

*W*hen Jo Foxworth, who founded her own advertising agency, was inducted into the American Advertising Hall of Fame in 1997, she was one of only six women to have received the honor. And to think that she was thrown out of Mississippi State College for Women for protesting a curriculum designed to make wives out of them. Foxworth earned a degree in journalism from the University of Missouri, and then went to work for a newspaper—selling advertising. For a number of years, she worked in the advertising departments of various stores. Eventually, Foxworth joined the McCann-Erickson advertising agency as a copywriter in 1955. After successful work on campaigns for companies such as Westinghouse, Procter & Gamble, and Coca-Cola, Foxworth, who espouses listening to your customer, founded her own firm in 1968.

Shut Up and Listen

Although the sound of one's own voice may be the sweetest music this side of Lincoln Center, the world and our own little plots of it in particular would probably be better if we'd shut up and listen more often. It boils down to this:

1. *Silence IS golden, no matter what they say at CBS and your friendly local disco.* As noise pollution rises, so does the premium on quiet. Please do not disturb the peace at the office any more than it is disturbed already.

2. *While "thinking out loud" may help you crystallize your own ideas, this may also keep other people from crystallizing theirs.* Since theirs can do you as much good as your own — maybe even more than yours — make your conversation an exchange, not a monologue.

3. *Do not let people outside your organization pick your brains unless they're good friends — or willing to pay.* What you know is worth money. Why give it away for the sake of a little ego trip?

   > ### Savvy Leadership
   > Don't overdecorate your office, she advises, because you want people to pay attention to you, not what's on the wall.

4. *Don't speak up at a meeting until you have something meaningful to contribute.* Talking to attract attention may call attention only to your blank spots.

5. *Do not interrupt busy or worried people with gratuitous advice and comment.* Do not present them with any problem or idea that can wait.

6. *Never, never under any circumstances talk when you don't know what you're talking about.* This is the most obvious dictum in business, yet it remains the one most often violated.

7. *When you do speak, control the volume.* The female voice under stress can be an extremely unpleasant sound. It's hard to remember this when you're angry, upset or excited, but try to keep your voice down.

Questions about Age, Salary, and Sex

In the immortal words of Casey Stengel, you don't have to tell nobody nuttin'. Practice smiling. And remember that an unanswered question is stickier for the asker than the askee. Keep the following points in mind:

1. *Don't tell your age to anybody.* You may be so proud of being the youngest executive in the history of the company that you'll be tempted to shout it from the air-conditioning tower, but you'll be another middle-aged executive someday and maybe not so eager to broadcast it.

2. *Don't tell your salary to anybody.* This is privileged information, and spreading it around can cause trouble to top management. Top managements hate trouble, and one of the first things you learn when you're running a company is why they're such bastards up there.

3. *Don't tell the fascinating story of your sex life to anybody.* Now that everybody's lurid sexual exploits are in the public domain, you can't impress your associates with yours anyway, and Mr. Omnipotence and his wife may be a pair of gold-seal prudes.

Theodore N. Vail

1845–1920

Although Alexander Graham Bell patented the telephone in 1876, it was Theodore Vail who pioneered the building of the infrastructure for the telephone. Vail, who was working for the U.S. Railway Service and was considered the foremost expert in mail delivery, was hired by Bell Telephone in 1878. His mission was to take on Western Union and replace the telegraph with the telephone as the most important device for communication. Implicit in this mission was the job of networking the country with telephone lines, just as Vail had done with his system for mail delivery. In 1880, Vail won his battle with Western Union when he convinced them to sell out their interests, and in 1885, Bell formally became American Telephone and Telegraph. As a pioneer, Vail knew all too well the importance of decisiveness and perseverance when it comes to success.

The Making of a Businessman

In the making of a businessman, and in the course of a business life, there are practices to be cultivated, things to be learned and habits to be formed that are most helpful to success. These are the most important of them:

Extreme Measures

Vail insisted that senior managers meet him on his yacht; he did not let them off until particular problems were solved or policies were agreed to.

- Concentration upon and application to the work in hand, to the exclusion, for the time being, of all other work.
- Definiteness of purpose and thoroughness in deciding on a pursuit, and in doing and learning all that is necessary to be done or known for its accomplishment.
- Observation, or the habit of noticing little things — instinctive recognition of anything wrong, or out of place. This is incidental to orderly habits, or the result of them. General deductions from single incidents should never be made. One incident may be accidental; many similar incidents come from a common cause.
- Foresight and precaution; there never was a successful leader who did not continue all precautions until the moment of success.
- Self-confidence, without overconfidence or offensive egotism; it should rest on a thorough knowledge of what is to be done, or on experience in the doing, or on both.
- Respect for the unknown; in every undertaking there are difficulties that only a familiar and practical acquaintance can reveal.
- Respect for the opinions of others.
- Deliberation over new ideas. Many thoughts that are seemingly wonderful lose their apparent value when slept over, or exposed to impartial criticism.
- Attention without interruption to anyone who is at all entitled to be heard. Cultivate the mind in many directions. To

know intelligently about many things is always valuable to a business man.

- Reciprocity in all the affairs of life. It is only by reciprocity that permanent success can be gained. Every exchange should benefit both sides.

Those who feel discouraged by hard conditions should remember that most successful men have started under discouraging conditions.

Henry Ford II
1917–1987

Filling the shoes of legendary Henry Ford was a herculean task, but Henry Ford II had little choice when his senile grandfather started running the Ford Motor Company into the ground in the 1940s. No one thought that young Ford would amount to much, but he enlisted in the Navy during World War II against the family's wishes to prove his independence and his worth. When his father Edsel Ford died in 1943, Henry II was permitted to leave the Navy to help run the car company, which needed a serious housecleaning. Even then, however, it took two years before he was made president. Henry II, who knew what he wanted in an employee and hired the best, is credited with turning around the company in the postwar years, and the famous Mustang was introduced during his watch in 1964.

What an Employer Wants

In considering a man for a management job or for other work, every employer must ask himself, "Would this applicant, if hired, be an asset to my company?" We know many of the qualities that make a man an asset to a business. Here are the main ones.

- *Proficiency in your field.* Your college training is the company's justification for hiring you. But you should remember that when an employer thinks about an applicant's college training, he thinks about more than a major in one field. He thinks about the applicant's reading speed and comprehension; his ability to write the English language and his knowledge of the principles of

---

Smart Habits

Henry Ford II insisted on complete order in his life; for example, he cataloged every single personal possession of consequence.

---

mathematics. These form the hard logical base not only of a successful education but of a successful career as well. Naturally, the better prepared you are in accounting or public relations, engineering or market research, product design or law, the better are your chances of matching the description of the job that is open. Never forget, however, that specialized training alone is not enough. It may get you that first job; but if it is all you have to offer an employer, it may also bury you in that first job.

- *Social competence.* This is the kind of unsatisfactory term that always means too many things. Perhaps I can clarify it somewhat by pointing out that the social skills a young man learns while in school will serve him well in a large corporation. The ability to cooperate with others in purposeful activity, congeniality, knowing how to follow and lead—all of these personal traits are important in school, and they are important in a company. I don't mean to suggest that an employer is going to be impressed automatically by a long list of extracurricular activities. Your chairmanship of the dance committee speaks highly for you. But for an employer, your chairmanships in the professional and honorary societies speak more highly—and more to the point. They indicate that you possess the kinds of skills which are highly prized in a company.

- *Analytical power.* You exercise this power in the classroom to the extent that you gather evidence, interpret it and draw logical conclusions. You will also exercise it in business, but there will be a difference—a big one. When you apply the scientific method to a problem in a classroom, usually you don't apply all of it. In a mathematics class, for example, a teacher gives you the problem, and you work out the solution to it. In business, you often have to find the problem before you can even start thinking about the solution. In business, recognizing the problem is just as important as knowing the method that will solve it.

> ### *Extreme Measures*
> Back in the 1940s, when Henry Ford II was reorganizing the Ford Motor Company and purging dubious individuals, he took to packing a gun to protect himself against reprisals.

- *Curiosity.* An employer is always on the lookout for questing minds. Many people with specialized training and the ability to reason can deal easily with accepted facts. Fewer people are blessed with the kind of curiosity that breaks up familiar patterns and starts fresh thoughts. This is the very source of innovation—the less costly manufacturing technique, the quicker accounting system, the more effective sales plan, the better design.
- *Integrity.* This is the quality that gives meaning to all the rest. You must have it first of all for yourself, of course, for without

it no person is whole. But individual integrity also makes group integrity and this is essential to a company. It is the guidance-and-control system that directs company performance. And by its performance over the long haul, a company lives or dies.

Andrew S. Grove

1936–

I ntel's chairman, Andrew Grove, made famous the motto, *"Only the paranoid survive"—a philosophy developed and necessary in his youth. Life was more than a challenge growing up Jewish in Hungary; during World War II, his father was taken to a labor camp, and his mother and he survived the Nazi occupation by obtaining false papers. When the Soviets invaded Hungary in 1956, Grove chose to escape to the United States. After earning a Ph.D. in chemical engineering from the University of California, Berkeley, Grove went to work for Fairchild Semiconductor, where he met the future founders of Intel, Gordon Moore and Robert Noyce. Grove, who has managed his career by continually asking himself how to add value, joined them at Intel in 1968 and became president in 1979. He later added the titles of CEO and chairman.*

Managing Your Own Career

As a general rule, you have to accept that no matter where you work, you are not an employee; you are in a business with one employee—yourself. You are in competition with millions of similar businesses, millions of others all over the world, picking up the pace, capable of doing the same work that you can do and perhaps more eager.

The point is, the cliches of globalization and the information revolution have real meaning—potentially deadly meaning—for your career. The sad news is, nobody owes you a career. You own it as a sole proprietor. I can offer you no sure-fire formula for success. But here are three key questions:

> *Savvy Leadership*
>
> To remain accessible to all employees, Grove works in an 8-foot by 9-foot cubicle.

1. Continually ask, Am I adding real value or merely passing information along? How do you add more value? By continually looking for ways to make things truly better in your organization. In principle, every hour of your day should be spent increasing the output or the value of the output of the people for whom you're responsible.
2. Continually ask, Am I plugged into what's happening around me? Inside the company? The industry? Are you a node connected to a network of plugged-in people or are you floating by yourself?
3. Are you trying new ideas, new techniques, and new technologies?—and I mean personally. Don't just read about them.

> *Smart Habits*
>
> To gather poignant information from others in an efficient manner, Grove recommends doing so by phone or through a quick exchange by just poking your head in their office/cubicle. Scheduled information-sharing meetings involve too much social etiquette and waste time.

People do not always face up to changes they have to deal with, yet you can't be ready for the future until you've survived the crucible of change. And the key to survival is to learn to add more value today, and every day.

Strategic Inflection Points

Major change in the competitive landscape can take many forms. It may be the introduction of new technologies, a new regulatory environment, or a sudden shift in customer preferences. But the change usually hits the organization in such a way that those of us in senior management are among the last to notice.

Such monumental changes represent what I call Strategic Inflection Points—events that cause you to fundamentally change your business strategy. At such moments in the life of an organization, nothing less will do.

The biggest difficulty with Strategic Inflection Points— aside from the havoc they create—is distinguishing them from the many changes that routinely impinge on your business. Obviously, not every change we respond to requires a dramatic reaction. But the answers to three questions may signal the onset of such a change:

- *Has the company of the entity that you most worry about shifted?* I have a mental "silver bullet" test. If you had one bullet, what would you shoot with it? If you change the direction of the gun, that is one of the signals that you may be dealing with something more than an ordinary shift in the competitive landscape.
- *Is your key complementor—a company whose work you rely on to make your product more available—changing?*

A shift in direction by a partner or market ally can be as decisive as a move by a competitor.

- *Do the people you have worked with for 20 years seem to be talking gibberish?* Are they suddenly talking about people, products, or companies that no one had heard of a year before? If so, it's time to pay attention to what's going on.

PART IV

Wall Street Wizards

Warren E. Buffett

1930–

The billionaire investor was said to have discovered money like "Mozart discovered music." Imagine: $10,000 invested with Warren Buffett in 1956 was worth $80 million in 1994. He has always worked hard; as a kid he had two paper routes, retrieved golf balls for resale, and managed pinball machines. After attending the University of Nebraska, he studied at Columbia University, where he met his mentor Benjamin Graham, the undisputed father of modern securities analysis. In 1956, Buffett started his own investing firm and then bought Berkshire Hathaway, turning it into a holding company for his investments. He made a killing by investing in companies with virtual monopolies in their industries such as Coca-Cola, Disney, and Gilette.

Investment Principles

- Rule No. 1: Never lose money. Rule No. 2: Never forget Rule No. 1.
- I never attempt to make money on the stock market. I buy on the assumption that they could close the market the next day and not reopen it for five years.
- The market is there only as a reference point to see if anybody is offering anything foolish. When we invest in stocks, we invest in businesses.

- The dumbest reason to buy a stock is because it's going up.
- Great investment opportunities come around when excellent companies are surrounded by unusual circumstances that cause the stock to be misappraised.
- We don't make judgments based on ratings. If we wanted Moody's and Standard & Poor's to run our money, we'd give it to them.

- Draw a circle around the businesses you understand and then eliminate those that fail to qualify on the basis of value, good management, and limited exposure to hard times.
- I can't be involved in 50 or 75 things. That's a Noah's Ark way of investing—you end up with a zoo that way. I like to put meaningful amounts of money in a few things.

Extreme Measures

When Buffett is asked how long he holds a stock, he answers, "My favorite time frame for holding a stock is forever." For example, he's owned Disney for more than 30 years.

- I read annual reports of the company I'm looking at and I read the annual reports of the competitors—that is the main source of material.
- We love the kinds of companies that can do well in international markets, obviously, particularly where they're largely untapped.
- You should invest in a business that even a fool can run, because someday a fool will.

Sir John M. Templeton

*S*ir John Templeton was a master at discovering international investment opportunities long before it became fashionable. For example, by the mid-1960s, Templeton and his venerable Templeton Funds were invested in Japan, where stocks were trading at 4 times earnings, whereas U.S. stocks were at 16. "To get a bargain price, you've got to look for where the public is most frightened and pessimistic," he said. Templeton was intrigued by foreign lands while growing up in rural Tennessee, and was so captivated by stories told by visiting Christian missionaries, he thought of becoming one. However, after attending Yale and Oxford as a Rhodes scholar, he realized his real forte was with money and finding great investments where others feared to tread.

The Time-Tested Maxims of the Templeton Touch

1. For all long-term investors, there is only one objective — "maximum total real return after taxes."
2. Achieving a good record takes much study and work, and is a lot harder than most people think.
3. It is impossible to produce a superior performance unless you do something different from the majority.

4. The time of maximum pessimism is the best time to buy, and the time of maximum optimism is the best time to sell.

5. To put "Maxim 4" in somewhat different terms, in the stock market the only way to get a bargain is to buy what most investors are selling.

6. To buy when others are despondently selling and to sell when others are greedily buying requires the greatest fortitude, even while offering the greatest reward.

7. Bear markets have always been temporary. Share prices turn upward from one to twelve months before the bottom of the business cycle.

8. If a particular industry or type of security becomes popular with investors, that popularity will always prove temporary and, when lost, won't return for many years.

9. In the long run, the stock market indexes fluctuate around the long-term upward trend of earnings per share.

10. In free-enterprise nations, the earnings on stock market indexes fluctuate around the replacement book value of the shares of the index.

11. If you buy the same securities as other people, you will have the same results as other people.

12. The time to buy a stock is when the short-term owners have finished their selling, and the time to sell a stock is often when short-term owners have finished their buying.

13. Share prices fluctuate much more widely than values. Therefore, index funds will never produce the best total return performance.

14. Too many investors focus on "outlook" and "trends." Therefore, more profit is made by focusing on value.

15. If you search worldwide, you will find more bargains and better bargains than by studying only one nation. Also, you gain the safety of diversification.

16. The fluctuation of share prices is roughly proportional to the square root of the price.

17. The time to sell an asset is when you have found a much better bargain to replace it.

18. When any method for selecting stocks becomes popular, then switch to unpopular methods. As has been suggested in "Maxim 3," too many investors can spoil any share-selection method or any market-timing formula.

> ### *Savvy Leadership*
> For some 30 years, Templeton led the Templeton Growth Fund directors in prayer at their meetings, that is, praying they make smart investments. Prayer, he believed, enabled them to think more clearly.

19. Never adopt permanently any type of asset or any selection method. Try to stay flexible, open-minded and skeptical. Long-term top results are achieved only by changing from popular to unpopular the types of securities you favor and your methods of selection.

20. The skill factor in selection is largest for the common-stock part of your investments.

21. The best performance is produced by a person, not a committee.

22. If you begin with prayer, you can think more clearly and make fewer stupid mistakes.

Bernard M. Baruch

1870–1965

As a boy, future Wall Street powerhouse Bernard Baruch picked cotton to earn money for powder and shot so he could hunt rabbits. He grew up in rural South Carolina, where whites and blacks clashed constantly, eventually prompting the family to move to New York City. After attending City College, Baruch went to Colorado in search of adventure and gold, but in 1891, he was back in New York, working as a clerk and then an analyst for an investing firm. Not long after, he struck out on his own, raising money from others to invest. Baruch, who moved in the right circles (e.g., the Rockefellers and the Guggenheims), made millions in the stock market with some help from his powerful friends. His key to success was employing a skeptical philosophy that was focused on separating facts from emotion.

My Investment Philosophy

Being so skeptical about the usefulness of advice, I have been reluctant to lay down any "rules" or guidelines on how to invest or speculate wisely. Still, there are a number of things I have learned from my own experience which might be worth listing for those who are able to muster the necessary self-discipline:

1. Don't speculate unless you can make it a full-time job.
2. Beware of barbers, beauticians, waiters—of anyone—bringing gifts of "inside" information or "tips."
3. Before you buy a security, find out everything you can about the company, its management and competitors, its earnings and possibilities for growth.
4. Don't try to buy at the bottom and sell at the top. This can't be done—except by liars.
5. Learn how to take your losses quickly and cleanly. Don't expect to be right all the time. If you have made a mistake, cut your losses as quickly as possible.
6. Don't buy too many different securities. Better have only a few investments which can be watched.

Smart Habits

Although hard to stomach, Baruch always analyzed his losses to determine his mistake(s). To do so, he would break away from Wall Street and find a quiet place to review what he'd done. The review always included a period of self-examination to understand his own failings.

7. Make a periodic reappraisal of all your investments to see whether changing developments have altered their prospects.
8. Study your tax position to know when you can sell to greatest advantage.
9. Always keep a good part of your capital in a cash reserve. Never invest all your funds.
10. Don't try to be a jack of all investments. Stick to the field you know best.

These "rules" mainly reflect two lessons that experience has taught me—that getting the facts of a situation before acting is of crucial importance, and that getting these facts is a continuous job which requires eternal vigilance.

Two Principal Mistakes

There are two principal mistakes that nearly all amateurs in the stock market make.

The first is to have an inexact knowledge of the securities in which one is dealing, to know too little about a company's management, its earnings and prospects for future growth.

The second mistake is to trade beyond one's financial resources, to try to run up a fortune on a shoestring. That was my main error at the outset. I had virtually no "capital" to start with. When I bought stocks I put up so small a margin that a change of a few points would wipe out my equity. What I really was doing was little more than betting whether a stock would go up or down. I might be right sometimes, but any sizable fluctuation would wipe me out.

John C. Bogle

1929–

*J*ohn Bogle founded The Vanguard Group, a highly successful *family of mutual funds, in 1974. After attending Princeton University, where he wrote his senior thesis on mutual funds, Bogle joined a Wall Street firm and worked with such drive that he suffered a heart attack at age 30. Not to be thwarted, he became a pioneer in creating index funds. A key factor in his success was keeping management costs to a minimum, relying heavily on computers for analysis and transactions—the average cost of the company's funds have been less than one-third of the industry average. Before Bogle retired in 1996 (after a heart transplant), he could boast that the size of his group's assets were second only to Fidelity, a monumental achievement built upon his 12 pillars of wisdom that espouse simplicity.*

Twelve Pillars of Wisdom

1. *Investing is not nearly as difficult as it looks.* The intelligent investor in mutual funds, using common sense and without extraordinary financial acumen, can perform with the pros. In a world where financial markets are highly efficient, there is absolutely no reason that careful and disciplined novices—those who know the rudiments but lack

the experience—cannot hold their own or even surpass the long-term returns earned by professional investors as a group. Successful investing involves doing just a few things right and avoiding serious mistakes.

2. *When all else fails, fall back on simplicity.* If you have a major investment decision to make, there are an infinite number of solutions that would be worse than this one: commit, over a period of a few years, half of your assets to a stock index fund and half to a bond index fund. Ignore interim fluctuations in their net asset values. Hold your positions for as long as you live, subject only to infrequent and marginal adjustments as your circumstances change. Occam's razor—a thesis set forth 600 years ago and often affirmed by experience since then—should encourage you: when there are multiple solutions to a problem, choose the simplest one.

3. *Time marches on.* Time dramatically enhances capital accumulation as the magic of compounding accelerates. At an annual return of +10%, the additional capital accumulation on a $10,000 investment is $1,000 in the first year, $2,400 by the tenth year, and $10,000 by the twenty-fifth year. At the end of 25 years, the total value of the initial $10,000 investment is $108,000, nearly a tenfold increase in value. Give yourself the benefit of all the time you can possibly afford.

4. *Nothing ventured, nothing gained.* It pays to take reasonable interim risks in the search for higher long-term rates of return. The magic of compounding accelerates sharply with even modest increases in annual rate of return. While an investment of $10,000 earning an annual return of +10%

grows to a value of $108,000 over 25 years, at +12% the final value is $170,000. The difference of $62,000 is more than six times the initial investment itself.

5. *Diversify, diversify, diversify.* It is hard to imagine that a principle as basic as investment diversification can be so valuable. By investing in mutual funds you can eliminate the risk of owning the stock or bond of a single enterprise that may deteriorate and never fully recover, or even fail altogether. The passage of time has no impact on this specific security risk. By owning a broadly diversified portfolio of stocks and bonds, only market risk remains. This risk is reflected in the volatility of the total value of your portfolio and should take care of itself over time as reinvested dividends and interest are compounded.

6. *The eternal triangle.* Never forget that risk, return, and cost are the three sides of the eternal triangle of investing. Remember also that the cost penalty may sharply erode the risk premium to which an investor is entitled. This is not to say that you should necessarily seek out the lowest-cost mutual fund option. Rather, you should understand unequivocally that investing in a fund with a relatively high expense ratio—more than 0.50% per year for a money market fund, 0.75% for a bond fund, 1.00% for a regular equity fund, or 0.30% for an index fund—bears careful examination. Unless you are confident that the higher costs you incur are justified by higher expected returns or enhanced value of service, select your investments from among the lower-cost no-load funds.

7. *The powerful magnetism of the mean.* In the world of investing, the mean is a powerful magnet that pulls financial mar-

The eternal triangle of investing.

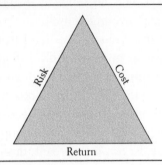

Return

ket returns toward it, causing returns to deteriorate after
they exceed historical norms by substantial margins and to
improve after they fall short. The mean is also the powerful
magnet that pulls the returns achieved by portfolio managers toward it, causing a fund's return to move, over time,
ever closer to the average returns achieved by other funds.
Regression to the mean is a manifestation of the immutable
law of averages that prevails, sooner or later, in the financial
jungle.

8. *Do not overestimate your ability to pick superior equity mutual
funds, nor underestimate your ability to pick superior bond and
money market funds.* In selecting equity funds, no analysis of
the past, no matter how painstaking, assures future superiority. In general, you should settle for a solid mainstream equity
fund in which the action of the stock market itself explains
about 85% or more of the fund's return. Combining several
low-cost equity funds to achieve this diversification is equally
sensible; so is the holding of a single low-cost index fund. But
do not approach the selection of bond and money market
funds with the same skepticism. Selecting the better funds in

these categories on the basis of their comparative costs holds remarkably favorable prospects for success.

9. *You may have a stable principal value or a stable income stream, but you may not have both.* Nothing could make this proposition more obvious than the contrast between a 90-day U.S. Treasury bill—with its volatile income stream and fixed value—and a 30-year U.S. Treasury bond—with its fixed income stream and extraordinarily volatile market value. Intelligent investing involves choices, compromises, and trade-offs, and your own financial position should determine which type of stability—or, more likely, which combination of the two—is most suitable for your portfolio.

10. *Beware of "fighting the last war."* Too many investors—individuals and institutions alike—are constantly making investment decisions based on the lessons of the recent, or even the extended, past. They seek stocks after stocks have emerged victorious from the last war, bonds after bonds have won, Treasury bills after bills have won. And they worry about the impact of inflation *after* inflation, having turned high real returns into so-so nominal returns, has become the accepted bogeyman. You should not ignore the past, but neither should you assume that a particular cyclical trend will last forever. None does.

Savvy Leadership

Although Bogle founded a mutual fund company, he advises investors to beware of "past performance syndrome" in mutual fund advertising. In other words, beware of those who claim that their fund is No. 1. Why? First, hundreds of funds can claim that they're No. 1 based on select criteria, and second, the chances of a fund repeating as a No. 1 performer in the near future is essentially zero, according to Bogle.

11. *You rarely, if ever, know something the market does not.* It is really not possible to do so. If you are worried about the coming bear market, excited about the coming bull market, fearful about the prospect of war, or concerned about the economy, the election, or indeed the state of mankind, in all probability your opinions are already reflected in the market. The financial markets reflect the knowledge, the hopes, the fears, even the greed, of all investors everywhere. It is nearly always unwise to act on insights that you think are your own but are in fact shared by millions of others.

12. *Think long term.* Do not let transitory changes in stock prices alter your investment program. There is a lot of noise in the daily volatility of the stock market, which too often is "a tale told by an idiot, full of sound and fury, signifying nothing." (Macbeth would doubtless agree.) Stocks may remain overvalued, or undervalued, for years. Patience and consistency are valuable assets for the intelligent investor. The best rule is: stay the course.

Caveat Emptor: The Best-Laid Schemes

There are intelligent ways to go about investing and less intelligent ways. Although the odds are heavily against them, some foolish investors are ever seeking to grow rich, using Dr. Johnson's words, "beyond the dreams of avarice." In the real world of investing, such dreams rarely become reality. But even pursuing the sensible, time-honored policies of conservative investing is no guarantee of financial enrichment. The most intelligent of plans often go awry. As Robert Burns warned, "the best laid schemes of mice and

---

men gang aft a-gley." So know yourself, educate yourself, determine for yourself the financial plan best suited to your own objectives, and have the wisdom, patience, and emotional discipline to stay the course that you have chosen. Finally, make your own careful judgments about all of the investment advice that you receive—including, dare I say, even the well-intentioned and experienced advice provided in this book.

Philip L. Carret

1896–1998

*W*arren Buffett declares that if there were ever a hall of fame for investment advisers, Philip Carret would be among the first inducted. Carret studied chemistry at Harvard and then trained as an aviator for World War I, but didn't see action. Afterward, he sold bonds, but then quit to become a reporter for Barron's. While there, he came up with the idea of pooling various individual's money for investment and left to found one of the first mutual funds, the Pioneer Fund, in 1928. Carret managed the fund until 1963, when he sold it and founded Carret and Co., a money management company. At the age of 101, he was still going to the office and forever remained cynical in evaluating companies, a trait that Carret believed went a long way when it comes to successful investing.

Twelve Commandments for Speculators

1. Never hold fewer than ten different securities covering five different fields of business.
2. At least once in six months reappraise every security held.
3. Keep at least half the total fund in income-producing securities.

4. Consider yield the least important factor in analyzing any stock.
5. Be quick to take losses, reluctant to take profits.
6. Never put more than 25% of a given fund into securities about which detailed information is not readily and regularly available.
7. Avoid "inside information" as you would the plague.
8. Seek facts diligently, advice never.
9. Ignore mechanical formulas for valuing securities.
10. When stocks are high, money rates rising, business prosperous, at least half a given fund should be placed in short-term bonds.
11. Borrow money sparingly and only when stocks are low, money rates low or falling, and business depressed.
12. Set aside a moderate proportion of available funds for the purchase of long-term options on stocks of promising companies whenever available.

Smart Habits

Carret always searched his immediate surroundings for investment ideas; for example, he used Neutrogena soap while staying in a Boston hotel, was impressed, and bought the stock. Years later, Johnson & Johnson was equally impressed and bought Neutrogena; Carret made a killing.

Smart Habits

Once you buy a stock, evaluate your holding once every six months. If you do so more frequently, Carret warned, you're more likely to sell it sooner than you should or churn your portfolio. It could take years for a stock price to reflect the value of the company.

Charles Schwab

M oney *magazine selected Charles Schwab, who has built a discount brokerage powerhouse, as one of seven people who most influences the economy. After receiving an MBA from Stanford University, Schwab entered the investment world in 1957. He was working for a small California investment adviser when he and two partners decided to start their own mutual fund company in 1971. Unfortunately, they failed to properly register with securities regulators and were closed down. Schwab went on to found Charles Schwab & Co. in 1974. Nine years later, he sold a controlling interest to BankAmerica to raise money for expansion, but then bought it back in 1987 and took the firm public that same year. Whether you be a novice or an experienced investor looking for diversity, he believes in a basic checklist for picking mutual funds.*

The Bottom Line on Mutual Funds

- To be a successful investor, you don't have to outperform the market; you only have to match it.
- I consider mutual funds to be the investment of choice for many of us. With one investment, you get diversification that might otherwise be impossible.

- No-load mutual funds are about the best investment you can make for an IRA.
- Index funds can be a great way to invest, for both first-time and experienced investors.
- Consider only funds that are listed in reputable financial publications.
- Consider only no-load mutual funds.
- Look for funds that have good performance records, not only for this year but over the life of the fund.
- A good way to diversify is to use a "core and explore" approach. You use index funds to form the core of your portfolio and selectively add actively managed funds for further diversification or to try to beat the market.

> ### Smart Habits
> As you follow the stock market, don't overindulge in your reading and research. Schwab prefers the *Wall Street Journal* as his daily paper and finds *Forbes* and *Money* to be the best magazines. While reading, pay attention to the advertisements—there might be an investing opportunity behind an ad.

- Unless you're an experienced investor, avoid sector funds.
- The best source I know of for timely fund information is the Internet.
- With mutual funds, as with other investments, the higher the risk, the greater the potential reward.
- Taxes can have a huge impact on mutual fund returns. Check the investment philosophy or strategy defined in the fund's prospectus. An investment that is suitable for a tax-deferred account (such as an IRA) may not be as appropriate for a taxable account.
- It's my feeling that international investing is a key part of asset allocation, and that every portfolio should include an international component.

Henry Clews

1834–1923

enry Clews was once a powerful figure on the Street and wrote several insightful books on the subject (often quoted by historians). While growing up in England, his parents expected him to join the family business of manufacturing china. However, when he accompanied his father to New York City in 1850, Clews became enthralled with the American lifestyle and never returned. He found a clerk position with a large importer and then moved into finance. Before long, he and some friends opened a private bank on Wall Street. Ever ambitious, Clews joined the New York Stock Exchange and survived battles with such notorious characters as Daniel Drew and Jay Gould, who ultimately taught him what kind of person to avoid on Wall Street.

The Study of the Stock Market

Next to the unwisdom of selecting and following bad or incompetent advisers in matters of speculation and investment, there are also certain persons whom, if you wish to do well and make a fortune honestly, you should be careful to avoid. You will not always know them by their appearance; in fact, that is often the worst rule to go by, for they are generally well disguised. It is in their walk, talk, and conversation that you will find them out, and, that this be the easier, I have made a collection of their characteristics, as follows:

Avoid a man

Who vilifies his benefactor;

Who unjustly accuses others of bad deeds;

Who never has a good word for anybody;

Who is always prating about his own virtues;

Who, when he drinks, habitually drinks alone;

Who boasts of the superiority of his family;

Who talks religion down-town in connection with his daily business affairs;

Who talks recklessly against the virtue of respectable women;

Who runs in debt with no apparent intention of paying;

Who borrows small sums on his note or check dated ahead;

Who won't work for an honest living;

Who looks down upon those who do;

Who imputes bad motives to those trying to do good;

Who betrays confidence;

Who lies;

Who is honest only for policy's sake;

Who deceives his wife and boasts of it to others;

Who chews tobacco in a public conveyance;

Who gets intoxicated in public places;

Who partakes of hospitality and talks behind his entertainer's back;

Who borrows money from a friend and then blackguards the lender.

With a population of 80,000,000* people, which this country now has, it is easy to find associates in life without selecting men possessed of any of these characteristics, and life is the better worth living without them.

You will both save and make money by strict observance of this short catalogue of avoidances. You are not called upon to do anything or to risk any money in the exercise of this discretion. It simply consists in letting such people severely alone, and if you have been in the habit of being imposed upon by such characters, you will find your happiness as well as your treasury greatly increased by prudently avoiding them.

Savvy Leadership

When it comes to deciding whether you should handle your own investment portfolio or seek professional guidance, Clews offered this advice: If you need legal help, you see a lawyer, and if you're sick, you see a doctor. Case closed.

---

*U.S. population in 1900, according to Clews.

Peter Lynch

1944–

*F*or his remarkable performance as manager of Fidelity's renowned Magellan Fund, Peter Lynch was named one of the greatest investors of all time by the Wall Street Journal. While growing up in a Boston suburb, he caddied at the local country club for big-shot executives who talked money, and the boy was hooked. Lynch attended Boston College on a caddy scholarship and then went to Wharton. In 1969, he was hired by Fidelity as a research analyst, specializing in the metals industry; in 1974, he was promoted to research director. Three years later, Lynch was handed Magellan, then worth $20 million with 45 stocks in its portfolio. By the time Lynch, who had a definitive checklist in evaluating companies, retired from active duty in 1990, the fund had diversified into more than 1,200 businesses and was worth almost $13 billion.

The Final Checklist

- Understand the nature of the companies you own and the specific reasons for holding the stock. ("It is really going up!" doesn't count.)
- By putting your stocks into categories you'll have a better idea of what to expect from them.

- Big companies have small moves, small companies have big moves.
- Consider the size of a company if you expect it to profit from a specific product.
- Look for small companies that are already profitable and have proven that their concept can be replicated.
- Be suspicious of companies with growth rates of 50 to 100 percent a year.
- Avoid hot stocks in hot industries.
- Distrust diversifications, which usually turn out to be diworse-ifications.
- Long shots almost never pay off.
- It's better to miss the first move in a stock and wait to see if a company's plans are working out.
- People get incredibly valuable fundamental information from their jobs that may not reach the professionals for months or even years.
- Separate all stock tips from the tipper, even if the tipper is very smart, very rich, and his or her last tip went up.
- Some stock tips, especially from an expert in the field, may turn out to be quite valuable. However, people in the paper industry normally give out tips on drug stocks, and people in the health care field never run out of tips on the coming takeovers in the paper industry.
- Invest in simple companies that appear dull, mundane, out of favor, and haven't caught the fancy of Wall Street.
- Moderately fast growers (20 to 25 percent) in nongrowth industries are ideal investments.
- Look for companies with niches.
- When purchasing depressed stocks in troubled companies,

seek out the ones with the superior financial positions and avoid the ones with loads of bank debt.
- Companies that have no debt can't go bankrupt.
- Managerial ability may be important, but it's quite difficult to assess. Base your purchases on the company's prospects, not on the president's resume or speaking ability.
- A lot of money can be made when a troubled company turns around.
- Carefully consider the price-earnings ratio. If the stock is grossly overpriced, even if everything else goes right, you won't make any money.
- Find a story line to follow as a way of monitoring a company's progress.

> ### *Smart Habits*
> Lynch would visit more than 500 companies a year, but some of his best investments were based on his use of a company's product; for example, he bought into Taco Bell after trying and enjoying one of their burritos on a road trip.

- Look for companies that consistently buy back their own shares.
- Study the dividend record of a company over the years and also how its earnings have fared in past recessions.
- Look for companies with little or no institutional ownership.
- All else being equal, favor companies in which management has a significant personal investment over companies run by people that benefit only from their salaries.
- Insider buying is a positive sign, especially when several individuals are buying at once.
- Devote at least an hour a week to investment research. Adding up your dividends and figuring out your gains and losses doesn't count.

- Be patient. Watched stock never boils.
- Buying stocks based on stated book value alone is dangerous and illusory. It's real value that counts.
- When in doubt, tune in later.
- Invest at least as much time and effort in choosing a new stock as you would in choosing a new refrigerator.

PART V

Gunslingers and the Entrepreneurial Drive

J. Paul Getty

1892–1976

J. Paul Getty was a master oilman who excelled during the Great Depression and pioneered the drilling of oil in the Middle East in the 1950s; however, his personal life was total chaos as he took lovers across the world, married new wives before he divorced prior ones, and estranged his children in the process. His origins were more humble, growing up a typical child in Minneapolis. His father, an insurance lawyer, was in Oklahoma when the state's first oil was being drilled and he caught the fever, moving the family there and becoming a wildcatter. When Getty graduated college, his father convinced him to join the family's oil business and the young man made his first million in 1916. Getty, who for all his flamboyance took a prudent approach to making his millions, was named the richest man in America by Forbes magazine in 1957.

You Can Make a Million Today

There are no absolutely safe or sure-fire formulas for achieving success in business. Nonetheless, I believe that there are some fundamental rules to the game which, if followed, tip the odds for success very much in the businessman's favor. These are rules which I've applied throughout my entire career—and which every millionaire businessman with whom I am acquainted has followed. The rules have worked for them—and for me. They'll work for you, too.

1. Almost without exception, there is only one way to make a great deal of money in the business world—and that is in one's own business. The man who wants to go into business for himself should choose a field which he knows and understands. Obviously, he can't know everything there is to know from the very beginning, but he should not start until he has acquired a good, solid working knowledge of the business.

2. The businessman should never lose sight of the central aim of all business—to produce more and better goods or provide more and better services to more people at lower cost.

3. A sense of thrift is essential for success in business. The businessman must discipline himself to practice economy wherever possible, in his personal life as well as his business affairs. "Make your money first—then think about spending it," is the best of all possible credos for the man who wishes to succeed.

4. Legitimate opportunities for expansion should never be ignored or overlooked. On the other hand, the businessman must always be on his guard against the temptation to overexpand or launch expansion programs blindly, without sufficient justification and planning. Forced growth can be fatal to any business, new or old.

5. A businessman must run his own business. He cannot expect his employees to think or do as well as he can. If they could, they would not be his employees. When "The Boss" delegates authority or responsibility, he must main-

tain close and constant supervision over the subordinates entrusted with it.

6. The businessman must be constantly alert for new ways to improve his products and services and increase his production and sales. He should also use prosperous periods to find the ways by which techniques may be improved and costs lowered. It is only human for people to give little thought to economies when business is booming. That, however, is just the time when the businessman has the mental elbow room to examine his operations calmly and objectively and thus effect important savings without sacrificing quality or efficiency. Many businessmen wait for lean periods to do these things and, as a result, often hit the panic button and slash costs in the wrong places.

> ### Savvy Leadership
> To test the knowledge of his petroleum engineers, Getty would randomly change critical technical data concerning a well site and then see if the engineers noticed.

7. A businessman must be willing to take risks—to risk his own capital and to use his credit and risk borrowed money as well when, in his considered opinion, the risks are justified. But borrowed money must always be promptly repaid. Nothing will write finis to a career faster than a bad credit rating.

> ### Extreme Measures
> If a roughneck in the oil field questioned Getty's authority (or manhood), Getty challenged him to a treacherous race to the top of an oil rig to settle their differences.

8. A businessman must constantly seek new horizons and untapped or under-exploited markets. As I've already said at some length, most of the world is eager to buy American products and know-how; today's shrewd businessman looks to foreign markets.

9. Nothing builds confidence and volume faster or better than a reputation for standing behind one's work or products. Guarantees should always be honored—and in doubtful cases, the decision should always be in the customer's favor. A generous service policy should also be maintained. The firm that is known to be completely reliable will have little difficulty filling its order books and keeping them filled.

10. No matter how many millions an individual amasses, if he is in business he must always consider his wealth as a means for improving living conditions everywhere. He must remember that he has responsibilities toward his associates, employees, stockholders—and the public.

Do you want to make a million? Believe me, you can—if you are able to recognize the limitless opportunities and potentials around you and will apply these rules and work hard. For today's alert, ambitious and able young men, all that glitters truly *can* be gold.

Dealing with Adversity

1. No matter what happens, do not panic. The panic-stricken individual cannot think or act effectively. A certain amount of trouble is inevitable in any business

career—when it comes, it should be met with calm determination.

2. When things go wrong, it is always a wise idea to pull back temporarily—to withdraw just long enough and far enough to view and evaluate the situation objectively.

3. In the opening stages of any developing adverse situation, it may be necessary and advisable to give some ground, to sacrifice those things which are least important and most expendable. But it should be a fighting withdrawal, a retrograde action that goes back only so far and no further. It must never be a disorderly retreat.

4. Next, all factors in the situation must be examined with meticulous care. Every possible course of action must be weighed. All available resources—cerebral as well as financial, creative as well as practical—must be marshaled.

5. Countermoves must be planned with the greatest care and in the greatest of detail—yet with allowances for alternative courses in the event unforeseen obstacles are encountered. Counteraction must be planned on a scale consistent with the resources available—and the goals set must be conceivably attainable. It is well to bear in mind, however, that the impetus of a properly executed counterattack very often carries the counterattacking force far beyond the point from which it was driven in the first place.

6. Once everything is ready, action should be taken confidently, purposefully, aggressively—and above all, enthusiastically. There can be no hesitation—and it is here that the determination, personality and energy of the leader count the most.

E. W. Scripps

1854–1926

E. W. Scripps built a media empire that included daily newspapers in 15 states, the United Press Association, and the United Feature Syndicate, among other enterprises. He preferred to work from his ranch outside San Diego or from his yacht. His reasons: he was difficult to get along with and he knew it, and to avoid the corruptive nature of wealth and fellow millionaires. "They [millionaires] get to thinking all alike, and their money not only talks, their money does their thinking, too," he said. Ethics was everything to Scripps, who left his empire and the following message to his son: "I would prefer that you should succeed in being in all things a gentleman, according to the real meaning of the word." Although he proclaimed to be an ethical man, his quirky personality and maverick rules for success might lead one to think different.

Some Outlandish Rules for Making Money

1. Never spend as much money as you earn. The smaller your expenditures are in proportion to your earnings the sooner you will become rich.
2. It is more blessed to pay wages than to accept them. At least, it is more profitable.

3. Never do anything yourself that you can get someone else to do for you. The more things that someone else does for you the more time and energy you have to do those things which no one else can do for you.

4. Never do anything today that you can put off till tomorrow. There is always so much to do today that you should not waste your time and energy in doing anything today that can be put off till tomorrow. Most things that you do not have to do today are not worth doing at all.

5. Always buy, never sell. If you've got enough horse sense to become rich you know that it is better to run only one risk than two risks. You also know that just as likely as not the other fellow is smarter than you are and that whether you buy or sell, in each case you run the risk of getting the worst of the bargain. By adopting my rule you will diminish by one-half your chances of loss.

6. Never do anything, if you can help it, that someone else is doing. Why compete with one person or many other persons in any occupation or line of business so long as it is possible for you to have a monopoly in some other field?

7. If circumstances compel you to pursue some occupation or to follow some line of business which is being pursued by some other person, then you do your work in some other way than that in which it is done by the other. There is always a good, better and best way. If you take the best way then the other fellow has no chance of competing with you.

8. Whatever you do once, whatever way you undertake to do a thing, don't do the same thing again or don't do the thing in the same way. If you know one way to do a thing you must know there is a better way to do the same thing.

9. If you're succeeding in anything you are doing, don't let anyone else know of your success, because if you do some other person will try to do the same thing and be your competitor.

10. When you become rich, as you will become rich if you follow my advice, don't let anyone know it. General knowledge of your wealth will only attract the taxgatherer, and other hungry people will try to get away from you something they want and something you want to keep.

11. One of the greatest assets any man can secure is a reputation for eccentricity. If you have a reputation of this kind you can do a lot of things. You can even do the things you want to do without attaching to yourself the enmity of others. Many an act which, if performed by an ordinary person, would arouse indignation, animosity and antagonism, can be performed by a man with a reputation for eccentricity with no other result than that of exciting mirth and perhaps pity. It is better to have the good will than the bad will, even of a dog.

12. Never hate anybody. Hatred is a useless expenditure of mental and nervous energy. Revenge costs much of energy and gains nothing.

13. When you find many people applauding you for what you do, and a few condemning, you can be certain that you are on the wrong course because you're doing the things that fools approve of. When the crowd ridicules and scorns you, you can at least know one thing, that it is at least possible that you are acting wisely. It is one of the instincts of men to covet applause. The wise man regulates his conduct rather by reason than by instinct.

14. It is far more important to learn what not to do than what to do. You can learn this invaluable lesson in two ways, the first of which and most inspired is by your own mistakes. The second is by observing the mistakes of others. Any man that learns all the things that he ought not to do cannot help doing the things he ought to do.

15. Posterity can never do anything for you. Therefore, you should invest nothing in posterity. Of course your heirs will quarrel over your estate, but that will be after you're dead and why should you trouble your mind over things which you will never know anything about?

16. A man can do anything he wants to do in this world, at least if he wants to do it badly enough. Therefore, I say that any of you who want to become rich can become rich if you live long enough.

17. After what I have said it goes without further saying that you should save money. But no man can save himself rich. He can only make himself rich. Savings are capital. It is only by doing things that one learns how to do things. It is only the capitalist who handles capital that learns how to handle capital profitably. The more capital you have the more skillful you become as a capitalist.

18. Fools say that money makes money. I say that money does not make money. It is only men who make money.

19. There are two cardinal sins in the economic world: one is giving something for nothing, and the other is getting

> ### *Smart Habits*
> Scripps was never an effective thinker while at the office, so to stimulate the creative juices he went riding, driving, rowing, or sailing. He averaged only two to three hours per day in his newspapers' editorial rooms.

something for nothing. And the greater sin of these is getting something for nothing, or trying to do so. I really doubt if anyone ever does get something for nothing.

(Don't marry a rich wife. Women are what they are. At best they are hard enough to get along with. They are always trying to make a man do something that he doesn't want to do, and generally succeeding. When a woman is conscious of the fact that she has furnished all or any part of your capital, her influence over you will be so great as to be the worst handicap you can carry.)

20. If you're a prospective heir of your father or some other relative, you should also consider that a handicap. I would advise you to refuse to be an heir.

21. Despise not the day of small things, but rather respect the small things. It is far easier to make a profit on a very small capital invested in any business than it is to make the same proportion of profit off of a large capital. It is true that after you have learned how to make a profit on a business that shows small capital, successively, as your capital grows, you learn how to handle it profitably. Then the time will come when the greater your capital becomes in this way the greater your proportion of profits on it should be. And, for an added reason, as your wealth and skill grow rapidly, your so-called necessary expenses grow much more slowly and in time cease to grow at all, so that beyond a certain limit all your income and added income becomes a surplus, constantly to be added to your capital.

22. It is far easier to make money than to spend it. As it becomes more and more difficult to spend money, you will spend less and less of it, and hence there will be more money to accumulate.

23. The hardest labor of all labor performed by man is that of thinking. If you have become rich, train your mind to hard thinking and hold it well in leash so that your thinking will all be with but one object in view, that of accumulating more wealth.

P. T. Barnum

1810–1891

*T*he Greatest Showman on Earth was raised on a Connecticut farm, but decided early in life that he preferred "laying plans for money making" over physical labor. As a young man, he worked as a clerk for local merchants and then bought his own shop in New York City. In 1835, he turned to entertainment when he bought and displayed Joice Heth, a black slave reputed to be 161 years old and to have been George Washington's nurse. Barnum, who applied sobering common sense to ruling over his wild empire, founded the American Museum in New York in 1841 to display all sorts of human curiosities and grisly items from around the world. His coup de grace was his extravagant Barnum Circus, founded in 1871, which lives on today as The Ringling Brothers and Barnum & Bailey Circus.

Barnum's Rules for Success in Business

1. *Select the kind of business that suits your natural inclinations and temperament.* Some men are naturally mechanics; others have a strong aversion to anything like machinery, and so on; one man has a natural taste for one occupation, and another for another. "I am glad that we

do not all feel and think alike," said Dick Homespun, "for if we did, everybody would think my gal, Sukey Snipes, the sweetest creature in all creation, and they would all be trying to court her at once."

I never could succeed as a merchant. I have tried it unsuccessfully several times. I never could be content with a fixed salary, for mine is a purely speculative disposition, while others are just the reverse; and therefore all should be careful to select those occupations that suit them best.

2. *Let your pledged word ever be sacred.* Never promise to do a thing without performing it with the most rigid promptness. Nothing is more valuable to a man in business than the name of always doing as he agrees, and that to the moment. A strict adherence to this rule gives a man the command of half the spare funds within the range of his acquaintance, and always encircles him with a host of friends who may be depended upon in almost any conceivable emergency.

3. *Whatever you do, do with all your might.* Work at it if necessary early and late, in season and out of season, not leaving a stone unturned, and never deferring for a single hour that which can be done just as well *now.* The old proverb is full of truth and meaning, "Whatever is worth doing at all, is worth doing well." Many a man acquires a fortune by doing his business *thoroughly*, while his neighbor remains poor for life because he only *half* does his business. Ambition, energy, industry, perseverance, are indispensable requisites for success in business.

4. *Sobriety. Use no description of intoxicating drinks.* As no man can succeed in business unless he has a *brain* to

enable him to lay his plans, and *reason* to guide him in their execution, so, no matter how bountifully a man may be blessed with intelligence, if his brain is muddled, and his judgment warped by intoxicating drinks, it is impossible for him to carry on business successfully. How many good opportunities have passed never to return, while a man was sipping a "social glass" with his friend! How many foolish bargains have been made under the influence of the *nervine* which temporarily makes its victim so *rich!* How many important chances have been put off until tomorrow, and thence for ever, because the wine-cup has thrown the system into a state of lassitude, neutralizing the energies so essential to success in business. The use of intoxicating drinks as a beverage is as much an infatuation as is the smoking of opium by the Chinese, and the former is quite as destructive to the success of the business man as the latter.

5. *Let hope predominate, but be not too visionary.* Many persons are always kept poor, because they are too *visionary.* Every project looks to them like certain success, and therefore they keep changing from one business to another, always in hot water, always "under the harrow." The plan of "counting the chickens before they are hatched" is an error of ancient date, but it does not seem to improve by age.

6. *Do not scatter your powers.* Engage in one kind of business only, and stick to it faithfully until you succeed, or until you conclude to abandon it. A constant hammering on one nail will generally drive it home at last, so that it can be clinched. When a man's undivided attention is cen-

tered on one object, his mind will constantly be suggesting improvements of value which would escape him if his brain were occupied by a dozen different subjects at once. Many a fortune has slipped through men's fingers by engaging in too many occupations at once.

7. *Engage proper employees.* Never employ a man of bad habits, when one whose habits are good can be found to fill his situation. I have generally been extremely fortunate in having faithful and competent persons to fill the responsible situations in my business, and a man can scarcely be too grateful for such a blessing. When you find a man unfit to fill his station, either from incapacity or peculiarity of character or disposition, dispense with his services, and do not drag out a miserable existence in the vain attempt to change his nature. It is utterly impossible to do so. "You cannot make a silk purse," etc. He was created for some other sphere. Let him find and fill it.

8. *Advertise your business. Do not hide your light under a bushel.* Whatever your occupation or calling may be, if it needs support from the public, *advertise* it thoroughly and efficiently, in some shape or other that will arrest public attention. I freely confess that what success I have had in my life may fairly be attributed more to the public press than to nearly all other causes combined. There *may* possibly be occupations that do not require advertising, but I cannot well conceive what they are.

Men in business will sometimes tell you that they have tried advertising, and that it did not pay. This is only when advertising is done sparingly and grudgingly. Homœopathic doses of advertising will not pay perhaps—

it is like half a potion of physic, making the patient sick, but effecting nothing. Administer liberally, and the cure will be sure and permanent.

Some say they cannot afford to advertise; they mistake—they cannot afford *not* to advertise. In this country, where everybody reads the newspapers, the man must have a thick skull who does not see that these are the cheapest and best medium through which he can speak to the public, where he is to find his customers. Put on the *appearance* of business, and generally the *reality* will follow. The farmer plants his seed, and while he is sleeping, his corn and potatoes are growing. So with advertising. While you are sleeping, or eating, or conversing with one set of customers, your advertisement is being read by hundreds and thousands of persons who never saw you, nor heard of your business, and never would, had it not been for your advertisement appearing in the newspapers.

The business men of this country do not, as a general thing, appreciate the advantages of advertising thoroughly. Occasionally the public are aroused at witnessing the success of a Swaim, a Brandreth, a Townsend, a Genin, or a Root, and express astonishment at the rapidity with which these gentlemen acquire fortunes, not reflecting that the same path is open to all who *dare* pursue it. But it needs *nerve* and *faith*. The former, to enable you to launch out thousands on the uncertain waters of the future; the latter, to teach you that after many days it shall surely return, bringing an hundred or a thousand fold to him who appreciates the advantages of "printer's ink" properly applied.

9. *Avoid extravagance; and always live considerably within your income, if you can do so without absolute starvation!* It

needs no prophet to tell us that those who live fully up to their means, without any thought of a reverse in life, can never attain to a pecuniary independence.

Men and women accustomed to gratify every whim and caprice, will find it hard at first to cut down their various unnecessary expenses, and will feel it a great self-denial to live in a smaller house than they have been accustomed to, with less expensive furniture, less company, less costly clothing, a less number of balls, parties, theatre-goings, carriage ridings, pleasure excursions, cigar smokings, liquor-drinkings, etc., etc., etc.; but, after all, if they will try the plan of laying by a "nest-egg," or in other words, a small sum of money, after paying all expenses, they will be surprised at the pleasure to be derived from constantly adding to their little "pile," as well as from all the economical habits which follow in the pursuit of this peculiar pleasure.

> ### Outrageous Promotion
>
> Barnum once asked an acquaintance to sue him for fraud for displaying a *supposed* bearded lady. When the case hit the courts it was a hit: The bearded lady proved to be legitimate, the newspapers had a field day, and the public thronged to Barnum's museum to see her.

The old suit of clothes, and the old bonnet and dress, will answer for another season; the Croton or spring water will taste better than champagne; a brisk walk will prove more exhilarating than a ride in the finest coach; a social family chat, an evening's reading in the family circle, or an hour's play of "hunt the slipper" and "blind man's buff," will be far more pleasant than a fifty- or a five-hundred-dollar party, when the reflection on the *difference in cost* is indulged in by those who begin to know the *pleasures of saving*.

Thousands of men are kept poor, and tens of thousands are made so after they have acquired quite sufficient to support them well through life, in consequence of laying their plans of living on too expensive a platform. Some families in this country expend twenty thousand dollars per annum, and some much more, and would scarcely know how to live on a less sum.

Prosperity is a more severe ordeal than adversity, especially sudden prosperity. "Easy come, easy go" is an old and true proverb. *Pride*, when permitted full sway, is the great undying cankerworm which gnaws the very vitals of a man's worldly possessions, let them be small or great, hundreds or millions. Many persons, as they begin to prosper, immediately commence expending for luxuries, until in a short time their expenses swallow up their income, and they become ruined in their ridiculous attempts to keep up appearances, and make a "sensation."

I know a gentleman of fortune, who says, that when he first began to prosper, his wife *would have* a new and elegant sofa. "That sofa," he says, "cost me thirty thousand dollars!" The riddle is thus explained:

When the sofa reached the house, it was found necessary to get chairs to "match," then sideboards, carpets, and tables, "to correspond" with them, and so on through the entire stock of furniture, when at last it was found that the house itself was quite too small and old-fashioned for the furniture, and a new one was built to correspond with the sofa and *et ceteras*; "thus," added my friend, "running up an outlay of thirty thousand dollars caused by that single sofa, and saddling on me, in the shape of servants, equipage, and the necessary expenses attendant upon keeping up a fine 'establishment,' a yearly outlay of eleven thousand dollars, and a tight pinch at that; whereas, ten years ago, we lived with much more real comfort, because much less care, on as many hundreds. The truth is," he continued, "that sofa would have brought me to inevitable bankruptcy, had not a most unexampled tide of prosperity kept me above it."

10. *Do not depend upon others.* Your success must depend upon your own individual exertions. Trust not to the assistance of friends; but learn that every man must be the architect of his own fortune.

With proper attention to the foregoing rules, and such observations as a man of sense will pick up in his own experience, the road to competence will not, I think, usually be found a difficult one.

Sam Walton

1918–1992

*The founder of Wal-Mart grew up in a poor farm commu-
nity of rural Missouri, right in the heart of the dust bowl
of the Great Depression. After attending the University of Missouri, Sam Walton joined JCPenney. World War II service
interrupted his career, after which he bought his own variety
store, called Ben Franklin, with $5,000 of his own money and
$20,000 that he borrowed from his father-in-law. Five years
later, he sold it and opened Walton's 5 & 10 in Bentonville,
Arkansas. He opened a second five-and-ten in 1952 and introduced the concept of self-service into retail to keep costs down.
Not until 1962 did Walton open his first Wal-Mart. The company went public in 1970, and in 1985, Forbes magazine
named Walton the richest man in America. A great motivator,
he never ceased playing cheerleader in building his business.*

Sam's Rules for Building a Business

Rule 1: Commit to your business. Believe in it more than anybody else. I think I overcame every single one of my personal shortcomings by the sheer passion I brought to my
work. I don't know if you're born with this kind of passion,
or if you can learn it. But I do know you need it. If you love

your work, you'll be out there every day trying to do it the best you possibly can, and pretty soon everybody around will catch the passion from you—like a fever.

Rule 2: Share your profits with all your associates, and treat them as partners. In turn, they will treat you as a partner, and together you will all perform beyond your wildest expectations. Remain a corporation and retain control if you like, but behave as a servant leader in a partnership. Encourage your associates to hold a stake in the company. Offer discounted stock, and grant them stock for their retirement. It's the single best thing we ever did.

Rule 3: Motivate your partners. Money and ownership alone aren't enough. Constantly, day by day, think of new and more interesting ways to motivate and challenge your partners. Set high goals, encourage competition, and then keep score. Make bets with outrageous payoffs. If things get stale, cross-pollinate; have managers switch jobs with one another to stay challenged. Keep everybody guessing as to what your next trick is going to be. Don't become too predictable.

Rule 4: Communicate everything you possibly can to your partners. The more they know, the more they'll understand. The more they understand, the more they'll care. Once they care, there's no stopping them. If you don't trust

> ### *Outrageous Promotion*
> Walton, who once dressed in a hula skirt to do a hula dance on Wall Street, encouraged a carnival-like atmosphere at his stores. For example, one store played hide-and-seek with a TV set. If you could find the TV (hidden somewhere in the store) you could buy it for 22 cents. The result: 500 to 600 customers stampeded the store and a pile of merchandise was sold.

your associates to know what's going on, they'll know you don't really consider them partners. Information is power, and the gain you get from empowering your associates more than offsets the risk of informing your competitors.

Rule 5: Appreciate everything your associates do for the business. A paycheck and a stock option will buy one kind of loyalty. But all of us like to be told how much somebody appreciates what we do for them. We like to hear it often, and especially when we have done something we're really proud of. Nothing else can quite substitute for a few well-chosen, well-timed, sincere words of praise. They're absolutely free—and worth a fortune.

Rule 6: Celebrate your successes. Find some humor in your failures. Don't take yourself so seriously. Loosen up, and everybody around you will loosen up. Have fun. Show enthusiasm—always. When all else fails, put on a costume and sing a silly song. Then make everybody else sing with you. Don't do a hula on Wall Street. It's been done. Think up your own stunt. All of this is more important, and more fun, than you think, and it really fools the competition. "Why should we take those cornballs at Wal-Mart seriously?"

Rule 7: Listen to everyone in your company. And figure out ways to get them talking. The folks on the front lines—the ones who actually talk to the customer—are the only ones who really know what's going on out there. You'd better find out what they know. This really is what total quality is all about. To push responsibility down in your organization, and to force good ideas to bubble up within it, you *must* listen to what your associates are trying to tell you.

Rule 8: Exceed your customers' expectations. If you do, they'll come back over and over. Give them what they want—and a little more. Let them know you appreciate them. Make good on all your mistakes, and don't make excuses—apologize. Stand behind everything you do. The two most important words I ever wrote were on that first Wal-Mart sign: "Satisfaction Guaranteed." They're still up there, and they have made all the difference.

Rule 9: Control your expenses better than your competition. This is where you can always find the competitive advantage. For twenty-five years running—long before Wal-Mart was known as the nation's largest retailer—we ranked number one in our industry for the lowest ratio of expenses to sales. You can make a lot of different mistakes and still recover if you run an efficient operation. Or you can be brilliant and still go out of business if you're too inefficient.

Rule 10: Swim upstream. Go the other way. Ignore the conventional wisdom. If everybody else is doing it one way, there's a good chance you can find your niche by going in exactly the opposite direction. But be prepared for a lot of folks to wave you down and tell you you're headed the wrong way. I guess in all my years, what I heard more often than anything was: a town of less than 50,000 population cannot support a discount store for very long.

Henry Ford

1863–1947

Henry Ford grew up on a farm, but was always fascinated by mechanical things. As a boy, he built his own watch and operated a steam-powered thrasher for a neighboring farmer whose workers feared it. His father gave him land, hoping he'd too be a farmer, but Ford left for Detroit to work for the Edison Company, where he rose to a superintendency position. In 1899, he left Thomas Edison's company to experiment fulltime with motor cars. Not until the age of 40 did he found his own company—twice before investors had pulled out. Ford, who devoutly believed in providing the customer quality and service, introduced the durable and best-selling Model T in 1908. Five years later, he instituted the conveyor belt assembly line in his factory, which cut production time per car down from 12-plus hours to 1½ hours.

Principles of Service

1. An absence of fear of the future and of veneration for the past. One who fears the future, who fears failure, limits his activities. Failure is only the opportunity more intelligently to begin again. There is no disgrace in honest fail-

ure; there is disgrace in fearing to fail. What is past is useful only as it suggests ways and means for progress.

2. A disregard of competition. Whoever does a thing best ought to be the one to do it. It is criminal to try to get business away from another man—criminal because one is then trying to lower for personal gain the condition of one's fellow man—to rule by force instead of by intelligence.

> ### *Outrageous Promotion*
> To prove his car design was the best and to attract both investors and customers, Ford took to what was then the extremely dangerous sport of auto racing. A week before New York's grand auto show, he even broke the current time record for one mile when he ran his "Model B" full throttle across a frozen lake.

3. The putting of service before profit. Without a profit, business cannot extend. There is nothing inherently wrong about making a profit. Well-conducted business enterprise cannot fail to return a profit, but profit must and inevitably will come as a reward for good service. It cannot be the basis—it must be the result of service.

4. Manufacturing is not buying low and selling high. It is the process of buying materials fairly and, with the smallest possible addition of cost, transforming those materials into a consumable product and giving it to the consumer. Gambling, speculating, and sharp dealing, tend only to clog this progression.

Robert Mondavi

1913–

*T*he founder of the Robert Mondavi Winery in Napa Valley
is one of the most respected leaders in the industry. Mondavi's parents immigrated to the United States from Italy, and
in 1919, the family moved to California, where his father went
into the grape business, buying and shipping the fruit east.
Mondavi, whose philosophy for success includes foremost having faith in yourself, studied economics and business administration at Stanford University. After graduating, he immersed
himself in the winery business, but not until 1943 did he, his
brother, and his father buy their own vineyard, the Charles
Krug winery. A family feud resulted in Mondavi leaving the
family winery in 1965. At age 52, he struck out on his own,
determined to compete with the best European wines.

Basic Components for Success

People often ask me, "Bob, what are the secrets to your success? What are the biggest lessons you have to share with people who are starting out or trying to remake their lives?" Well,
as I've tried to illustrate in the preceding chapters, in my philosophy of life there are some basic tenets that I believe lead to
success in business—and in almost every other life endeavor.

To succeed in business or in life I don't think you need fancy schooling or highly technical expertise. What you need is common sense, a commitment to hard work, and the courage to go your own way. This is the necessary foundation. On top of this foundation, there are fifteen other qualities that have served me well, and I think of them now as the basic components of my philosophy for success:

- First and foremost, you must have confidence and faith in yourself.
- Second, whatever you choose to do, make a commitment to excel, and then pour yourself into it with your heart and soul and complete dedication.
- Third, interest is not enough—you must be passionate about what you do if you want to succeed and have a happy life. Find a job you love and you'll never have to work a day in your life.
- Fourth, establish a goal just beyond what you think you can do. When you achieve that, establish another and another. This will teach you to embrace risk.

> ### *Extreme Measures*
> To iron out their differences in managing the family winery, Mondavi and his two sons went to see a psychotherapist. The result: Mondavi became more of a father and mentor, not a micromanager.

- Fifth, be completely honest and open. I never had secrets. I would share my knowledge and experience with others if they would share with me. I always had confidence that there was enough room for all of us.
- Sixth, generosity pays. So learn to initiate giving. What you give will enrich your life and come back to you many times over.

- Seventh, only make promises and commitments you know you can keep. A broken promise can damage your credibility and reputation beyond repair.
- Eighth, you must understand that you cannot change people. You might be able to influence them a little, but you can't change anyone but yourself. So accept people the way they are. Accept their differences and try to work with them as they are. I learned this late in life, and it is amazing what peace of mind I found when I finally understood it.
- Ninth, to live and work in harmony with others, don't be judgmental. Instead, cultivate tolerance, empathy, and compassion. And never berate people, especially your children, in front of their cohorts. This can be dispiriting and damaging to them, and it's counterproductive for you. As I've learned, if you want to teach someone to fly, you don't start by clipping his wings.
- Tenth, human beings experience the same thing in very different ways. Two people can live through the exact same experience and come away with totally different understandings of what happened. So between people there is always a large space for misunderstanding. Always be alert for misunderstandings and tread lightly, especially when it comes to politics, religion, or moral standards.
- Eleventh, it is very important that we understand one another. We need to learn how to bridge those spaces of misunderstanding. To do this, listen carefully, and when you talk, be sure people understand you. On important issues, have people repeat back to you what you've said, to make sure there are no areas of confusion or conflict.
- Twelfth, rarely will you find complete harmony between two human beings. But if you find it, maintaining this harmony

requires individuals or soul mates to have complete confidence in one another. Make time to be alone, to share experiences and appreciate together precious moments and the beauty of life. Open all of yourself to that person—emotionally, physically, spiritually, and intellectually. And always, always leave time for playfulness and laughter. There is no better tonic for keeping love alive and vibrant than laughter and good cheer.

- Thirteenth, in both life and work, stay flexible. Whether in a country, a company, or a family, the same holds true: Dictatorship and rigidity rarely work. Freedom and elasticity do.
- Fourteenth, always stay positive. Use your common sense. And remember this: America was built on the can-do spirit and will continue to thrive on the can-do spirit.
- Fifteenth, out of all the rigidities and mistakes of my past, I've learned one final lesson, and I'd like to see it engraved on the desk of every business leader, teacher, and parent in America:

The greatest leaders don't rule. They inspire.

Victor Kiam

1926–

*V*ictor Kiam made a name for himself by appearing in his own TV ads and declaring that he loved the Remington razor so much, he bought the company in 1978. After he graduated from Harvard Business School in 1951, he joined Lever Brothers as a management trainee. For four years, he found himself selling cosmetics to backcountry pharmacists, who had a habit of mixing up cold medicines in their basement that "had the kick of low-grade bourbon." Kiam jumped companies to Playtex in 1955 and rose to the position of executive vice president. But then, in 1968, he attended a conference that included a panel discussion on entrepreneurship. Kiam was so enthralled with the speakers that he quit Playtex that same year to pursue his own interests, but not before looking at himself in the mirror and asking some hard questions.

The Man-in-the-Mirror Test

What does it take to be an entrepreneur? Do you have the go-getter's version of the right stuff? To find out, all you have to do is take the advice found in a Michael Jackson hit song. Consult your "Man in the Mirror" and ask:

1. Do I Have Confidence in Myself: You have to believe you can move the Himalayas if that is what your ultimate success demands. In a corporation, you'll want the people working for or with you to follow your lead. You want your superiors to give you as much authority as you can handle. They have to respect your judgment.

   If you're running your own enterprise, you may want investors. Your clients have to believe you will do your very best work for them or that your products are of the highest quality. They have to catch your enthusiasm. How can you pump them up if you don't believe in yourself? As an entrepreneur, you always want to stand out. How can you hold center stage if you don't think yourself worthy of it?

2. Do I Have Confidence in My Venture: When you make an investment in an enterprise, what are you betting on? The idea or the people behind it? The answer is always both. Your time is one of your most valuable commodities. If you become involved in a venture it must be worth your total commitment. If you start a venture plagued by doubts, you are going to run into the self-fulfilling prophecy. When the hard times hit—and, believe me, even the most successful entrepreneur encounters some turbulence on his flight to paradise—you are going to be hard pressed to give your project the support it needs if you doubt its chances for survival.

3. Are You Willing to Make Sacrifices: Nine to five has no real meaning for you. An entrepreneur is not a clock watcher. Business is a game. You will often need more than eight hours to score the winning touchdown.

4. Am I a Decision Maker: You have to be. An entrepreneur wants to assume the ultimate responsibility for his or her project. The buck not only stops at the true entrepreneur's desk, it starts there also. You are often on your own. If you're running a business or a division, no one can make the tough decisions for you.

5. Do I Recognize Opportunity: This is vital. Are you often berating yourself because you've passed by yet another chance of a lifetime? You can't allow too many of those to slip by. Get used to looking over all the nuances of every proposition. Approach each idea thinking, "How can I make this work for me?"

6. Can I Keep My Cool: Do you feel a bit of tightness in your throat when pressure is applied to you? Do the butterflies flap up a Wagnerian opera whenever crunch time comes? That's OK, it's a typically human response. But do others around you pick up on that nervousness? If they do, you could be in trouble. The entrepreneur is a general. If his troops are about to enter the valley of death, his mere presence must say, "Our strategy is sound. This army is ready. We will fight our way through this dangerous terrain without serious casualties." Your army will be able to take a cool, reasoned approach to any obstacle. Such a stance represents the first step toward winning. On the other hand, if your troops sense you are as bewildered as they are, that the hand mapping the strategy is an unsteady one, you are in big trouble. While you might delude yourself that you are still a leader of men, you will rapidly discover there are no men left to lead.

7. Do I Have High Levels of Energy and Stamina: Entrepreneurs shouldn't have any shortage of energy. We're much

too involved; we feed off life's opportunities. If you find yourself looking forward to your afternoon siesta or constantly thinking about the nice warm tub waiting for you at the end of the day, don't even think about getting into the entrepreneurial life. While you're napping or unwinding in the bath, some competitor is out on the prowl and picking up points at your expense. Remember, you can't always outthink, outplan, or outspend a rival. But you can outwork anyone.

Outrageous Promotion

To ensure that his would-be customers remembered his pitch, Kiam rented a monkey to bring along on sales calls.

8. Am I Willing to Lead by Example: You can't ask your troops to walk on water for you if you choose to ride the *Queen Mary* over the same route. You want your team to put in fourteen-hour workdays when it is needed? Make sure you are willing to do the same. I've never asked an employee to do something I wasn't willing to do. I feel a responsibility to work harder than the people who work for me.

While we're on the subject, never, ever ask an employee to act as a gofer. When I am on the road with one of my salesmen and he tries to take my bag, he has a real fight on his hands. I just won't give it to him. I want him to know we are partners and that we are in this thing together. You want to motivate the people around you. Leading by example is one of the best methods.

Lillian Vernon

1927–

Very few mailboxes have not received Lillian Vernon catalogs, which are renowned for striking the consumers' tastes. However, Vernon's tale is one of both triumph and tragedy. She was born in Germany, where her father had built a prosperous lingerie business, but when Hitler came to power in 1933, life changed dramatically for this Jewish family. After her older brother was attacked by Nazi thugs, they emigrated to Amsterdam and then to the United States. Vernon's brother was later killed in World War II, but she persevered through the tragedy. Married and pregnant in 1951, Vernon was convinced that she had some greater purpose in the working world and decided to start her mail-order business with $2,000. With the odds stacked against her as a woman entrepreneur in the 1950s, Vernon's catchwords became commitment and hard work.

Are You an Entrepreneur?

If you're thinking of starting your own business, here are ten questions you should ask yourself before you begin. Your answers should help you make your decision.

1. Do you have the necessary commitment? To succeed, you must feel passionate about the work you have chosen.

Lukewarm enthusiasm will not sustain you through the challenges you will face in a start-up business.

2. Are you prepared to work extremely hard? Launching your own business demands long hours of labor. Are you sure you want to give up a good part of your social life: your weekends, golf games, and vacations? For your developing business to succeed, you will need to focus all your energies on it.

3. Are you sure you have the mental stamina and concentration to meet the demands your project will impose on you? If your attention flags, you may jeopardize your venture.

> ### Outrageous Promotion
>
> Lillian Vernon created the waspy-sounding name of her company by combining her first name with Mount Vernon, the name of the Westchester County, New York, town where she lived as a newly-wed. She later legally changed her own name from Lillian Hochberg to the company's name.

4. Do you accept new ideas easily? Do you treat other people's ideas with respect? Are you able to make decisions right away? An entrepreneur must be open-minded, flexible, and able to respond to new ideas.

5. How do you deal with problem solving? Are you prepared to spend time analyzing a problem and finding a solution? Or do you just close your eyes and hope for the best? No matter how carefully you plan, you are bound to run into an unforeseen problem now and then. Be prepared to cope with such a situation.

6. Are you ready to commit to the long term? A company's success is never an overnight miracle. That is one reason you must be absolutely certain that you love your work — there will be a lot of it.

7. What back-up resources do you have? Banks and other financial institutions seldom lend money to start-up businesses. Will family members or friends invest in your company or tide you over during a rough patch?

8. Are you good at concentrating on detail? Often, no one but you will be able to take care of small items. An entrepreneur's life is not one of ideas alone.

9. Are you ready to sit down and write a careful analysis of your business prospects? Without a best case/worst case scenario to guide you through the first years, you may be in for an unpleasant surprise or two. Be aware and be prepared.

10. Are you by nature an optimist? Mistakes and setbacks are bound to occur. Can you—without getting derailed or discouraged—learn from your mistakes?

PART VI

~

The Gurus

Warren Bennis

1925–

*A*s founding chairman of The Leadership Institute at the University of Southern California's Marshall School of Business, where he has taught since 1979, Warren Bennis is recognized the world over as an expert on leadership. Bennis, who has written more than 25 books and 1,500 articles on management and leadership, earned his undergraduate degree from Antioch College in 1951 and a Ph.D. from MIT in 1955. He stayed at MIT for several years as a faculty member of the Sloan School of Management and then taught at Harvard and Boston Universities. Bennis himself took a management job as president of the University of Cincinnati, before heading west.

Five Key Skills

1. The ability to accept people as they are, not as you would like them to be. In a way, this can be seen as the height of wisdom—to "enter the skin" of someone else, to understand what other people are like on *their* terms, rather than judging them.
2. The capacity to approach relationships and problems in terms of the present rather than the past. Certainly it is true that we can learn from past mistakes. But using the

present as a takeoff point for trying to make fewer mistakes seemed to be more productive for our leaders—and certainly was more psychologically sound than rehashing things that are over.

3. The ability to treat those who are close to you with the same courteous attention that you extend to strangers and casual acquaintances. The need for this skill is often most obvious—and lacking—in our relationships with our own families. But it is equally important at work. We tend to take for granted those to whom we are closest. Often we get so accustomed to seeing them and hearing from them that we lose our ability to listen to what they are really saying or to appreciate the quality—good or bad—of what they are doing. Personal feelings of friendship or hostility or simple indifference interfere.

   There are two aspects to this problem of overfamiliarity. The first is that of not hearing what is being said: selective deafness leads to misunderstandings, misconceptions, mistakes. The second is the matter of feedback we fail to provide to indicate our attentiveness.

4. The ability to trust others, even if the risk seems great. A withholding of trust is often necessary for self-protection. But the price is too high if it means always being on guard, constantly suspicious of others. Even an overdose of trust that at times involves the risk of being deceived or disappointed is wiser, in the long run, than taking it for granted that most people are incompetent or insincere.

5. The ability to do without constant approval and recognition from others. Particularly in a work situation, the need for constant approval can be harmful and counterproductive. It should not really matter how many people *like* leaders. The

important thing is the quality of work that results from collaborating with them. The emotionally wise leader realizes that this quality will suffer when undue emphasis is placed on being a "good guy." More important, it is a large part of the leader's job to take risks. And risks by their very nature cannot be pleasing to everyone.

Smart Habits

To force yourself to reflect on and learn from your experiences, especially failures, Bennis recommends keeping a diary and reading biographies—biographies, he believes, inspire self-reflection.

Dale Carnegie

1888–1955

*D*ale Carnegie is best remembered for his ever-popular public speaking courses and his 1937 book, How to Win Friends and Influence People, *which sold over 1.3 million copies alone before his death. He was raised on a Missouri farm and joined the high school debate team. However, after attending the State Teachers' College in Missouri, Carnegie pursued a career in sales. As a salesman for the International Correspondence School, he sold only one course before quitting, and then moved to Chicago to work in sales at Armour & Co. From there, it was to New York City in 1911, where he tried his hand at acting. Finally, Carnegie started teaching public speaking at a YMCA, during which time he refined his ideas on how to lead people without commanding them. He then founded the Carnegie Institute for Effective Speaking and Human Relations.*

Be a Leader

A leader's job often includes changing your people's attitudes and behavior. Some suggestions to accomplish this:

PRINCIPLE 1
Begin with praise and honest appreciation.

PRINCIPLE 2
Call attention to people's mistakes indirectly.

PRINCIPLE 3
Talk about your own mistakes before criticizing the other person.

PRINCIPLE 4
Ask questions instead of giving direct orders.

Outrageous Promotion

Not long before delivering a lecture at Carnegie Hall, Dale changed the spelling of his name from *Carnegey* to *Carnegie* so that his audience would associate him with the highly successful king of steel, Andrew Carnegie.

PRINCIPLE 5
Let the other person save face.

PRINCIPLE 6
Praise the slightest improvement and praise every improvement. Be "hearty in your approbation and lavish in your praise."

PRINCIPLE 7
Give the other person a fine reputation to live up to.

PRINCIPLE 8
Use encouragement. Make the fault seem easy to correct.

PRINCIPLE 9
Make the other person happy about doing the thing you suggest.

Peter F. Drucker

1909–

*P*eter Drucker, management-consultant extraordinaire, was born in Vienna where his father was a prominent lawyer. Drucker studied law at the University of Hamburg and at the University of Frankfurt in Germany. When Adolf Hitler came to power in 1933, he knew it was time to leave Germany. For the next four years he worked in England as an economist, and then in 1937, his wife and he emigrated to the United States. At the outbreak of World War II, a series of insightful articles on Germany's economy written by Drucker caught the attention of both Washington's policy makers and U.S. business leaders, enabling him to launch his consulting business in 1940. Drucker also taught at Bennington College, New York University, and the Claremont Graduate School in California.

Lessons for Leading People

The three people from whom I learned the most in my work were all very different. The first two were exceptionally demanding; the third was exceptionally brilliant. All three taught me a lot.

My first boss founded the economics department in a European private bank. He went to France when Hitler came to power, rose to be a full general under De Gaulle, and commanded French resistance troops in Africa. The second was among the last in the great 19th-century tradition of liberal journalism in Europe, a stern disciplinarian. I learned more from him than from anybody else. The third was a London banker who built a private bank from scratch. It became the first newcomer to the London Clearinghouse Association—the club of private banks—in 50 years, and today is part of a financial conglomerate.

Five lessons from those remarkable men still apply today:

- *Treat people differently, based on their strengths.* My first boss, the banker, simply didn't know that there were such things as beginners, and so he had me work out a merger of the European artificial silk industry—rayon, the first synthetic. It was a merger of the German and Dutch, Italian and French companies. And at age 19 I worked it out, period. I was a securities analyst trainee and knew nothing about anything. When I went in to ask a question he looked at me and said, "Have you looked it up? Don't come and ask me a question until after you have looked it up." So I looked things up, and I learned something.

   There were four or five of us, and he treated each of us differently—the way we needed to be treated, which for me was very rough. He demanded enormous things from me. He looked at people, what they should be doing, and then demanded it at a high professional level, far beyond our capacity, and did not stop until we did work that had that quality.
- *Set high standards, but give people the freedom and responsibility to do their jobs.* My next job was for Frankfurt's leading afternoon newspaper. It was the second largest afternoon paper on the continent—a 600,000 circulation, with an editorial staff of

14 people. We didn't know enough to know that we were over-worked; we just loved it.

I went to work as financial and foreign writer on my 20th birthday. The oldest was perhaps 26—largely because this was 10 years after the end of World War I, and the people that should have held those jobs were lying in officers' graves all over Europe. There were no educated 30-year-olds, liter-ally none.

You began work at 6:00 in the morning. I took the first streetcar, which stopped outside the office at 6:02. My first morning I climbed up the three stairs to the editorial offices and there was the editor, 6 foot 5, whom I had never met—the publisher had hired me—with a watch in his hand looking at me. He said, "Young man, if you don't come in five minutes to six tomorrow morning you don't have to come in at all." I explained that the first streetcar didn't leave until 5:35. He picked up the telephone at 6:00 in the morning and got the mayor of Frankfurt out of bed. The next day the first streetcar left at 5:07, and I was on it.

I had a 6:50 deadline each morning—less than an hour in which to write the second and third editorials each day, six days a week. One needed to be 900 words, the other 600 words. The editor had to approve them, but the topics were entirely up to me—and did I learn. The discipline this imposed forced me to be resourceful, but allowed me to be creative. Yes, the editor was stern, forbidding, demanding, relentless. But his demands were based not on the mindless exercise of authority but on accountability and the delivery of results.

- *Performance review must be honest, exacting, and an inte-gral part of the job.* The same editor provided a very powerful performance-assessment model. The fourth Saturday of every month, instead of going home at noon, when the paper had gone to press, we adjourned to a private room in a tavern and stayed until 2:00 in the morning. We paid for the sausages they served; the beer was furnished by the paper.

So we began around the table. The first was usually the one woman on the staff, because her name began with a B. We each made a presentation about the last month's work, what we thought we had done outstandingly well and why, what we thought needed improvement, where we had botched things, and what we could learn from those.

It was not just a performance review, it was a performance, period. Each of us—all 14—took 20 or 30 minutes. That's seven hours. The editor didn't say a word; we all asked questions, and he only took a few notes. So by that time, we had another round of sausage and beer. Then the editor would ask for comments, 10 minutes or 15 minutes from each of us. Finally he would sum up for three hours without once looking at the notes. We just loved it—and learned everything there was to know about where we stood and how to do better.

- *People learn the most when teaching others.* My third employer was the youngest of three senior partners of a bank. I mostly worked for him as the firm's economist and London securities analyst.

Once a week or so, he would sit down with me and talk about the way he saw the world. He used me as an audience, and in the process, he demonstrated how to think. He talked the same subject over and over again until it clicked. I learned an enormous amount listening to him and seeing a first-rate mind work. The clarity, the aesthetic rigor he demanded of himself was a joy to behold.

He insisted that since I was the firm's economist, I had better learn some economics, which as a brash young man I thought was quite unreasonable. But he used his influence to get me into a prestigious economics seminar at Cambridge. When I left the firm I told him, "I'm not going to be a banker; money bores me silly." He said, "I've known that all along." He simply needed someone who could listen, who could allow him to work out his ideas. In the end, I think he learned more than I did from our little talks.

> ## Savvy Leadership
> To measure employees' development, Drucker espouses designing a scorecard. It should judge expectations against actual performance, especially for those employees who are promoted.

- *Effective leaders earn respect—but they don't need to be liked.* Each of my three mentors won my respect, but I doubt any of them considered himself my friend. It would never have occurred to the editor, for instance, to feel affection for a staff member; it was irrelevant. At the end he made me one of three senior editors, but I never even had lunch with him. I never sat down with him except on business. Yet I knew that if I did my job I could trust him totally—and that if I didn't, I would be out, period.

  When I went back to Europe in 1953 for the first time since the war, I went to Frankfurt and called on him. He was very gracious, and I told him how much he taught me in those monthly review sessions, how much I learned. And he looked at me and said, "That never occurred to me. The only thing I was interested in was next month's papers." The only bond we had was the task at hand.

★

Each of these three leaders taught me valuable lessons. But they were, to use an often-abused phrase, "just doing their jobs." They focused on performance and responsibility for results. Intuitively, they understood that the manager's job is to make human strength effective and human weakness irrelevant. Perhaps that was the biggest lesson of all.

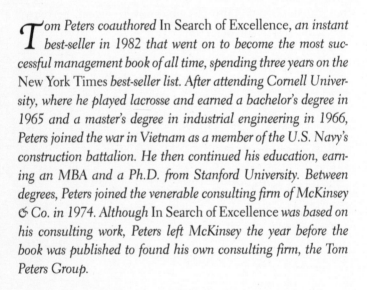

Tom Peters

1942–

*T*om *Peters coauthored* In Search of Excellence, *an instant best-seller in 1982 that went on to become the most successful management book of all time, spending three years on the* New York Times *best-seller list. After attending Cornell University, where he played lacrosse and earned a bachelor's degree in 1965 and a master's degree in industrial engineering in 1966, Peters joined the war in Vietnam as a member of the U.S. Navy's construction battalion. He then continued his education, earning an MBA and a Ph.D. from Stanford University. Between degrees, Peters joined the venerable consulting firm of McKinsey & Co. in 1974. Although* In Search of Excellence *was based on his consulting work, Peters left McKinsey the year before the book was published to found his own consulting firm, the Tom Peters Group.*

Eight Attributes of Innovative Companies

1. A *bias for action,* for getting on with it. Even though these companies may be analytical in their approach to decision making, they are not paralyzed by that fact (as so many others seem to be). In many of these companies the standard operating procedure is "Do it, fix it, try it." Says a Digital

Equipment Corporation senior executive, for example, "When we've got a big problem here, we grab ten senior guys and stick them in a room for a week. They come up with an answer *and* implement it." Moreover, the companies are experimenters supreme. Instead of allowing 250 engineers and marketers to work on a new product in isolation for fifteen months, they form bands of 5 to 25 and test ideas out on a customer, often with inexpensive prototypes, within a matter of weeks. What is striking is the host of practical devices the excellent companies employ, to maintain corporate fleetness of foot and counter the stultification that almost inevitably comes with size.

2. *Close to the customer.* These companies learn from the people they serve. They provide unparalleled quality, service, and reliability—things that work and last. They succeed in differentiating—*à la* Frito-Lay (potato chips), Maytag (washers), or Tupperware—the most commodity-like products. IBM's marketing vice president, Francis G. (Buck) Rodgers, says, "It's a shame that, in so many companies, whenever you get good service, it's an exception." Not so at the excellent companies. Everyone gets into the act. Many of the innovative companies got their best product ideas from customers. That comes from listening, intently and regularly.

3. *Autonomy and entrepreneurship.* The innovative companies foster many leaders and many innovators throughout the organization. They are a hive of what we've come to call champions; 3M has been described as "so intent on innovation that its essential atmosphere seems not like that of a large corporation but rather a loose network of laboratories and cubbyholes populated by feverish inventors and

dauntless entrepreneurs who let their imaginations fly in all directions." They don't try to hold everyone on so short a rein that he can't be creative. They encourage practical risk taking, and support good tries. They follow Fletcher Byrom's ninth commandment: "Make sure you generate a reasonable number of mistakes."

4. *Productivity through people.* The excellent companies treat the rank and file as the root source of quality and productivity gain. They do not foster we/they labor attitudes or regard capital investment as the fundamental source of efficiency improvement. As Thomas J. Watson, Jr., said of his company, "IBM's philosophy is largely contained in three simple beliefs. I want to begin with what I think is the most important: *our respect for the individual.* This is a simple concept, but in IBM it occupies a major portion of management time." Texas Instruments' chairman Mark Shepherd talks about it in terms of every worker being "seen as a source of ideas, not just acting as a pair of hands"; each of his more than 9,000 People Involvement Program, or PIP, teams (TI's quality circles) does contribute to the company's sparkling productivity record.

5. *Hands-on, value driven.* Thomas Watson, Jr., said that "the basic philosophy of an organization has far more to do with its achievements than do technological or economic resources, organizational structure, innovation and timing." Watson

---

Extreme Measures

To cultivate "out-of-the-box thinking," Peters advises taking vacations to the Far East or other exotic places (as opposed to two weeks at the beach), trying unique food, listening to foreign languages, noticing how the people act, and generally exploring things that are strange to you.

and HP's William Hewlett are legendary for walking the plant floors. McDonald's Ray Kroc regularly visits stores and assesses them on the factors the company holds dear, Q.S.C. & V. (Quality, Service, Cleanliness, and Value).

6. *Stick to the knitting.* Robert W. Johnson, former Johnson & Johnson chairman, put it this way: "Never acquire a business you don't know how to run." Or as Edward G. Harness, past chief executive at Procter & Gamble, said, "This company has never left its base. We seek to be anything but a conglomerate." While there were a few exceptions, the odds for excellent performance seem strongly to favor those companies that stay reasonably close to businesses they know.

7. *Simple form, lean staff.* As big as most of the companies we have looked at are, none when we looked at it was formally run with a matrix organization structure, and some which had tried that form had abandoned it. The underlying structural forms and systems in the excellent companies are elegantly simple. Top-level staffs are lean; it is not uncommon to find a corporate staff of fewer than 100 people running multi-billion-dollar enterprises.

8. *Simultaneous loose-tight properties.* The excellent companies are both centralized and decentralized. For the most part, as we have said, they have pushed autonomy down to the shop floor or product development team. On the other hand, they are fanatic centralists around the few core values they hold dear. 3M is marked by barely organized chaos surrounding its product champions. Yet one analyst argues, "The brainwashed members of an extremist religious sect are no more conformist in their central beliefs." At Digital the chaos is so rampant that one executive

noted, "Damn few people know who they work for." Yet Digital's fetish for reliability is more rigidly adhered to than any outsider could imagine.

Most of these eight attributes are not startling. Some, if not most, are "motherhoods." But as Rene McPherson says, "Almost everybody agrees, 'people are our most important asset.' Yet almost none really lives it."

Savvy Leadership

At his consulting company, no one is allowed a business card with their title on it. Peters' point: all are significant contributors.

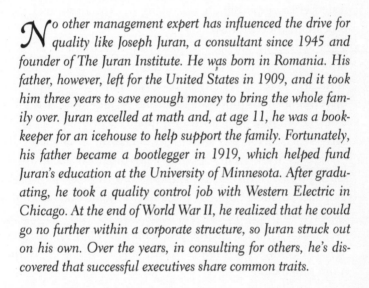

Joseph Juran

1904–

*N*o other management expert has influenced the drive for quality like Joseph Juran, a consultant since 1945 and founder of The Juran Institute. He was born in Romania. His father, however, left for the United States in 1909, and it took him three years to save enough money to bring the whole family over. Juran excelled at math and, at age 11, he was a bookkeeper for an icehouse to help support the family. Fortunately, his father became a bootlegger in 1919, which helped fund Juran's education at the University of Minnesota. After graduating, he took a quality control job with Western Electric in Chicago. At the end of World War II, he realized that he could go no further within a corporate structure, so Juran struck out on his own. Over the years, in consulting for others, he's discovered that successful executives share common traits.

Thirteen Common Success Factors

- They make product quality and customer service their priorities. Quality becomes top priority among company goals, and customer satisfaction becomes the focus in customer relations.
- They train all managers in quality improvement processes. This training usually starts at the top and then cascades down.

- They enlarge the business plan to include quality-related goals — goals to improve customer satisfaction, to meet competitive standards, to reduce costs of poor quality, and to improve key processes.
- They use benchmarking as a means of setting ambitious (but attainable) goals.
- They identify the actions needed to meet the goals. They also assign clear responsibility for taking those actions, and they provide the needed resources.
- They accelerate the pace of quality improvement far beyond prior practice. This translates to thousands of improvements annually — a revolutionary pace. Every improvement project includes business processes as well as factory processes.
- They develop new measures for quality. For example, in its early years, Xerox was stunningly successful financially. Its executives were well supplied with financial measures — sales, profits, return on investment, and the like. However, they lacked such essential measures of quality as customer satisfaction and competitive quality. Lacking such measures, they learned of their quality problems only after severe damage had already been done, making their comeback all the more remarkable.
- They regularly review performance against quality goals, just as they review performance against financial goals.
- They publicly acknowledge persons and teams who achieve superior performance.
- Self-audits. They use self-audits to identify the strengths and weaknesses of divisions and support services and to assist in making decisions. Such self-audits are often conducted against the criteria of the Malcolm Baldrige National Quality Award. Some companies, such as AT&T, also have internal awards.

- Partnership with suppliers. They take steps to change from adversarial relationships with suppliers to partnerships. They shrink their supplier base by about two-thirds or more and require the surviving suppliers to take steps toward attaining world-class quality. They share information, and participate in planning improvement projects. Some even serve notice to the colleges which supply them with recruits: "If you want us to continue sending our recruiters to your campus, you will make the following quality improvements at your college."

> ### Savvy Leadership
> To promote quality work at all levels, Juran suggests preparing exhibits that show how the product is used by customers so that every employee understands how the results of his or her job affect the customer—this show-and-tell process can be used to benefit both external and internal customers.

- Business process quality management. They trace many quality problems to the business processes rather than factory processes. Often key business processes lack clear ownership. The steps in the process may have owners, but the overall process does not. Deeming this to be unacceptable, they assign owners to the key business processes, and spell out the responsibilities of owners. This results in dramatic improvements in customer service, error rates, productivity, time cycles, and costs.
- Self-directing teams. They train and empower workers to run processes with minimal help from supervisors or from specialists, such as process engineers. To make this work, they create self-directing teams. Jobs cross former functional lines; jobs become team jobs; workers become team members; quality and productivity improve; the ratio of workers to managers rises, as team members both plan and execute.

Human Obstacles to Quality

The obstacles that are removable by motivation include

1. *Unawareness.* People are not aware that they are creating quality problems.
2. *Competition in priorities.* People are unable to achieve quality because other goals that have higher priority get in the way.
3. *Suboptimization.* The achievement of quality locally gets in the way of overall quality.
4. *Cultural myths.* People hold certain sincere beliefs that are related to quality but that are not based on fact. These "myths" can be an obstacle to constructive efforts to achieve quality leadership.

In most companies, these obstacles have their origin in prior managerial practices. It is therefore important to avoid any atmosphere of blame. The emphasis should be on what to do differently, and on the methods for making the needed changes.

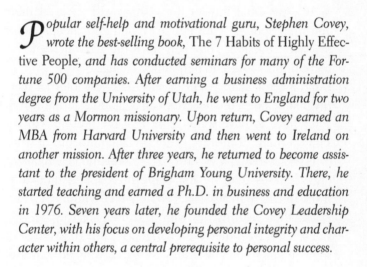

Stephen R. Covey

1932–

*P*opular *self-help and motivational guru, Stephen Covey, wrote the best-selling book,* The 7 Habits of Highly Effective People, *and has conducted seminars for many of the Fortune 500 companies. After earning a business administration degree from the University of Utah, he went to England for two years as a Mormon missionary. Upon return, Covey earned an MBA from Harvard University and then went to Ireland on another mission. After three years, he returned to become assistant to the president of Brigham Young University. There, he started teaching and earned a Ph.D. in business and education in 1976. Seven years later, he founded the Covey Leadership Center, with his focus on developing personal integrity and character within others, a central prerequisite to personal success.*

Ten Keys to Transformation

1. Transformation starts with increased awareness of the need for change. We need an increased awareness of where we are in relation to where we want to be. We can't be in a state of denial about the need for change or about the kind of commitment and effort that it will take. Often increased aware-

ness comes from 360-degree feedback that makes denial difficult and from a stakeholder information and accountability system that drives the transformation process.

2. The next step is to enter into a "co-missioning" process, aligning your personal mission with the mission of your organization. This "co-missioning" is best done through involvement and participation. People must decide for themselves what impact the change will have on them and their sphere of influence. When your people share the same mission, you then have the natural reinforcement in the culture to perpetuate change.

3. Build a sense of internal security. The less internal security people have, the less they can adapt to external reality. They have to have some sense that the ground will not shift on them. If they try to get predictability out of structure and systems, they only create bureaucracy-fossilized organizations that are incapable of adapting quickly to shifts in the marketplace. People won't willingly change unless their security lies within. If their security lies outside themselves, they see change as a threat. We need a sense of permanency and security. Living on unstable ground all the time is like living through an earthquake every day.

4. You next have to make change legitimate at the personal level. If you give people a profound learning experience on listening with empathy, for example, the next day they can do something about it. But if you ask them to do something the day before, they'll rebel against it. They might say: "What are you trying to do? What's wrong with the way we are doing it now?" People must acknowledge:

"I need something that I don't have now." And they know that it won't come by just hoping for it and envisioning it. It involves a change in mind-set and skill set. They must pay the price in a development process to get it.

5. Take personal responsibility for results. Executives and employees often debate the question, "How much of that development should be the duty of the organization, and how much the role and responsibility of the individual?" I think that in the last analysis, competency is up to the individual. The individual should say, "The organization is a resource to me. I can draw upon this resource or go to other resources. If the organization proves not to be a resource to me, then I will have to get the knowledge, skills, and training on my own."

But if we look at training from the chief executive's point of view, I would say: "Yes, the individual is ultimately responsible, but we need to create a supportive environment and provide some resources to help people develop the competency that we need to be competitive." Many governments now give tax credits for training and development to encourage companies to invest in the health of the "goose" that lays the golden eggs.

6. Bury the old. Often there needs to be a "baptism" — a symbolic burial of the old body and taking up of a new body, new name, new position, new place, new language, and a new spirit. This symbolizes not that you have rejected the old, but that you are building upon the old and moving forward. I have seen this done very successfully where people get together and bury the old practices and old ways and all of the guilt associated with them. It becomes a

transition time. In her book *Passages*, Gail Sheehy writes: "Like the lobster, we, too, must shed a protective structure with each passage from one stage of human growth to the next. We are left exposed and vulnerable—but also yeasty and embryonic again, capable of stretching in ways we hadn't known before."

These times of passage also become something that people can look at and laugh about. If they don't take themselves so seriously, they can say: "We'll be making changes the rest our lives. This change process is not a one-shot deal."

7. Embrace the new way with a spirit of adventure. The very process of changing has to change. First, the organization should be centered on natural laws and enduring principles, because those laws are going to operate, regardless. You can't transform a politicized workplace into a quality culture unless you build on principles; otherwise, you won't have the foundation to support reform initiatives.

Principle-centered leaders create a common vision and seek to decrease the restraining forces. Profit-centered leaders often try to increase the driving forces. Temporarily they can make improvements, but these create tensions—and those tensions break out in new problems, requiring new driving forces. Performance dips as people become fatigued and cynical. Management by drives will lead to management by crises.

8. Be open to new options. Major change requires a spirit of adventure since you are in unknown territory. You don't know what will happen or what hand you are going to be dealt, but you are excited to discover what it is so you can appropriately respond to it.

I suggest that you enter into a negotiation or a transformation saying, "Let's begin with the end in mind. The end in mind is that we will have a solution that will be better than what either of us now proposes. We do not know what the end will be. It is something that we will work out between us. Synergy is what we seek. Having an open mind will give us more of an immunity to dichotomous, either-or thinking. So the next time we run into a problem with each other, we can go for something better—a third alternative." If the "end in mind" is more of a spirit or philosophy or relationship than it is a specific outcome, you can be open to new options.

9. Seek synergy with other stakeholders. I was visiting with a CEO the other day, helping him prepare an important speech in which he wanted to deal with the "worsening relationships" inside the organization. I suggested to him that strained relationships are often symptomatic of deeper ills inside the culture—ills such as the spirit of contention and the spirit of adversarialism in the way people solve their problems. I showed the CEO how the habits of interdependency, empathy, and synergy represent a way to deal with difficult issues and still maintain good working relationships. He said, "The other day, I met with an adversary, and said, 'Let's let the spirit of synergy be the spirit of our interaction with each other.' He agreed, and our meeting was fruitful! I was thrilled, but now we are back to our old fighting stances."

I said, "Why don't you be the model of the concept that we solve our problems through synergy. If the trust isn't sufficient for synergy, at least you can have a respectful compromise. But no more name calling or labeling. Set yourself up as the model, and if you falter, acknowledge it by saying, 'I have faltered in the past, and I may falter in the future, but I will acknowledge it in order to set a new pattern of civil dialogue inside our organization.' "

An appreciation of diversity allows for synergy, and synergy creates transformation. When people feel understood and valued, they can transform in their own way instead of according to some norm, clone, or mandate. The chief characteristic of cancer is that it makes all cells the same. It robs them of what makes them unique.

10. The key thing is the transcendent purpose. Today, we are so buried by private and special interests that we don't share a transcendent purpose. The other day, as I met with a group of military generals, I noticed that it was much more difficult for them to create mission statements in peace time as opposed to war time. They're more focused when they have an "enemy." But most turf battles block transformation because you're too concerned about protecting your special interests to have the incentive and motivation to transform. When you see the world in terms of "us versus them," you get into transacting, not transforming.

Transformation of people and organizations happens faster once we have shared awareness and pain. We can then bury the old and get on with the new without carrying all the baggage of "what-might-have-been" deals

---

Extreme Measures

Imagine your funeral, Covey suggests, and there are to be four speakers: a family member, a friend, a work associate, and a member from your community. Imagine what character traits and what achievements you would want each of them to talk about. Now live it.

and "us-versus-them" relationships. Effective leaders "transform" people and organizations—changing them in mind and heart; enlarging vision, insight, mind and understanding; clarifying purposes; making behavior congruent with beliefs, principles, or values; and bringing about permanent, self-perpetuating, and bringing about momentum-building changes.

The Seven Habits of Highly Effective People

1. Be Proactive
   "It means more than merely taking initiative. It means that as human beings, we are responsible for our own lives."
2. Begin with the End in Mind
   "It's based on *imagination*—the ability to envision, to see the potential . . . If you want to have a successful enterprise, you clearly define what you're trying to accomplish."
3. Put First Things First
   "Effective management is putting first things first. While leadership decides what 'first things' are, it is management that puts them first, day-by-day, moment-by-moment. Management is discipline, carrying it out."
4. Think Win/Win
   "Win/Win is a frame of mind and heart that constantly seeks mutual benefit in all human interactions."

(Continued)

5. Seek First to Understand, then to Be Understood
   "When we really, deeply understand each other, we open the door to creative solutions and third alternatives. Our differences are no longer stumbling blocks to communication and progress."
6. Synergize
   "The essence of synergy is to value differences—to respect them, to build on strengths, to compensate for weaknesses."
7. Sharpen the Saw
   "It's preserving and enhancing the greatest asset you have—you. It's renewing the four dimensions of your nature—physical, spiritual, mental, and social/emotional."

PART VII

~

Builders of Culture

Ben Cohen and Jerry Greenfield

1951– , 1951–

*E*very ice cream connoisseur knows Ben and Jerry, who are *famous for their wild flavors and social activism. They met in a high school gym class in their Long Island hometown, and realized they shared a love for food, not athletics. In 1969, they went their separate ways to college, with Ben eventually failing to become a potter and Jerry failing to get into medical school. In 1977, they reunited to start their own business. They mulled over bagels and pizza, but settled on making ice cream where there was little competition: Burlington, Vermont. Ben and Jerry, whose aspirations include building a community as opposed to just a workplace, were cowinners of the 1988 National Small Business Person of the Year Award. It was presented to them by President Ronald Reagan, even though the two were campaigning against Reagan's military buildup.*

Our Aspirations

To BE REAL: We need to be who we say we are, both inside and outside the company. We are all custodians of the reputation of Ben & Jerry's. We will strive to put into practice the words we use to describe ourselves: Friendly, Enthusiastic, Exciting, Caring, High-Quality, Progressive, Off-beat, Innovative, Cutting-Edge, Funny, Lighthearted, Encouraging, Informal, Activist, Honest, Childlike, Down-Home.

TO BE THE BEST: If our customers are euphoric about our products, we will prosper. Our future together depends upon our ability to outperform the competition. That's our business strategy. We want to be the best ice cream company in the world. We want to be viewed as master ice cream makers. We are passionate about giving customers what they want, when they want it, every single time.

TO IMPROVE CONTINUOUSLY: Every time we do something, we should be checking to see if our methods worked and figure out how we can do it better the next time. From the minute we join the company we are responsible for helping to shape and improve what goes on around us.

TO LEARN CONTINUOUSLY: We want people to have the opportunity to develop their potential to contribute to the company. We'll need to keep growing skills in three areas: technical skills to achieve excellence in day-to-day work, personal skills to give life and vitality to these aspirations, and business knowledge to understand the companywide implications and importance of what each of us does.

TO BE INCLUSIVE: We embrace individual differences. The right to be ourselves contributes to our sense of ownership. We perform better and serve the marketplace better when men, women, gays, lesbians, and people of different races, nationalities, ethnicities, and backgrounds work together. Building a diverse staff contributes to excellent performance, not just to societal good.

To Be Creative: Our creativity is our strength. We want to see beyond conventional thinking and come up with ideas that work, that excite our customers and reflect our values.

To Build Community: No one at Ben & Jerry's should feel alone or apart. When one of us needs help, we reach out to help. People from outside feel our energy when they visit us. We have a zest for life, a sense of humor, and we enjoy one another's company. We share the excitement of succeeding at the game of business and we'll try to have fun while we do it.

To Be Open and Trusting: Rationales, strategy, and the truth should be shared. We want to be open about our concerns and admit our mistakes and failings. We need to make sure people feel safe to speak up about things they care about. If we trust one another's good intentions, we'll feel better about trying new things and about speaking up about things that concern us. It's expected that we'll all do the right thing even when nobody is looking.

Outrageous Promotion

To promote ice cream sales in winter, the twosome would take a penny off the cost of a cone for every degree below 0°C, otherwise known as Penny Off Per Celsius Degree Below Zero Winter Extravaganza, or POPCDBZWE. Because their first store was located in Burlington, Vermont, the promotion turned a liability (the cold weather) into an asset.

To Celebrate and to Give Meaningful Recognition: When we reach or exceed our targets, we should cheer. Celebration establishes a sense of accomplishment, which leads to more accomplishments. Celebrations don't need to be elaborate. Recognition is the currency of leadership. We should make recognition a contagious part of everyday life.

TO USE CONSULTIVE DECISION MAKING AND ACTIVE LISTENING: When making decisions we'll involve people with special expertise and people likely to be affected. We'll also give those with a contrary point of view an opportunity to be heard. However, Ben & Jerry's is not a democracy. Leaders need to make calls based on facts, data, and input. In order to practice consultive decision making and to create the conditions for people to contribute their best thinking, we must be active listeners.

TO HOLD OURSELVES ACCOUNTABLE: We all need to do what we said we were going to do and be clear about who's responsible and what's expected. When we don't do our part it affects everybody. We put the company at risk when we tolerate poor performance.

TO BE GREAT COMMUNICATORS: Leaders are responsible for effectively and consistently communicating pertinent information in a timely way. Good leaders have well-informed teams. We're each responsible for absorbing the information offered through company communication vehicles like postings, staff meetings, and *The Rolling Cone*.

TO BE UP-FRONT: People aren't going to do better unless they understand what they need to do to improve. Good straight feedback is essential to improvement. Talking about someone's performance to people other than the person does harm to the individual and to the company.

TO BE PROFITABLE BY BEING THRIFTY: We believe in investing wisely and with a sense of frugality. When we save the company money, we do a service to our shareholders and ourselves.

Ben and Jerry's Social Mission Statement

We have a progressive, nonpartisan social agenda.

We seek peace by supporting nonviolent ways to resolve conflict.

We will look for ways to create economic opportunities for the disenfranchised.

We are committed to practicing caring capitalism.

We seek to minimize our negative impact on the environment.

We support family farming and sustainable methods of food production.

Howard M. Schultz

1953–

As CEO of Starbucks, the international chain of coffee bars, Howard Schultz put romance back in the coffee bean. He grew up in Brooklyn, where his blue-collar family struggled to make ends meet. Fortunately, Schultz won a football scholarship to Northern Michigan University. After earning a business degree in 1975, he became a sales rep for Xerox, and two jobs later joined Seattle-based Starbucks (then just a coffee bean wholesaler) in 1982. After four years, Schultz left the company to start a chain of coffee bars, only to buy Starbucks in 1987 for $3.8 million. He took the company public in 1992 and, as of 1999, the company was operating more than 2,800 stores around the world. Success has depended upon Schultz never compromising his principles when it comes to coffee quality and store atmosphere.

Starbucks Mission Statement

Establish Starbucks as the premier purveyor of the finest coffee in the world while maintaining our uncompromising principles as we grow. The following six guiding principles will help us measure the appropriateness of our decisions:

Provide a great work environment and treat
each other with respect and dignity.

Embrace diversity as an essential component
in the way we do business.

Apply the highest standards of
excellence to the purchasing,
roasting, and fresh delivery
of our coffee.

Develop enthusiastically
satisfied customers all
of the time.

Smart Habits

On the way to work, Schultz
stops by one of several dozen
Seattle-area Starbucks for a cup
of java; it jump-starts his day and
keeps him in touch with the front
lines.

Contribute positively to our communities
and our environment.

Recognize that profitability is essential
to our future success.

Capturing the Customer's Imagination

A taste of romance. At Starbucks stores, people get a five-
or ten-minute break that takes them far from the routine of their daily lives. Where else can you go to get a
whiff of Sumatra or Kenya or Costa Rica? Where else
can you get a taste of Verona or Milan? Just having the
(Continued)

chance to order a drink as exotic as an *espresso mac-chiato* adds a spark of romance to an otherwise unremarkable day.

An affordable luxury. In our stores you may see a policeman or a utility worker standing in line in front of a wealthy surgeon. The blue-collar man may not be able to afford the Mercedes the surgeon just drove up in, but he can order the same $2.00 cappuccino. They're both giving themselves a reward and enjoying something world class.

An oasis. In an increasingly fractured society, our stores offer a quiet moment to gather your thoughts and center yourself. Starbucks people smile at you, serve you quickly, don't harass you. A visit to Starbucks can be a small escape during a day when so many other things are beating you down. We've become a breath of fresh air.

Casual social interaction. One of the advertising agencies that pitched for our business interviewed Los Angeles–area customers in focus groups. The common thread among their comments was this: "Starbucks is so social. We go to Starbucks stores because of a social feeling."

John Wanamaker

1838–1922

John Wanamaker was a pioneer of the modern department store, involved and innovative right up until his final years—he also had quite a reputation for filling notebooks full of maxims in the spirit of Ben Franklin. At age 13, he went to work as an errand boy for a publishing house, earning $1.25 a week. Not long after that, he joined a men's clothing business and rose to salesman, but was then hired by the Philadelphia chapter of the Young Men's Christian Association in 1857. Four years later, Wanamaker and his brother-in-law had saved enough money to buy their own men's clothing business, and then Wanamaker opened his own shop in 1869. It was another seven years until he bought an old freight depot and converted it into "a new kind of store"—a collection of specialty shops under one roof that evolved into today's department store.

The Knows, the Keeps, the Takes, the Gives

Know yourself.
Know your merchandise.
Know how to present yourself and your merchandise.
Keep your mind on your work.
Keep sweet.

Keep listening to your customer rather than talking yourself.

Keep wide awake to effect the sales.

Keep steady at each transaction until goods are wrapped and on the way to delivery.

Take care to be accurate.

Take trouble to be punctual and prompt.

Take pains to spell back the name, number, street and town of the addresses given you.

Take no offence under any circumstances.

Take firm hold of anything that displeases a customer and set it right before leaving it.

Take sufficient time to avoid mistakes.

Give sufficient care to suit the customer, so that goods will stay sold.

Give yourself a little rest between customers, if possible.

Give a call to the medical director, at his office, if in the least sick, so that you will quickly mend a cold and not have to be absent when the store needs you.

Extreme Measures

To force himself to save money, little by little, Wanamaker took out 62 life insurance policies. (At age 50, he was more insured than any other American; at age 57, his policies were worth more than $1.5 million.)

Smart Habits

To enliven his advertising copy, which he personally wrote, Wanamaker studied the dictionary and made his own collection of the most interesting words.

Dave Thomas

1932–

*A*s an adopted child who moved 12 times in 15 years, the founder of Wendy's restaurant chain only knew work to be a "constant companion." During the Korean War, he volunteered and attended the army's Cook and Baker School. Feeding 2,000 hungry soldiers a day taught him "some important skills about the big picture of feeding a lot of people." After the army, he worked as a short-order cook for a man who owned four Kentucky Fried Chicken franchises. The franchises were failing, so Thomas was offered a deal: If he could turn around the KFCs, he would get 45 percent ownership. He made good and then cashed out for $1 million in 1968 to start Wendy's. Thomas, who appears in the company's humorous and disarming TV commercials, enjoys razzing his people to keep them on their toes.

Dave's Rules for Successful Harassment

1. **Make sure people trust you.** I remember when Denny Lynch, our vice president of communications, first started working for us. Denny was so intense, I kept on harassing him to get him to loosen up. One day, I teased him to the brink, and he shot back, "Mr. Thomas, are you questioning my veracity?" I said, "I don't know." Then, I teased him for

three more days for using a word I didn't understand. The more I saw Denny, the more uptight he looked. Finally, it dawned on me that Denny didn't trust me. He thought that since I was always on his case I was one step away from canning him. That wasn't my idea at all. Later I read something in a book called *Leaders* by Warren Bennis and Burt Nanus that stuck with me. In it, they say that Los Angeles Rams coach John Robinson "never criticizes his players until they're convinced of his unconditional confidence in their abilities." That's a good outlook to have.

As for Denny and harassment, he's totally sold on the program now. The other day, I overheard him talking to another guy I'd been badgering. "Don't worry," Denny said. "If he's harassing you, it means he likes you. If he didn't think you could take it or that you were a zero, he wouldn't say a thing."

2. *Start early.* I first met Charlie Rath, our executive vice president of marketing, in 1977. He had just "sold" Wendy's on being the local sponsor for Grand Prix Tennis—the Columbus stop on the professional tennis circuit. Every time I saw Charlie I would ask him when the signs would go up to let people know about the event. Finally, we were getting pretty close to the day the matches would start. Charlie maintained it was about three months before the tournament. I said three days. It was probably more like three weeks. Well, Charlie finally went out and did something. He had a bunch of signs screen-printed and nailed one on each of the nearly five hundred telephone poles between my house and the tennis stadium.

3. *Tell people when they're almost perfect . . . but do it nice.* When Charlie finally got the signs up, I made sure that I

thanked him for the great job. Then I gave him a slip of paper with the addresses of the two phone poles he missed.

4. *Make 'em feel guilty when they do nothing.* One thing I can't stand is people who don't act on a situation. I'd rather that people make mistakes than sit around and not do something.

5. *Don't put up with excuses.* Poor results are bad enough, but weak excuses are even worse. I visit about fifty different markets each year to see Wendy's operations. When I'm on the road, I'll visit as many restaurants as I can.

Extreme Measures

Thomas believes most entrepreneurs get into trouble by offering too many products; so Wendy's, with its down-home atmosphere, kept the exact same limited menu of hamburgers, chili, french fries, Frosty shakes, and various beverages for 10 years.

Most of the time, I'm happy with what we see, but sometimes not. Nothing makes me more unhappy than when I get weak excuses and alibis to explain poor performance. So, I always try to go easier on bad performance than when somebody is punting or lying.

6. *Don't let up until they go out there and find out.* Whenever our marketing people come in and tell me about somebody else's new sandwich, the first thing I'll ask is, "Did ya try it?" If somebody comes up with a new store design, I want to know what it looks like in real life. The same thing goes for problems inside your business. You can get all the reports in the world—most of them written to cover up what the real problems are—but there is no substitute for going out there and nosing around yourself.

You've got to be real careful when you harass people. I just don't think harassment works for managers who are not perceived as nice people by their team. And if people don't know you like them and you start harassing them, they'll just clam up on you or even serve you a knuckle sandwich. But harassment can work. Why? So much of any business is detail and execution, and any manager has to stay on top of it. Harassment is personal communications. It's not some dumb, dull memo that you could just as well address "To Whom It May Concern."

Smart Habits

Every month, Wendy's polls 500 customers to see what they think of the menu, food quality, and the restaurant itself.

7. *Batch things for people.* People tell me that I always have a bunch of lists going on in my head with messages for people. I'm a laundry list type of guy, and I've been blessed with a pretty good memory. When I see somebody, I try to go through my whole list with them. It's really just "packaging," and it's a lot better than writing a bunch of stupid memos. It's not much different from what you do with your kids as they go sailing out the door: "When did you say you were going to clean the basement? The cat's not happy with the litter box . . . and don't forget your galoshes."

8. *Make harassment fun.* Businesses focus too much on "productivity" and too little on fun. I've made more money by having fun than I have not having fun. That would be true for most people, if they gave themselves the chance. A little well-meant harassment is the best way I know to connect hard work and having fun. To me the perfect employee is someone who has fun doing the job.

Mark McCormack

1930–

*I*t took only one client to put Mark McCormack on the road to becoming the most powerful person in sports—the legendary golfer Arnold Palmer, whom he signed in 1959. After earning an undergraduate degree at William & Mary, McCormack attended Yale's Law School and then joined a Cleveland, Ohio, law firm. Not long after, Palmer walked through the door looking for help. Realizing the opportunities that sports agenting and marketing presented, McCormack quit the law firm and founded the International Management Group (IMG) with $500 in start-up capital. Over the years, McCormack added a variety of characters to his stables, from the violinist Itzhak Perlman to tennis star Chris Evert to Tiger Woods, and the firm now has 76 offices in 31 countries. A key to his success has been developing honest relationships devoid of duplicity.

The Ten Most Toxic Lies in Business

The fact is, the workplace is a far healthier environment because of all the little lies that we allow to float harmlessly among us. I'm especially in favour of the white lies that spare other people's feelings, the ones where you don't say what you really think of their unfortunate haircuts or their ridiculous new glasses or their poorly researched reports. Why start a fight or bruise an ego when a few words of innocuous approval will suffice?

However, there is a wholly different sector of lies that are far less benign. These are the clichés and verbal mantras that many people employ to mask their failings at work. These catchphrases are hard to argue with, but you should perk up when you hear them because they often come out of the mouths of people who mean exactly the opposite of what they are saying. Here are 10 of the most common and therefore most dangerous lies in business:

1. "I can keep a secret."

   In my experience people who can keep a confidence don't brag about it because the alternative, namely betraying a confidence, is not an issue with them. People who tell you they can keep a secret invariably don't.

   This is similar to people who say, "I always meet my deadlines," or "I always deliver on time." Punctuality isn't an issue with people who are always on time. They take it for granted. It only matters to people who tend to miss their deadlines.

2. "This was a rational decision."

   People say this in order to take the personal sting out of a decision that will adversely affect you. As if a rational decision deserves a rational response from you. Don't be fooled. There are no perfectly rational decisions. Every decision, even that based on hard numbers, is a series of either/or choices that are founded as much on intuition or personal inclination as anything else. In other words "This was a rational decision" really means "I wanted to do this."

3. "I want totally honest feedback."

When bosses say "I want to know what you really think" they probably mean it. It's the moment after you tell them what you really think that the statement becomes a lie because they don't react to your blunt opinion in a welcoming manner. Whether they resent it or they're hurt by it or they don't believe it, very few are grateful to you for saying it. Consciously or not, they will usually punish you for it.

> ### *Smart Habits*
> McCormack has preferred waking up early enough to spend an hour reading, relaxing, and exercising, before getting ready for work—even if it means setting the alarm for 5:00 A.M. Result: no rushing around and no feeling that work imposes on personal time.

There are plenty of occasions to tell the boss the unvarnished truth. Ironically, when the boss asks for it is not one of them.

4. "The cheque is in the mail."

This is the grandaddy of business lies, so egregious and trite that people laugh about it as they are saying it. Of course the accompanying laugh track doesn't make this lie more palatable. When you hear this the truth is plain and simple: you have a collection problem.

5. "You're the only one we're talking to."

This is the lie about exclusivity. When people tell me I'm the only one they're talking to about a project they're probably telling the truth. What's missing from this sentence, however, is the phrase, ". . . but if things don't go our way we won't hesitate to talk to other people too."

There's nothing wrong with this. We're all adults in business. In any transaction I realize that I don't have the field all to myself. I just wish more people would state their real intentions.

6. "It's business. It's not personal."

You can thank The Godfather for this one.

The truth is everything is personal. All things being equal in business people won't shaft you if they personally like you. In fact they'll go out of their way to help a friend even when all things are less than equal. Likewise they won't hesitate to decide against you if there is no personal connection.

This phrase is not a lie so much as a contradiction. If it's business it only means that there was nothing significantly personal between you.

7. "The customer comes first."

Quite often this is true. But in even the noblest of service businesses people shade the truth. They're selective. They treat customers differently depending on what they think they can get away with. Big customers get taken care of because doing so clearly benefits the business. Little customers get ignored if people perceive there is little risk to their business.

Smart Habits

To avoid interruptions in his workday, McCormack rarely takes a phone call. He also prefers to initiate the phone call so he can prepare what he wants to say and control the flow of conversation.

---

8. "I'll call you right back."

This is more a verbal tic than a lie. People say it to end a phone conversation or because they have to take another call. Unless it serves their interest to call back immediately, people rarely deliver on this promise.

If you're one of those people who are still waiting for the return call, you shouldn't.

9. "We judge people on their performance."

If this were true the workplace would be a perfect meritocracy. The truth is more like "We judge your performance based on how much we like you." People don't get fired for not doing their jobs well. They get canned because someone in authority doesn't like them. It's that simple.

10. "The boss is clueless."

This is more a myth than a lie. It's uttered by every subordinate who thinks he or she is smarter than their boss. It's also a convenient excuse when an unpopular decision needs explaining. Don't believe it. There are usually sounder reasons for an unpopular decision than the boss' purported ignorance.

> ### Extreme Measures
>
> If you want to get in with an *inaccessible* bigwig for business reasons, McCormack advises befriending a friend of the bigwig and then using your now mutual acquaintance as a reference to gain access.

*R*ene McPherson was a maverick CEO whose progressive management style at the Dana Corporation made him famous. After a stint in the USAAF, he earned a B.S. degree from Case Institute of Technology and an MBA from Harvard in 1952. He then joined Dana, an auto parts manufacturer with a strong international presence, eventually becoming CEO. The company was wallowing in bureaucracy, so he cut 350 people from a corporate staff of 500, decentralized operations, encouraged employees to participate in the Dana stock plan, and established Dana University (a premier in-house training program). In addition, McPherson, whose maverick policies created an extremely productive climate, oversaw the purchase of 24 companies from 1963 to 1980 to diversify and to improve the company's financial performance.

Creating a Productive Climate

There are a few contributions toward a productive climate that are basic enough to fit any organizational application:

- *Nothing more effectively involves people, sustains credibility or generates enthusiasm than face-to-face communication. As a* total group, both within departments and on an individual basis, our people must meet regularly to discuss goals, objectives, financial performance, the status of suggestions, the future or whatever else is on their minds. I do not believe in corporate procedures; they are counterproductive and restrict the flexibility of people to respond to the unpredictable. They also retard the inventiveness, professional development and accountability of managers. Among the few corporate policies that must survive, however, is the one requiring managers and leaders to meet with *all* of their people regularly—to talk, to explain and to *listen*.

- *It is critical to provide and discuss all organizational performance figures with all of our people.* Bad news is as important as good news, and candor is essential. If we are managing well, our people have tough goals to meet, and they must know how they are doing as judged against performance yardsticks. Regular meetings help ensure that our goals are understood, and offer the opportunity to share the recognition for having met the challenges.
- *We have an obligation to provide training and the opportunity for development to our productive people who want to improve their skills, expand their career opportunities or simply further their general education.* Tailor the programs to their specific requirements and listen to their evaluations of those programs. Forget about trying to cost-justify education; rely instead on instinct. Everyone responds positively to needs that are, or can be, satisfied. Smart companies during the last recession used the period as an opportunity.
- *This is the most difficult: It is essential to provide job security for our people.* Concentrate on eliminating cyclitility and

business fluctuation as well as on establishing an environment where layoffs and work shortages are not considered
to be as inevitable as they once were. Most of our people
are well insulated from the shock of a layoff to their earnings through a series of income-protection plans. But no
matter how sheltered our peo-
ple are by supplemental unem-
ployment benefits, layoffs are
bad. They create an attitude of
uncertainty, disrupt productive
programs, undermine our credibility and erode the spirit of
optimism and aggressiveness so
important in our work areas.
They have the effect of saying
to our people, "As hard as you
work, and as valuable as your
ideas are, we don't need you
right now." We do need them,
and we need to correct situations that cause employment
interruptions. It takes excellent leaders and exceptional
long-term planning to accomplish this.

> ### *Extreme Measures*
> When McPherson became CEO, he replaced 17-inch-thick company manuals with concise policy statements, put an end to management reports that generated over 400 pages each month, terminated the use of memos for communication so managers would meet face-to-face, and removed all time clocks from their facilities.

- *Create incentive programs that rely on ideas and suggestions,
  as well as on hard work, to establish a reward pool.* Then distribute this pool as a percent of income to *everyone* in the
  particular operation, without respect to rank. Group cohe-
  sion is vital.

I learned years ago that most organizations are too large to
be run from one office or through the sheer dynamism of a few

individuals. I also learned that if we do not listen to our people, encourage them to participate and recognize the immense talent they have, we shall fall short of our growth expectations and our obligation to provide our constituencies the performance they expect.

Mary Kay Ash

$\mathcal{M}$ary Kay Ash is perhaps best recognized by the pink car she awards top cosmetics saleswomen. Ash, who infuses her management philosophy with the Golden Rule, attributes her success to her mother. While growing up in Texas, her father suffered from tuberculosis and her mother supported the family. Subsequently, Ash had more than her share of household chores, so her mother encouraged her with the mantra: "You can do it." After working 11 years as a sales rep for Stanley Home Products, Ash quit to start her own business when a male assistant, who'd been with the company less than two years, became her boss. Unfortunately, a month before Mary Kay Cosmetics was to open in 1963, her husband had a fatal heart attack and all seemed lost. She later reflected, however, "No matter what anyone thought, I just couldn't give up my dream."

Treat People Fairly

Solving management problems by applying the Golden Rule means treating people fairly and according to merit, not merely using them for self-serving purposes. To some this seems in conflict with a company's profit motive; I think, however, the two can be harmonious. For instance, a person may ask for an unreasonably high increase in salary, one that does not give the company a fair return for services rendered. "My wife lost her job, and we have two kids in college," an employee may plead; "I need a raise." A good manager will be sympathetic, but he can't always comply with even the most justifiable wants and needs of his employees. In order to balance responsibilities to the company, the employee, and all other employees, every manager must be able to say no.

I understand that this can be unpleasant. But instead of approaching the job as a task to be endured—I try to turn it into a positive situation. I want that employee to turn a "no" into the motivation for accomplishing more. And I do this with four simple steps.

Extreme Measures

Ash wrote her goals on her bathroom mirror at home, so that she would have to face them every morning.

---

1. It is imperative that each employee be confident that no decision will be arbitrary. And so the first thing I do is to listen and then restate the question. This reassures the employee that I do indeed understand the scope of his problem.
2. I clearly list the logical reasons why his request cannot be granted.
3. I give a direct "no" statement. This is so important if you are to build trust and respect among people. It's not fair to expect someone else to surmise or guess your real intent.
4. And finally I try to suggest how the employee's goal may be reached by some other path. For example, to this hypothetical employee I might say, "Bill, I am truly sorry about

your wife's misfortune. But you know, she may be on the threshold of a whole new career. This could be your opportunity to help her discover her real talents. God didn't have time to make a nobody; we all have the capacity for greatness. Why don't you sit down with her tonight and talk about what she would really like to accomplish next?"

> ### Smart Habits
>
> Whether speaking with a work associate or a friend, Ash espouses looking them directly in the eye at all times—a wandering eye equates to a wandering mind.

A good manager will confront problems of this nature with sensitivity and seek the best solutions. But the solutions cannot compromise his responsibility to his company or to other people within the organization.

Establishing Yourself

- Always be *truthful* with your employees. If they ask for information you cannot reveal, say so. If they ask something that you don't know—say that as well. Most people are very quick to discern a smoke screen.
- Be *consistent* in facts and attitude. Not only will this help employees understand you, but it will also allow them to function with security.
- Be *relaxed* and *confident* when dealing with others. Even something as obvious as using a calm tone of voice can put

your employees at ease. Think things through before you say them (be certain you are saying what you mean) and be yourself.

- Whenever possible, *use "we" instead of "I"* when discussing your people with others. Word will definitely get back that you accept and respect their contributions.
- Finally, always *remember where you came from,* and bear in mind that your future in management depends upon your ability to work well with people. While pomp is something that fascinates all of us on occasion, pomposity is never admirable—least of all in a manager.

Thomas J. Watson, Jr.

1914–1993

*B*ack in 1987, Fortune *magazine selected IBM CEO Thomas Watson as "the greatest capitalist in history." Yet, while growing up he was known as "Terrible Tom;" in prep school he tried marijuana; and he barely graduated from Brown University. Watson was commissioned a second lieutenant in the air force, and quickly learned how to manage the men under his command during World War II. He realized "that I had the force of personality to get my ideas across to others." After the war, Watson was prepared to work as a pilot for United Air Lines, but his commanding general convinced him to return to IBM, where he'd been in sales before the war. He quickly rose through the ranks, became president in 1952, and succeeded his father as chairman in 1956. It was a period of tumultuous change, but Watson succeeded by focusing on good old human relations.*

What Growth and Change Have Taught Us

In looking back on the history of a company, one can't help but reflect on what the organization has learned from its years in business. In thinking specifically of the period since the war when IBM faced the twin challenges of great technological change and growth, I would say that we've come out with five key lessons. They may not be applicable to all companies. All I can do is attest to the great value these five lessons had for us.

1. There is simply no substitute for good human relations and for the high morale they bring. It takes good people to do the jobs necessary to reach your profit goals. But good people alone are not enough. No matter how good your people may be, if they don't really like the business, if they don't feel

   ### Savvy Leadership

   Never hesitate to promote someone you don't like, Watson advised. He preferred scratchy, harsh, unpleasant folks who told it like it was. If a promoted lieutenant erred, Watson put him/her in his so-called penalty box, which amounted to a boring job off the fast track, until they redeemed themselves.

   totally involved in it, or if they don't think they're being treated fairly—it's awfully hard to get a business off the ground. Good human relations are easy to talk about. The real lesson, I think, is that you must work at them all the time and make sure your managers are working with you.

2. There are two things an organization must increase far out of proportion to its growth rate if that organization is to overcome the problems of change. The first of these is communication, upward and downward. The second is education and retraining.

3. Complacency is the most natural and insidious disease of large corporations. It can be overcome if management will set the right tone and pace and if its lines of communication are in working order.

4. Everyone—particularly in a company such as IBM—must place company interest above that of a division or depart-

ment. In an interdependent organization, a community of effort is imperative. Cooperation must outrank self-interest, and an understanding of the company's particular approach to things is more important than technical ability.

5. And the final and most important lesson: Beliefs must always come before policies, practices, and goals. The latter must always be altered if they are seen to violate fundamental beliefs. The only sacred cow in an organization should be its basic philosophy of doing business.

The British economist Walter Bagehot once wrote: "Strong beliefs win strong men and then make them stronger." To this I would add, "And as men become stronger, so do the organizations to which they belong."

PART VIII

~

Maxims for Life

Al Neuharth

1924–

*W*hen the future founder of USA Today and Gannett chairman was only 22 months old, his dad died, and at age 10, Neuharth took a newspaper delivery job at 12 cents a week to help fill the family coffers. In high school, he first pursued journalism, and he was editor of the school's paper in his senior year. After serving in World War II, he studied at the University of South Dakota (his home state), and then cofounded SoDak Sports, a newspaper that was dedicated to sports. It folded after two years. Neuharth, who merrily refers to himself as an S.O.B., went on to work for the Miami Herald and the Detroit Free Press, and was eventually offered the job of managing two of the Gannett's 16 papers. Neuharth lived by his own rules, which included how to avoid burnout, and eventually became Gannett's chairman, launching USA Today in 1982.

An S.O.B.'s Ten Secrets to Success

- Expect others to do unto you what you would do unto them.
- Somebody wants something you have. Protect it.
- Somebody has something you want. Go for it.
- Be as nice as possible, only as nasty as necessary.
- Treasure your family and your roots but never turn back.

Outrageous Promotion

To ensure that he received a standing ovation when it came time to announce the launch of *USA Today* to 400 Gannett executives, Neuharth had a few allies placed strategically throughout the crowd with instructions to start the "spontaneous standing ovation" at the right moment.

- Explore the byways as well as the highways of life.
- Think Big. Big dreams. Big risks. Big rewards.
- Scramble to the top and don't tiptoe while you're there.
- Bow out while all your marbles are still intact.
- Life's a game. Play it to win. And to enjoy.

How to Avoid Burnout

Whether at home or away, I take care of myself.

Executives who pride themselves on hard work but ignore fun and fitness are candidates for career burnout.

People ask me why I appear so relaxed after a long day of work or days of travel: It's simple. Be very particular about what you put into your body and how you use it. You too can feel great if you:

- Eat only when you're hungry.
- Drink only when you're thirsty.
- Sleep only when you're tired.
- Screw only when you're horny.

There may be more scientific ways to achieve fun and fitness in a first-class way, but I haven't found them yet.

Kemmons Wilson

1913–

$\mathcal{K}$emmons Wilson, founder of Holiday Inns and father of the modern hotel, was just nine months old when his own father died. To help support the family, he dropped out of high school and worked as a stock boy for a cotton broker, and then he built up a pinball machine franchise. During the Great Depression, he bought cheap property and built homes. The idea for a motel chain came to him when he drove his family from Memphis to Washington, D.C. in 1951—motel choices were limited and not kid-friendly. Beginning in 1952, he built four motels around Memphis, just off the highways to cater to travelers. When Wilson retired in 1979, there were 1,759 Holiday Inns in 50 countries—the result of his down-to-earth beliefs that draw upon a positive mental attitude.

Twenty Tips for Success

1. Work only a half a day; it makes no difference which half—it can be either the first 12 hours or the last 12 hours.
2. Work is the master key that opens the door to all opportunities.

3. Mental attitude plays a far more important role in a person's success or failure than mental capacity.
4. Remember that we all climb the ladder of success one step at a time.
5. There are two ways to get to the top of an oak tree. One way is to sit on an acorn and wait; the other way is to climb it.
6. Do not be afraid of taking a chance. Remember that a broken watch is exactly right at least twice every 24 hours.
7. The secret of happiness is not in doing what one likes, but in liking what one does.
8. Eliminate from your vocabulary the words, "I don't think I can" and substitute, "I know I can."
9. In evaluating a career, put opportunity ahead of security.
10. Remember that success requires half luck and half brains.
11. A person has to take risks to achieve.

Smart Habits

To save time while on the road, at restaurants Wilson would order and eat his dessert while waiting for his main course.

---

12. People who take pains never to do more than they get paid for, never get paid for anything more than they do.
13. No job is too hard as long as you are smart enough to find someone else to do it for you.
14. Opportunity comes often. It knocks as often as you have an ear trained to hear it, an eye trained to see it, a hand trained to grasp it, and a head trained to use it.
15. You cannot procrastinate—in two days, tomorrow will be yesterday.
16. Sell your wristwatch and buy an alarm clock.

17. A successful person realizes his personal responsibility for self-motivation. He starts himself because he possesses the key to his own ignition switch.

18. Do not worry. You can't change the past, but you sure can ruin the present by worrying over the future. Remember that half the things we worry about never happen, and the other half are going to happen anyway. So, why worry?

> ### *Extreme Measures*
> To find great hotel locations, Wilson flew his own plane—often upside down for a better view—and more than once almost crashed in his excitement.

19. It is not how much you have but how much you enjoy that makes happiness.

20. Believe in God and obey the Ten Commandments.

Carley Fiorina

1954–

*A*s the first outsider to be named CEO of Hewlett-Packard (HP), Carley Fiorina has her work cut out. Founded by William Hewlett and Dave Packard in 1938 in a Palo Alto garage, HP is considered the birthplace of Silicon Valley, and has a rich and staid culture that tends to resist change. After graduating from Stanford University in 1976 with degrees in medieval history and philosophy, Fiorina taught English in Italy. She then received an MBA from the University of Maryland and subsequently joined AT&T. Fiorina, who has a reputation for dogged determination and clear vision, helped execute the Lucent Technologies spin-off in 1996 and was named chief of Lucent's $20 billion Global Service Provider business. HP recruited her in 1999, and at that time, she became one of only three women running Fortune 500 companies.

Seven Principles for Personal and Business Growth

- Recognize the power of the team; no one succeeds alone.

- "Never, never, never, never give in," to quote Winston Churchill. Most great wins happen on the last play.

- Strike a balance between confidence and humility—enough confidence to know that you can make a real difference, enough humility to ask for help.

- Love what you do. Success requires passion.

- Seek tough challenges: they're more fun.

Savvy Leadership

After giving a speech to employees, Fiorina shouts, "Send me 'The 10 Stupidest Things We Do!' I'll read it!"

- Have an unflinching, clear-eyed vision of the goal, followed by absolute clarity, realism and objectivity about what it really will take to grow, to lead and to win.

- Understand that the only limits that really matter are those you put on yourself, or that a business puts on itself. Most people and businesses are capable of far more than they realize.

Conrad Hilton

1887–1971

*T*he *founder of the Hilton Hotels Corporation knew both poverty and glamour: Conrad Hilton grew up in New Mexico in the same "primitive adobe" that housed his father's general store; he later married and divorced Zsa Zsa Gabor and became the proud owner of the Waldorf-Astoria. After attending the New Mexico School of Mines for two years and serving in the army during World War I, Hilton desperately wanted to be an independent banker. An old friend advised him to seek his fortune in Texas, because where there's oil there's action. When Hilton tried to find a hotel bed his first night in Texas, he couldn't and he knew immediately what to buy—not a bank, but a hotel. Hilton was always a big dreamer who refused to cling to the past, two elements he lists in his art for living.*

There Is an Art to Living

Find Your Own Particular Talent: As surely as none of us was given the exact same thumb print, so surely none of us possesses the exact same talent. This does not mean there will not be two housewives, two carpenters, two artists or two hotel men.

We each have two thumbs. But the individual print is uniquely our own.

Emerson says, "Each man has his own vocation. The talent is the call . . . He inclines to do something which is easy for him, and good when it is done, but which no other man can do . . . His ambition is exactly proportioned to his powers. The height of the pinnacle is determined by the breadth of the base."

Finding this particular talent or vocation is the first step in the art of successful living. Great frustration and the *feel* of failure can be present in the face of material success if we follow someone else's footsteps rather than our own. . . .

Be Big: Think Big. Act Big. Dream Big.

Your value is determined by the mold you yourself make. It doesn't take any more energy to expect to be the best housewife, the finest cook, the most capable carpenter.

It has been my experience that the way most people court failure is by misjudging their abilities, belittling their worth and value. Did you ever think what can happen to a plain bar of iron, worth about $5.00? The same iron when made into horseshoes is worth $10.50. If made into needles, it is worth $3,250.85, and if turned into balance springs for watches its value jumps to $250,000.

The same is true of another kind of material—You! . . .

Be Honest: What I have in mind is something more than the negative virtues of not cheating, not lying, not stealing. It is a bold, direct, open stand for the truth as we know it, both to ourselves and others. My mother had two old-fashioned quotations she dished out with our oatmeal. The first was Shakespeare: "To thine own self be true, and it must follow as the night the day, Thou canst not then be false to any man." The second was Sir Walter Scott: "Oh, what a tangled web we weave, when first we practice to deceive!"

Once you start it, there's no place that deception can stop— and of course it has to start with self-deception, even if it's only the self-deception of believing we can get away with it. True, sometimes we are not "discovered." But all of modern psychology and psychiatry is based on the belief that our self-deceptions drive things into our subconscious where they make all kinds of trouble. . . .

Live with Enthusiasm: It has been my experience that there is nothing worth doing that can be done without it. Ability you must have, but ability sparked with enthusiasm. Enthusiasm is an inexhaustible force, so mighty that you must ever tame and temper it with wisdom. Use it and you will find yourself constantly moving forward to new forms of expression.

If you have enthusiasm for life you cannot ever know an inactive time of life. Sir Christopher Wren, the famed architect who built fifty-two churches in London, retired from public life at eighty-six. After that he spent five years in literary, astronomical and religious pursuits. Cato, at eighty, studied Greek; and Plutarch, almost as old, Latin. Titian painted a masterpiece at ninety-eight. Verdi wrote his great opera, *Othello*, at seventy-four, and *Falstaff* at eighty. What is that but continued enthusiasm for life?

Everyone faces hardships along their chosen path. What carries them through? Makes them work and pray with no thought of quitting? Enthusiasm! After working long and hard to accumulate his first $50, Frank Woolworth saw three of his first five chain stores fail. The *Saturday Evening Post* lost $800,000 for Cyrus H. K. Curtis before a single dollar of profit came in. Twenty-seven million dollars and eleven years of work were behind the first pound of Nylon sold by DuPont.

There is no such thing as being "a little bit enthusiastic." You either are or aren't. If you aren't you face failure and boredom. You can't take it by the spoonful. . . .

Don't Let Your Possessions Possess You: I have in my lifetime had everything—and nothing. In my Bible it doesn't say that *money* is the root of all evil, but the *"love of"* money. I believe that to be true and I believe the exact same to be true about possessions.

They are very nice to have, to enjoy, to share. But if you find even one that you can't live without—hasten to give it away. Your very freedom depends on it.

We have all heard of the lack of sense of the monkey who will put his paw into the narrow mouth of a bottle, grasp a desired nut or bit of food, and refuse to let it go even though the fist he has made makes his hand too large to draw it from the bottle again. "Silly thing," we say, "he hasn't really got the food— and he's attached to the bottle. All he has to do is open his hand and let go."

We laugh. But is it so funny? The monkey has lost his freedom. Do we guard ourselves from falling into the same trap?

Don't Worry about Your Problems: The successful life is a balanced life and includes thought, action, rest, recreation. The artist in living will neither work himself to death nor play until he reaches satiety. Now the chronic worrier is all out of balance. He is like a dog with a bone. Problems, and we all have them, are puzzles offered us for solution and we solve them by keeping in balance, alert mentally and well physically, or we handicap ourselves. To worry your difficulties after the sun is set and you have done all you can for the day is useless—and an act of distrust. . . .

Don't Cling to the Past: Not through regret. Not through longing. To do so is to tie yourself to a memory, for yesterday is gone. It is wisdom to profit by yesterday's mistakes. It is fatal to hang onto yesterday's victories. You limit yourself. The future should be expanding. Yesterday's experiences are the foundation on which you build today.

A man walking with his eyes turned backward is very apt to fall into a ditch. It has been said that I would never part with certain hotels. This is not true. If I have had to let go of a success (and I have had to many times) to build an expanding future, then I've released yesterday. We can only act *now* and then look forward to more activity, greater fulfillment.

To be haunted by past failures or satisfied with past successes is to arrest forward motion. . . .

Look Up to People When You Can—Down to No One: Who and what is your neighbor? Do you know him?

Let's take a man standing at 50th Street and Park Avenue in New York City; he is waiting for the light to turn. Who is he? To the statistician standing at the window high above, he is one unit in a crowd. To the biologist he is a specimen; to the physicist a formula of mass and energy; to the chemist a compound of substances. He is of interest to the historian as one of the billions of beings who have inhabited this planet of ours; to the politician as a vote; to the merchandiser as a customer;

to the mailman as an address. The behaviorist sees him from his office across the street and tags him as an animal modified by conditioned reflexes; and the psychiatrist in the next suite as a particular mental type deviating in one way or another from the alleged normal.

> ### Extreme Measures
> To finance his growing hotel empire, Hilton borrowed against his own life insurance policy, even though he had a wife and three children to worry about should the worst happen.

Each science pinpoints the poor fellow from some particular angle and makes him look foolish, like the candid camera shot that catches you in the middle of a yawn. Let any one of these specialists pigeonhole you and get you to look at yourself through his single eye and what you will see will not be a man, but a fragment of a man. . . .

As we strive to know more about people, to understand rather than to be understood, we are in a better position to fulfill the commandment to "love our neighbor as ourselves."

Assume Your Full Share of Responsibility for the World in Which You Live: Develop your own policy, domestic and foreign. Give it thought. And then effort. Stand on it! Stand for it! Live it!

The whole purpose of democracy is for the participation of the individual. The will of the people. You cannot have "government of the people, by the people, for the people" without the active participation of those people.

Nor can your life be a personal success unless, as a citizen, tourist, voter, you share in shaping your own world. . . .

The successful American will not be indifferent. He will let his enthusiasms sweep into his patriotism and be an *individual* cog in the wheels that lead to a better world. President Eisenhower has truly said: "We are not helpless prisoners of history. We are free men." But only so long as the individual desires it! And works for it!

Henry J. Kaiser

Industrialist Henry Kaiser's firm was a major partner in building both the great Boulder and Grand Coulee dams, and he became a World War II hero due to his company's shipbuilding achievements. To help support the family, he dropped out of school at age 11 and was an errand boy for a local photographer. Before reaching age 20, Kaiser had saved enough money to buy the photographer out. In 1906, he became a salesman for a construction company, and in 1913, he founded his own street paving company. Kaiser, who had great faith in himself, soon moved into heavy construction and the manufacturing of steel, aluminum, and cement, among other ventures. Boulder Dam was completed in 1935 and Coulee in 1941. When World War II started, his company had never built a ship, but went on to construct almost 1,500.

Imagine Your Future

1. Know yourself and decide what you want most of all to make out of your life. Then write down your goals and a plan to reach them.

   What would you rather accomplish than anything else in the world?

Do you want to be a millionaire?—And if so, I hope you will include becoming a *millionaire in the real things of life*, as well as in money. Do you want to become a great engineer, teacher, businessman, industrialist, statesman, farmer, or home-maker, or what?

Before you can decide clearly and rightly upon your inmost desires in life, you need to analyze what you have to offer. . . .

2. *Use the great powers that you can tap through faith in God and the hidden energies of your soul and sub-conscious mind.*

Over and over, in an infinite number and variety of proofs in the lives of folks, I have seen how man can draw upon the High Power and the soul within him.

Call it the sub-conscious mind or the soul, there is in every human being a reservoir of inspiration and intuitions—the source from which spring the emotions and the driving force for good.

3. *Love people and serve them.*

This is practical. I can think of hundreds of successful persons whose careers prove that it works. A pervading, fundamental love of people—all people—is an unfailing mark of the finest characters. An ingrained attitude of, "What will I get out of it?" leads up a blind alley to failure.

4. *Develop your positive traits of character and personality.*

You don't have to blow the top off an I.Q. test or be the son or daughter of genius to succeed. You don't have to be at the head of your class, in order to pass by the

---

Smart Habits

To keep a positive mental attitude, Kaiser adopted "Oh, What a Beautiful Morning" as his number one theme song.

ones who were first in grades but lacking in fundamental aspects of character and personality.

5. *Work! Put your life's plan into determined action and go after what you want with all that's in you.*

My mother used to say to me from the days of my earliest memories, "Henry, nothing ever is accomplished without work. If I left you nothing else but a will to work, I would leave you the most priceless gift."

B. C. Forbes

1880–1954

*T*he founder of Forbes *magazine and a publishing empire was 1 of 10 children born to a tailor in Scotland. At the age of 14, B. C. Forbes agreed to a seven-year apprenticeship as a compositor for a local newspaper, thinking he'd learn to write, but to his chagrin, he discovered it meant grueling typesetting work. So he took a shorthand writing course (a prerequisite for journalists) and convinced the newspaper to make him a reporter. In 1902, he left Scotland for South Africa in search of adventure during the Boer War, which pitted Great Britain against white South Africans. In 1904, Forbes immigrated to the United States, where he found work in New York City, writing for several publications. Forbes founded his namesake in 1917, and after years of rubbing elbows with top executives and managing his own business, he developed quite a checklist for success.*

Keys to Success

Your success depends upon you.
Your happiness depends upon you.
You have to steer your own course.
You have to shape your own fortune.
You have to educate yourself.

You have to do your own thinking.

You have to live with your own conscience.

Your mind is yours and can be used only by you.

You come into the world alone.

You go to the grave alone.

You are alone with your inner thoughts during the journey between.

You must make your own decisions.

You must abide by the consequences of your acts.

"I cannot make you well unless you make yourself well," an eminent doctor often tells his patients.

You alone can regulate your habits and make or unmake your health.

You alone can assimilate things mental and things material.

Said a Brooklyn preacher, offering his parishioners communion one Sunday: "I cannot give you the blessings and the benefits of this holy feast. You must appropriate them for yourselves. The banquet is spread; help yourself freely.

"You may be invited to a feast where the table is laden with the choicest foods, but unless you partake of the foods, unless you appropriate and assimilate them, they can do you no good. So it is with this holy feast. You must appropriate its blessings. I cannot infuse them into you."

You have to do your own assimilation all through life.

You may be taught by a teacher, but you have to imbibe the knowledge. He cannot transfuse it into your brain.

You alone can control your mind cells and your brain cells.

You may have spread before you the wisdom of the ages, but unless you assimilate it you derive no benefit from it; no one can force it into your cranium.

You alone can move your own legs.

You alone can use your own arms.

You alone can utilize your own hands.

You alone can control your own muscles.

You must stand on your feet, physically and metaphorically.

You must take your own steps.

Your parents cannot enter into your skin, take control of your mental and physical machinery, and make something of you.

You cannot fight your son's battles; that he must do for himself.

You have to be captain of your own destiny.

You have to see through your own eyes.

You have to use your own ears.

You have to master your own faculties.

You have to solve your own problems.

You have to form your own ideals.

You have to create your own ideas.

Smart Habits

Don't be afraid to kick your feet up on your desk, close your eyes, and do some serious thinking, Forbes advised. At the very least, Forbes said that one or two nights a week should be dedicated to intense thought about both business and life. In the hustle and bustle of the world, not enough people set aside time for undisturbed, reflective thinking.

You must choose your own speech.

You must govern your own tongue.

Your real life is your thoughts.

Your thoughts are of your own making.

Your character is your own handiwork.

You alone can select the materials that go into it.

You alone can reject what is not fit to go into it.

You are the creator of your own personality.

You can be disgraced by no man's hand but your own.

You can be elevated and sustained by no man save yourself.

You have to write your own record.

You have to build your own monument—or dig your own pit.

Which are you doing?

Benjamin Franklin

1706–1790

B enjamin Franklin is the archetypal American entrepreneur *and businessman, and is renowned for his puritan maxims that appeared in his* Poor Richard's Almanac. *It did not come easy. Franklin was a poor student who failed in math, and at the age of 12, he was forced into an apprenticeship under his older brother, a printer, that was supposed to last until he was 21. By age 17, Franklin had had enough, and escaped Boston for Philadelphia, where he worked for another printer before he founded the* Pennsylvania Gazette *in 1728 and built a renowned print shop. He printed books, started* Gazettes *in Rhode Island and South Carolina, became the "public" printer for several states, and published the priceless* Poor Richard's Almanac *from 1732 to 1757—not to mention that he was a respected diplomat and helped draft the* Declaration of Independence.

Thirteen Virtues

1. TEMPERANCE
   Eat not to dullness; drink not to elevation.

2. SILENCE
   Speak not but what may benefit others or yourself; avoid trifling conversation.

3. ORDER

Let all your things have their places; let each part of your business have its time.

4. RESOLUTION

Resolve to perform what you ought; perform without fail what you resolve.

5. FRUGALITY

Make no expense but to do good to others or yourself; *i.e.,* waste nothing.

6. INDUSTRY

Lose no time; be always employ'd in something useful; cut off all unnecessary actions.

7. SINCERITY

Use no hurtful deceit; think innocently and justly; and, if you speak, speak accordingly.

8. JUSTICE

Wrong none by doing injuries, or omitting the benefits that are your duty.

9. MODERATION

Avoid extreams; forbear resenting injuries so much as you think they deserve.

10. CLEANLINESS

Tolerate no uncleanliness in body, cloaths, or habitation.

Smart Habits

Franklin made a grid with the days of the week across the top and 13 virtues down the side, and at the end of each day he would mark what virtues he had violated. Each week he would focus on a particular virtue, hoping that after a 13-week period he would have much greater strength of character.

TEMPERANCE. EAT NOT TO DULLNESS; DRINK NOT TO ELEVATION.							
	S.	M.	T.	W.	T.	F.	S.
T.							
S.	*	*		*		*	
O.	**	*	*		*	*	*
R.			*			*	
F.		*			*		
I.			*				
S.							
J.							
M.							
C.							
T.							
C.							
H.							

11. TRANQUILLITY

Be not disturbed at trifles, or at accidents common or unavoidable.

12. CHASTITY

Rarely use venery but for health or offspring, never to dulness, weakness, or the injury of your own or another's peace or reputation.

13. HUMILITY

Imitate Jesus and Socrates.

The precept of *Order* requiring that *every part of my business should have its allotted time,* one page in my little book contain'd the following scheme of employment for the twenty-four hours of a natural day.

THE MORNING. *Question.* What good shall I do this day?	5 6 7	Rise, wash, and address *Powerful Goodness!* Contrive day's business, and take the resolution of the day; prosecute the present study, and breakfast.
	8 9 10 11	Work.
NOON.	12 1	Read, or overlook my accounts, and dine.
	2 3 4 5	Work.
EVENING. *Question.* What good have I done to-day?	6 7 8 9	Put things in their places. Supper. Music or diversion, or conversation. Examination of the day.
	10 11 12	
NIGHT.	1 2 3 4	Sleep.

Acknowledgments

I was having lunch with Ed Knappman, my agent, and naming all the business legends who had their own unique list of habits and/or tips for success. Surely, I said, the lists could be combined to create the ultimate capitalist manifesto. Ed responded: "The better book would be a collection of those lists, plain and simple." He was right, and I tip my hat to Ed. Thanks also to my good friend, Ruth Mills, who took on the project, and to Airié Dekidjiev, who is now my caretaker. It's also very important to acknowledge the many authors and editors who had the foresight to distill respective business philosophies to the pithy templates found in this book. As always, thanks to Sasha Kintzler, to many others at John Wiley & Sons whom I have yet to meet, and to North Market Street Graphics. Diana, Pierson, Alex, and Julia—you're the best.

Credits and Sources

renewed © 1964 by Donna Dale Carnegie. Revised edition copyright © 1981 by Donna Dale Carnegie and Dorothy Carnegie.

"12 Commandments for Speculators" from *Art of Speculation* by Philip Carret. Published by *Barron's*, 1930.

"The Study of the Stock Market" from *The Wall Street Point of View* by Henry Clews. Published by Silver, Burdett and Company, 1900.

"Our Aspirations" from *Ben and Jerry's Doubledip* by Ben Cohen and Jerry Greenfield. Copyright © 1997 by Ben Cohen and Jerry Greenfield. Reprinted with the permission of Simon & Schuster.

"Keys to Transformation" by Stephen Covey, from *Executive Excellence*, December 1995. Used with permission of Excellence Publishing.

"The Competitive Edge" from *Direct from Dell* by Michael Dell with Catherine Fredman. Copyright © 1999 by Michael Dell. Reprinted by permission of HarperCollins Publishers, Inc.

"Lessons for Leading People" by Peter F. Drucker, from *Leader to Leader*, Fall 1996. Copyright © 1996 by Peter F. Drucker. Reprinted by permission of Jossey-Bass, Inc., a subsidiary of John Wiley & Sons, Inc.

"Seven Principles for Personal and Business Success" by Carley Fiorina, from *The New York Times*, September 29, 1999.

"Keys to Success" from *Keys to Success* by B. C. Forbes, 1917.

"Principles of Service" from *My Life and Work* by Henry Ford with Samuel Crowther. Published by Doubleday, Page & Company, 1922.

"What an Employer Wants" by Henry Ford, II, from *Listen to Leaders in Business*, edited by Albert Love and James Saxon Childers. Copyright © 1963 by Tupper & Love, Inc.

"Shut Up and Listen" from *Lady Boss* by Jo Foxworth. New York: Thomas J. Crowell, Publishers, 1978.

"Thirteen Virtues" from the *Autobiography* by Ben Franklin. John Bigelow, ed., *The Complete Works of Benjamin Franklin*, 1904.

"New Rules for the Age of Information" from *Business at the Speed of Thought* by Bill Gates. Copyright © 1999 by William H. Gates, III. Used by permission of Warner Books, Inc.

"You Can Make a Million Today" from *How to Be Rich* by J. Paul Getty. Copyright © by HMH Publishing Co., Inc.

"Succeeding in a Business Career" from *Managing* by Harold S. Geneen and Alvin Moscow. Copyright © 1984 by Harold S. Geneen and Alvin Moscow, Inc. Used by permission of Doubleday, a division of Random House.

"Managing Your Own Career" by Andrew Grove, from *Fortune*, September 18, 1995. Copyright © 1995 Time Inc. Reprinted by Permission.

"There Is an Art to Living" from *Be My Guest* by Conrad Hilton. Copyright © 1957 by Conrad Hilton, renewed 1985 by Mary Frances Hilton, Constance F. Hilton, William Baron Hilton, and Erik Michael Hilton.

"My Little Commandments of Management" from *Talking Straight* by Lee Iacocca. Copyright © 1988 by Lee Iacocca. Used by permission of Bantam Books, a division of Random House, Inc.

"How to Sell Anything in Five Minutes or Less" from *Succeeding Against the Odds* by John H. Johnson. Copyright © 1989 John H. Johnson. Reprinted by permission of Amistad Press, Inc.

"Management Principles" by John E. Jonsson, from the American Management Association's *General Management Series*, Number 185.

"Thirteen Common Success Factors" by Joseph Juran. Used by permission of Joseph Juran.

"Imagine Your Future" by Henry Kaiser, from a commencement address before the University of Nevada, Reno, June 7, 1948.

"The American Businessman" from *Random Reminiscences of Men and Events* by John D. Rockefeller. Published by Doubleday, Page & Company, 1909.

"Starbucks Mission Statement" and "Capturing the Customer's Imagination" from *Pour Your Heart Into It* by Howard Schultz and Dori Jones Yang. Copyright © 1997 Howard Schultz and Dori Jones Yang. Published by Hyperion, 1997.

"The Bottom Line of Mutual Funds" from *Charles Schwab's Guide to Financial Freedom* by Charles R. Schwab. Copyright © 1998 by The Charles Schwab Corporation. Reprinted by permission of Crown Publishers, a division of Random House, Inc.

"Some Outlandish Rules for Making Money" from *Damned Old Crank* by E. W. Scripps. Copyright 1951 by Harper & Brothers. Reprinted by Permission of HarperCollins Publishers, Inc.

"The GE Values Guide" from *Jack Welch and the GE Way* by Robert Slater. Copyright © 1998 by Robert Slater. Used by permission of The McGraw-Hill Companies.

"The Time-tested Maxims of the Templeton Touch" by Sir John Templeton, from *The Templeton Touch* by William Proctor. Copyright © 1983. Used by permission of John Templeton.

"Dave's Rules for Successful Harassment" from *Dave's Way* by David Thomas. Copyright © 1991 by R. David Thomas.

"No-No's" from *Up the Organization* by Robert Townsend. Copyright © 1970 by Robert Townsend. Reprinted by permission of Alfred A. Knopf, a division of Random House, Inc.

"The Making of a Businessman" by Theodore Vail, from *Youth's Companion*, September 1913.

"Are You an Entrepreneur?" from *An Eye for Winners* by Lillian Vernon. Copyright © 1996 by Lillian Vernon. Reprinted by permission of HarperCollins Publishers, Inc.

Author Index

Subject Index

THE
SPANISH
GAMBIT

Also by Stephen Hunter

The Master Sniper
The Second Saladin

THE
SPANISH
GAMBIT

A Novel by
Stephen Hunter

Crown Publishers, Inc. New York

Grateful acknowledgment is made for the following:
"We are the hollow men." From "The Hollow Men" in *Collected Poems 1909–1962* by T. S. Eliot,
Copyright 1936 by Harcourt Brace Jovanovich, Inc.; Copyright © 1963, 1964 by T. S. Eliot.
Reprinted by permission of Harcourt Brace Jovanovich, Inc. and Faber and Faber Ltd.
"These in the hour when heaven was falling." From "Epitaph for an Army of Mercenaries" from
The Collected Poems of A. E. Housman, Copyright 1922 by Holt, Rinehart & Winston.
Copyright 1950 by Barclays Bank Ltd. Reprinted by permission of
Holt, Rinehart & Winston, Publishers.
"If I should die, think only this of me. There's some foreign field that is forever England."
From Rupert Brooke's "The Soldier."

This is a work of fiction. The characters, incidents, and dialogues are products of the author's imagination and are not to be construed as real. The author's use of names of actual persons, living or dead, and actual places are incidental to the purposes of the plot and are not intended to change the entirely fictional character of the work.

Published by Crown Publishers, Inc., One Park Avenue, New York, New York 10016 and simultaneously in Canada by General Publishing Company Limited
CROWN is a trademark of Crown Publishers, Inc.
Manufactured in the United States of America
Library of Congress Cataloging in Publication Data
Hunter, Stephen, 1946–
The Spanish gambit.
I. Title
PS3558.U494S6 1985   813'.54   85-459
ISBN 0-517-55731-2

Design by Lenny Henderson

10 9 8 7 6 5 4 3 2 1
First Edition

This one, as promised,
is for Amy

The Ruy-Lopez, or Spanish Gambit, is more popular than any other king pawn opening. . . . The Gambit is astonishingly complicated, embodying as it does a perpetual intertwining of grandiose strategical planning with an alarming maze of difficult tactical finesses and combinative motifs. It is no exaggeration to affirm that mastery of the Spanish Gambit is a requisite for anyone aspiring to become a strong chess player.

Adapted from James Mason,
The Art of Chess,
London, April 1898

PROLOGUE

THE TRIAL OF THE ASSASSIN BENNY LAL IN THE OLD COURT-house at Moulmein, lower Burma, in February of 1931, caused a bit of a stir in its own day, but its memory has not lingered. It was a forgotten moment in the history of a vanished empire.

Yet a case could be made that it changed the political history of our century, however secretly, however subtly. Still, in the mind of one man, the event was important for exactly what it was, and not for what it eventually made possible. He was, on the last day of the trial, the Crown's chief witness, a tall, not unpleasant-looking young officer in the service khaki of the India Imperial Police. It was his duty to put the noose around the neck of Benny Lal.

The blades of the overhead fan moved through the air in a stately whirl, yet without palpable effect. Robert Florry stared at the motion, its easy, hypnotic blur fascinating him.

"Assistant superintendent?"

The magistrate's voice. Florry swallowed awkwardly and, blinking, embarrassed, redirected his vision toward the bench. He hoped his discomfort did not show, knowing of course that it did. He swallowed again. It had taken such a long time for this moment to arrive, but now it rushed at him with the power of the undeniable future.

"Assistant superintendent?"

Florry attempted a wretched smile. The courtroom, jammed with other Imperial Policemen and natives, was as still as a photograph. He could feel their scrutiny: it had the weight of accusation.

"Yessir," he said. His own voice always bothered him. It was a reedy, thin instrument and tended to disappear in key moments such as this one.

"The man I saw—" he said a bit more smartly, raising his finger to point—

At the defense table, under the slow whirl of the fan, amid a collection of more fortunate members of his race, sat a Hindu.

He was small and had that furtive, shifty, almost liquid swiftness in which the wogs seemed to specialize. He had a shock of thick dark hair and two darting black eyes, his skin so mocha-chocolate that it made his white teeth blaze like diamonds in the firelight. For Benny Lal was smiling; he always smiled. He was an idiot.

"That's the man," said Florry, suddenly finding his policeman's voice. "That's the man I saw running from the deceased on Tuesday last, half past eleven in the evening, outside the Moulmein officers' club. Sir."

He added the bit of recapitulation as if in testimony to his own efficiency, which was on trial here, too. Yet surely every officer and every native in the courtroom would have known that Tuesday last at half-eleven, a drunken Burmese merchant named U Bat had had his throat opened all over his white suit not fifty paces from the veranda of the club where Florry, nursing his fifth gin of the night, had sat trying to write Georgian poetry in the lamplight, amid moths and fancies. Only slightly drunk, the young officer had rushed to the still form in the dust as a smaller, quicker shape had dashed by him. Perhaps, it was being said in certain quarters, a man with more wit about him (or less gin in him) would have made the pinch right there. But Florry, stunned by the suddenness with which the violence had occurred and a little dotty not only with drink but also with dreams of literature and then still further staggered by his first exposure to the gaudy wreckage of a human body

soaking in its own blood in the dust, had let the villain slip away in the shadows of an alley.

A manhunt organized rather like a tiger drive had come upon the naked Benny Lal sleeping in blissful abandon by the side of the road a few miles away early the next morning. It developed swiftly, under blunt methods of investigation, that he had once been a houseboy in the domicile of U Bat and a frequent target of the drunken merchant's weekly rages. Under questioning Benny Lal, idiot child of the East, neither confessed nor defended himself. He merely smiled pleasantly at everybody and tried not to offend the British.

Was he in fact the guilty party?

If Florry could not really say yes, neither could he really say no. Yet he could not say nothing. These were tricky times, it had been explained to him by a fellow in the Intelligence Department. Already ugly rumors were afoot. The British themselves, it was said, had been behind the slaying. U Bat, in certain quarters, was being inflated into some kind of nationalist saint, not the black brute he'd been in reality. It would do, the chap explained with sweet reason and abundant charm on his side, it would do to be done with this matter quickly. It was a duty; sometimes one had to see the bigger picture.

"You're certain, then?" said the magistrate.

"I am sure, sir, yessir, I am," said Florry in a clear, unwavering voice.

"Mr. Gupta? Have you any questions?"

Mr. Gupta, who had been fanning himself this long time, at last arose. He was a tiny Hindu lawyer, up at no fee save mischief from Rangoon to speak for Benny Lal. He offered Florry a broad, extremely pleasant smile.

"How much, Constable Florry, would you—"

Conscious of the contest and eager not to fall behind from the start, Florry aggressively corrected the man. "Assistant superintendent please," he said, and in the instant he said it, realized he'd been snookered.

"Oh!" said the lawyer, in mock astonishment. "Oh, I am begging the officer's pardon," his smile radiating heat, "oh, I am so sorry of the mistake. Then you have received so recently a promotion? For duties of spectacular success?"

"I don't see what the devil dif—" Florry began with an extra measure of sahib's bluster, but the sudden swell of bright laughter from the unsympathetic Hindus in the back of the courtroom drowned him out.

"Mr. Gupta, the bench does not quite see what relevance the assistant superintendent's recent promotion has to do with the facts at issue," said the magistrate coolly.

"I meant no disrespect, your honored self. A simple mistake, in which no harm was meant nor even intended or implied. I congratulate the new assistant. If I have it right, over the year, the difference in moneys is about one hundred pounds, is this not so?"

"Perhaps counsel could explain what relevance to the case of the accused is meant by this?" the magistrate requested.

"Apologies, apologies, many and profuse," said Gupta, his cynicism as broad as his smile. "I only mean it to remark on the fortune of some and the misfortune of others in this cruel world. I mean never to imply or infer any kind of payment for services ren—"

"Now see here!" began Florry.

"Mr. Gupta, your client's case will not be helped by impertinence. Indeed, it will most likely be harmed."

"Then the subject of money shall be forever avoided from this moment onward. Now, Mr. Assistant Superintendent, I understand that you are a poet, is this not correct?"

Florry squirmed. He was a tall man, or boy, actually, twenty-three, with a long thin face, sandy hair, and a husky, big-boned body. He looked strong and English and a bit too decent for anybody's good. He was an Eton boy—though he'd been wretched there—but of an odd English class. The son of an India Company clerk, he'd gone to his fancy school on account of having been at one time thought promising. He was in service because no university would have him after a disastrous finish to his years at the

college. Worse, he felt here, as he felt at Eton—as he felt _everywhere_
—somewhat fraudulent.

"Scribble a verse now and then, yes," he said.

"Ah," said the Indian, as if having made a remarkable discovery.
"And would you not say that a poet is rewarded for his _imagination,_
Mr. Assistant Superintendent?"

"And his sense of rhyme, his moral vision, his beautiful command of the language, his higher range of exalted thought, his—"
Florry looked like a copper but he thought he was a poet, and if he
was wholly neither, he was still capable of speaking eloquently on
this one subject alone. But the magistrate cut him off.

"See here, Gupta, where's all this headed?"

"Honored judge of men, I wish only to see if the assistant superintendent is the sort of chappy who sometimes sees things that
aren't there in his poems. Or I wonder if he doesn't, in the honored
tradition of such as Shakespeare and Spenser, sometimes _improve_ the
way things are for the sake of the beauty and soul of his no doubt
significant poetics. I only mean to find the officer's sense or defini-
tion of the truth."

Benny Lal smiled. A lick of drool, like a gossamer filament in a
dream, drifted from his mouth.

"My poems are my poems," said Florry sullenly, embarrassed to
be depicted as such a dreamy ninny before the other officers, "and
duty is duty. Separate and apart. The way it should be."

"Leaving aside which is the most important to you, let me ask
you this, Mr. Assistant Superintendent. You were off duty, relax-
ing, cooling down at the end of a hot day's duty in service to your
mighty engine of empire. A man in these circumstances, sir, has
been known to have a drink of spirits. May I inquire, sir, if you
had done so, and if you had, to what extent?"

"A gin," Florry lied. "Maybe two."

"You are sure?"

"Quite."

"Not so much for an Englishman?"

"I'm sure I wouldn't know."

"Your Honor, I have here—ah—oh, yes—*here*—Assistant Superintendent Florry's bar chit for the previous month."

He held aloft the pink form that the young policeman, with sinking feeling, recognized immediately.

"And perhaps in the excitement of the night's events, the assistant superintendent forgot to sign that night. Yet in the weeks proceeding, it's quite clear he was accustomed to drinking as much as five gins a night. My goodness, here's one night when he drank *nine*! Yet on the night in question, he would have us believe he had drunk only two. My goodness. Perhaps, Mr. Assistant Superintendent, you could amplify."

"Ah—" Florry began, feeling a tide of liar's phlegm rising in his throat, "perhaps I may have had more than two. Perhaps I had three. It's difficult to remember. Four gins is not a lot. Certainly not enough to affect my vision, which is what is important in this matter. My vision was intact, sir, it was. Yes, sir, four, four it was."

Actually, it *had* been five. But the curious thing was, it hadn't really affected him. He could drink grotesque amounts of liquor without much damage.

"Well then, that should clear *that* up, shouldn't it?" said the magistrate.

"You see," hastened Florry, "I had had an idea for a poem that day. And when I write a poem, I never drink a lot. Dulls the senses."

"Then you had not written a poem for some time?"

"No," said Florry, wondering what the little devil was up to.

"And yet, here I have—oh, now where?—yes, *here,* here it is!—" and the little Hindu milked the theme of the missing document like some bad actor in a West End melodrama for some time until at last—"here it is, indeed. Your postal chit."

He displayed it triumphantly to the courtroom.

"Yes," Mr. Gupta continued merrily, "your postal chit. And on Friday before you had dispatched a large envelope—the bill was a

pound six—to an address in London. In Bloomsbury. Here it is. Number 56 Bedford. At Russell Square. SW1. Correct?"

"Well—"

"And two weeks before. And a week before that. Would you tell the court what the address is?"

Florry paused bitterly before issuing the grim answer. "It's the address of *The Spectator*. A literary quarterly. The best literary quarterly." They never took his poems. Nobody ever did.

"And so you have been writing poetry and you have been drinking and you were lost in the worlds of your own poetry. You heard the scream. You rushed off the veranda to the body you have just noticed. You have so testified, is this not true?"

"Yes," said Florry.

"And a shape flies past you. There's precious little light. And the distance must be thirty feet and the time must be, oh, one would gauge it to be only seconds, eh?"

Florry said nothing.

"Yet you recognized—please point to him."

Florry raised his finger to point.

Damn the wog.

Two smiling Hindus sat at the defense table. To Florry they were identical. Gupta and his tricks.

Florry's rising finger grew heavy. Pick one, he thought. Then he remembered a line from a poem: *In the end, it's all the same/In the end, it's all a game.* Brilliant Julian had written it. It was from the famous "Achilles, Fool," which had made him such a thing in London these days.

Julian, Why did you hurt me so? The pain of it, five years gone, was never adequately buried and now came up like a rotting odor.

Pick one, he thought. It doesn't matter. It's just a game.

"How can I pick one," said Florry, with a sudden icy coolness, "when *neither* is the right chap?"

There was a roar from the courtroom gallery. And then an En-

glish cheer. Gupta stared at him. The message was hatred. Florry stared back.

Benny Lal now sat three places down the table, in a blue coat. He was trying, under what must have been instruction from his lawyer, not to smile. Florry's eyes linked with his in an odd second and beheld, behind the gaze, exactly nothing.

Benny Lal smiled at him.

Three weeks after the murder of U Bat, Benny Lal was to be hanged.

Florry found himself standing in a small group of officials in the muddy parade ground of the prison. It was the sort of thing one could not avoid. The day was hot and gassy and he could feel his tunic clinging to his skin and the prickles of sweat in his hairline under his sun helmet. The prison building, an old hulk of a place that had once been a fort, loomed above them. The latrines were hard by and the stench hung in the air.

"Ever seen a hanging, Mr. Florry?" asked Mr. Gupta, with his bright smile. The lawyer had also come to watch the event.

"No. Isn't the sort of thing a chap goes to every day."

"Oh, here he comes," Mr. Gupta suddenly chirped. "Look, assistant superintendent. The treacherous, the cunning, the despicable villain, Benny Lal, off to meet his just desserts."

Benny, in the center of a small troop of guards, had emerged in handcuffs from the building. He walked, at an unhurried pace, toward the gallows.

Benny Lal grinned and Florry looked away.

"Certainly cheery about it, isn't he?" observed Mr. Gupta.

"Well, you're a cold-blooded fellow," said Florry with more emotion than he'd intended to show. "He was your client and now he's going to meet his maker."

"The British Empire was his maker, assistant superintendent, just as it is his destroyer."

Florry watched now as the little man climbed the ladder to the platform.

"Mr. Florry, perhaps some day you'll write a poem about all this. Think of the colorful literary details: the stench, the hot sun, these officials, the ever-obedient Benny Lal—and your own ambivalences." He smiled wickedly.

"And you, Mr. Gupta."

"Oh, surely I am too insignificant for poetry," said Mr. Gupta.

The executioner had placed the hood on Benny Lal. He struggled with the noose and Florry could see Benny lower his head cooperatively to make it easier on the chap.

"Benny Lal, you stand convicted on the capital crime of murder under the Crown's law," shouted the warden, in accordance with the ceremony. "What say you in these last moments?"

Benny, hooded, was silent. Then he began to cry. "Please, sirs. Please, sirs."

The Hindu, his scrawny bound body taut under the frame of the gallows, the cords of his neck standing out in vivid relief, continued to sob.

"Please, sirs. Sirs, I beg you. Sirs, I—"

With a snap, the trap sprang, and Benny Lal hurtled through the opening, disappearing into silence.

"Tally-ho, Benny," said Mr. Gupta.

Florry swore, watching the slow pendulum of the rope, tense with the terrible weight of the dead man, that he would never again work for the Empire.

It was a promise, however, he would not be permitted to keep.

Part I

ROBERT

1

LONDON, LATE FALL OF 1936

MR. VANE AND MAJOR HOLLY-BROWNING FOUND A PARK-ing space on Woburn Place at Russell Square, just across from the Russell Hotel. Mr. Vane, who drove the Morris with a delicacy that was almost fussiness, pulled into the gap with some grunting and huffing. He was not a physically graceful man or a strong one, and mechanical tasks came to him with some difficulty. He removed the ignition key and placed it in his vest pocket. Neither man made a move to leave the auto. They simply sat in the little car, two drab men of the commercial class, perhaps, travelers, little clerks, barristers' assistants.

It was a bright blue morning in Bloomsbury, a fabulous morning. In the elms of the square, whose dense leaves had begun to turn russet with the coming of colder weather, squirrels chattered and scrambled; squads of ugly, bumbling old pigeons gathered on the lawn. Some even perched upon the earl of Bedford's copper shoulders at the corner of the park. The chrysanthemums in the beds alongside the walks had not yet perished, though they would within the fortnight.

"He's late, of course," said Vane, examining his pocket watch.

"Give him time, Vane," said Major Holly-Browning. "This is a big day in his life, and the chap's sure to be nervous. *This* chap in particular."

Major Holly-Browning was in his fifties, ten years older than Mr. Vane, and wore a vague mustache, a voluminous mackintosh despite the clear skies, and a bowler. On closer examination, he

didn't look commercial at all but rather military. He had the look of a passed-over officer, with a certain grayness to the skin, a certain bleakness to the eyes, and a certain formality to his carriage. He looked like the man who hadn't quite managed the proper friends in the regiment and was therefore doomed to a succession of grim assignments in the outposts of the Empire, far from the parades, the swirling social life, the intrigues of home duty.

In fact, the major was head of Section V, MI-6, that is, the counterespionage section of the Secret Intelligence Service; he was, in the lexicon of the trade, V (a); Mr. Vane, his number two, was V (b). There was no V (c); they were the entire division. The major took a deep breath inside the little car. One of his headaches was starting up. He touched his temple.

"Tired, sir?"

"Exhausted, Vane. Haven't slept in weeks."

"You must go home more often, sir. You can't expect to remain in the proper health living as you do, those long nights in the office."

The major sighed. Vane could be an awful prig.

"I suppose you are right, Vane."

"He is now seven minutes late."

"He will be here. The bait is far too tempting for him not to swallow."

"Yessir."

They sat again in silence.

"*Sir!* There he is."

"Don't stare, Vane."

The major waited calmly and at long last the object of his well-controlled curiosity appeared. The fellow'd gotten off at the Russell Square tube station, as they'd expected, and come up Bernard Street. He waited patiently for the walk signal, then crossed to their side of the street and ambled by a few feet beyond them: it was the tall, diffident figure of a Mr. Robert Florry.

"The great Julian's ex-chum. Not an impressive man, is he?"

observed the major, who for all his efforts in the matter had not before this second laid eyes upon the man.

"Nobody has ever been greatly impressed with Mr. Florry," said Mr. Vane, the Florry expert. "Whatever can such a Robin Goodfellow of Society as the great Julian Raines have seen in him?"

"He only saw it for a bit," said the major, knowing a little something of the broken-off schoolboy friendship, the cometlike ascension of one of the partners and the disappearance into ignominy of the other.

Florry was turned out, after the fashion of the day, to the maximum limits of his wardrobe, but on his severely limited budget he could only manage to appear a notch beyond the shabby. The coat was almost fifteen years old, a tweed thing that was as lumpy as it was frayed, and flecked with a dozen tawny colors. The rest of Florry's attire was in perfect accordance with the coat: floppy wool trousers, a gaudy Fair Isle sweater, and a bumpkin's well-beaten walking shoes. He had on his officer's khaki service tie and his shirt was of dark blue, worn shiny and limp from countless washings.

"I must confess I'd expected someone with a bit more bearing. The fellow was an officer, wasn't he?" said the major.

"Of sorts," said Vane. "More a copper, actually."

Florry continued to navigate the sidewalk as he headed toward his destination, which lay on the far side of the square, across still another street. Yet even having cleared this, a final obstacle stood in his way. The early edition of the afternoon *Mail* had just come out and a news board hawked the leader in a crude child's scrawl.

MADRID BOMBED, SURROUNDED
HOW LONG CAN REDS LAST?

This information brought the young man to a sudden halt. He stared at it gravely for some time.

"Why on earth did *that* have to be there?" wondered Mr. Vane.

Florry finally pulled himself away from the announcement and made his way another few yards down the street, where he assaulted the marble steps of a red-brick house at Number 56 Bedford, at Russell Square.

Major Holly-Browning sat back but could not relax. A cold sore inside his lip began to throb and his headache had not abated at all. He believed himself, and not without some evidence, to be quietly disintegrating. He knew now the most difficult part of the day was upon him, the awful waiting while certain steps were taken to bring upon him that most awkward and tender moment of the operation. Florry would be wooed—delicately if possible, brutally if necessary —but at all costs *successfully*. The major, having partaken in so many similar seductions over the years, had no illusions about the process of recruitment. Florry must be taken and owned and directed. It was more important than Florry himself.

"I say, Vane, can you stay here and keep watch?" the major suddenly said. "I imagine it will still be a bit. I must move. The old leg, it's beginning to smart up, eh?"

"Of course, sir," Vane replied.

The major opened the door, pulled himself onto the curb, and closed the door behind him, absorbing great drafts of fresh air in the process. The car had seemed a prison; sometimes, confined, he had the sudden screaming urge come over him to stretch and breathe and feel the cool air in his nose and the soft grass underneath his feet. It was a feeling that could come hurtling over him without warning, until he could no longer stand it. It had begun in Lubyanka, with Levitsky.

The major found his way to a bench near the gigantic old tree that stood at the center of the park. He sat down, trying to calm himself. Yet what returned to him was not calm but memory. Perhaps it was the drama of recruitment being played out at that moment not a hundred yards off in the office of *The Spectator,* or perhaps it was the sure and steady approach of a moment when he, Holly-Browning, must himself act, the pregnant moment of equipoise, when Florry, perched delicately between worlds and lives,

must be nudged into the right one. Or perhaps it was simply time again to remember, for the memory had returned as regularly as a train, twice a week, every week since 1922.

For in that year, he himself had been the object of just such a ritual as was now transpiring so close at hand. His impersonation of one Golitsyn, the furrier's son and Bolshevik officer of cavalry, had been penetrated by a clever Cheka agent. The major, who had fought Zulus and wogs before the '14–'18 show, who'd gone over the top twice in suicidal assaults during it, and who'd fought in seven battles of the civil war in Russia under his fictitious identity, had never until that moment been truly frightened. But Levitsky had sliced through him as a sharp knife goes into a plump goose's breast.

He could not but think of his own session in the cell. The same shame flooded over him. It came to sit on his chest like an ingot, suffocating him.

Levitsky, he thought, *you were so shrewd.*

"Sir!"

It was Vane, out of the car.

"Look!"

The major looked across the green park and could see the upper shade of Number 56, the arched window above the entrance: the shade had been raised.

Vane approached, looking flushed.

"He's bitten. He has taken the hook."

"He has indeed," said the major. "And now it's time to land him."

The sherry was extraordinary. Florry had never tasted anything quite like it.

"Well, Florry," said Sir Denis heartily, returning from the window whose shade he had just raised, admitting a shaft of pale London sun, "I can't tell you how delighted we all are here."

"Nor I, sir," said Florry, still trembling with excitement.

"The Spectator has never sent a man abroad. Much less to a revolution."

"Well, you can certainly count on me to master my Spanish politics before I leave, sir. I shan't mix up the POUM and the PSUD again."

"No, it wouldn't do. That's PSUC, old boy. The Trotsky fellows are the first group, the dreamers, the new architects of society, the poets, the artists. The fashionable folk, if you will. The PSUC would have precious little patience for *that.* They're the Comintern lads, the professional Russian and German revolutionaries. Bloody Joe Stalin's pals. Best not to mingle them together. They hate each other enough as it is. And they may end up cutting each other's throats before too long. It's all in the initials. Memorize the initials and the Spanish revolution becomes as clear as a bell. You might read Julian's stuff in *Signature.* He's got it down pat."

"Yessir," said Florry, almost contritely. *Damn* Julian. Of course he'd have it down pat. That was Julian, the art of getting things down pat. The art of the easy success, the swift climb, the importance of connections. Florry felt the old pain, the old hate mixed with regret.

Yet another name from Florry's complicated past seemed present, in the form of that constant nagging little dog that always told him he didn't quite deserve that which he was about to receive. This new life, this life he had dreamed about and wanted so badly for so long—no more dreadful nights in dreadful bed-sitters up scribbling away on novels and poems nobody would publish—had developed by virtue of his one piece of professional writing. And a damned good piece it was, too, if effort had anything to do with it: he'd rewritten it over thirteen times until he felt he'd gotten every one of its five thousand words exactly *right*; still, he'd been dumbstruck when the note from Sir Denis had arrived.

FLORRY:

Your piece on the hanging superb. Delighted to have it. It'll go in the late February number. By the way, how about

dropping by the office Tuesday, half-tennish. I have a proposition for you.

YOURS, MASON

Benny Lal, six years among the worms, was still doing his best to accommodate.

The phone rang. Sir Denis picked it up.

"They are? Fine, show them in," he said. "Now Florry, there is one small thing."

"Of course."

"Two chaps from the foreign office. They'd like a word with you."

"The F.O.?"

"Or some such. Something governmental. I never pay much attention to that sort of thing. Fellow named Holly-Browning. Knew him at Magdalen. First-rate chap, you'll like him."

"Well, I certainly—"

But Sir Denis rose and crossed the room to open the door.

"Hullo, James. Vane."

"Denis. And how are you?"

"Ah, the same. And how's Marjorie?"

"Blooming."

"You married the most beautiful woman of our time, that's for certain, James."

"She's still quite beautiful, but I see her so infrequently these days, one forgets."

"Is he working too hard as usual, Vane?"

"Yessir. To midnight, most nights, and later even on many others."

"Good heavens, James, after all you've been through! Well, here's young Mr. Robert Florry, our new Spanish political correspondent."

Florry rose to encounter a large, sad man, dourly turned out, with huge hands and a hulking body. There was something implacable about him, and his beaten but pugnacious face somehow held

the promise of secret zealotry that Florry sensed immediately. Florry knew one other thing instantly, having been one himself for five years: he knew he was among coppers.

"Florry, I'm Major Holly-Browning. This is my assistant Mr. Vane."

"Ah, pleased—" began Florry, extending a hand that nobody seemed to notice.

Sir Denis had quietly slipped out and Florry discovered himself being ushered to a window alcove, where three old leather chairs sat about a low table full of African masks and old numbers of *The Spectator*.

"The F.O., do I understand?" said Florry.

"His Majesty's government, shall we say. Please sit. Tea?"

"Er, yes, thanks."

"Vane, see about some tea, will you?"

Florry, sitting, felt his exultation begin to transform into confusion.

"May I ask, Mr. Florry, are you a red?"

At first Florry thought he had said "Are you well-read?" and he'd begun to compose what seemed an intelligent reply, when it occurred to him that that wasn't it at all.

"But what possible business is it of yours?"

The major stared at him levelly, admitting the light of no surprise into his dim eyes.

Florry wasn't fuddled. Though tense and suddenly aware he was in murky waters, his mind flooded with lucidity. "Is this how they do it, nowadays, major? In my time, we were a little subtler. I was a copper. Been in on a few sessions like this myself. I know how it works. The affability and good companionship to put the poor fellow at his ease. Then, with no warning, a hard question. Catch the poor bastard off guard, goad him into something silly. Yes, I can see it now. Perhaps we could spare each other the poking about and get right to it."

Something very like a little smile crossed the major's pug face.

"Here's tea," sang Vane, wheeling in triumphantly with a tray. "I also found some marvelous buns. Care for a bun, Mr. Florry?"

"No," said Florry.

"One lump or two, Mr. Florry?"

"One should do, I would think."

"One it is, then."

"Vane, I'll have two. And lots of milk."

"Yessir."

"And a bun. Are they crisp?"

"_Very_ crisp, sir."

"A bun, then. I've just asked Florry if he's a red."

"Oh?" said Vane distractedly, pouring tea and sorting buns, "and what did he say?"

"He wouldn't answer. Got his back up."

"Bully good for him, I say. Now don't let the major push you about, Mr. Florry. He can be an awful brute."

"Now then, Florry," said the major, "suppose we were on the lookout for just such a chap. Let's say, for a matter of argument, a genuine red. Oh, I'm not talking your harmless parlor revolutionary, all hot air and castles in Spain, your blowsy English eccentric who likes to stand on soap boxes in Hyde Park on Sunday and harangue the passers-by. No, let's just suppose that somewhere there is a fellow who in his heart of hearts really _wants_ Uncle Joe Stalin to come over here, lock us in chains, turn his secret policemen loose, and teach our children to read Russian. Do you follow me so far?"

"Where is all this heading?" said Florry warily.

"We have information from a source we're not permitted to reveal that such a chap as we're describing in this highly theoretical conversation may in fact exist."

It suddenly dawned on Florry. These men were spies! In the service, they'd been called "politicals," though perhaps the term had gone out of use by now. These were the chaps that Kipling wrote about in _Kim,_ the great game fellows.

"You're smiling, Mr. Florry. Something funny here?"

"No."

"Ever hear of the Official Secrets Act, Mr. Florry? Nasty bit of legislation, went into effect in 'thirty-two. Could put a chap away for seven years in the Scrubs. What I'm about to tell you is protected by the Official Secrets Act, Mr. Florry. It must never leave this room. Understand?"

"I must say, I don't see how I can be of any help to you."

"Oh, you can be of great help, Mr. Florry. Now listen closely. In 1931, while you were off having adventures in Burma for the Crown, a Russian secret intelligence operative named Levitsky recruited a Cambridge University student—young, gifted, clever, a lad with connections, with charm, with immense potential—to spy for Russia. As the first step of bringing Uncle Joe and his ways over here."

"Why, that's revolting," blurted Florry, not quite sure himself how he meant it.

"Indeed it is," said the major.

"But what has all of this to do with me? I never went to Cambridge. I can't help you find him."

"Oh, we need no help in finding him, Mr. Florry," said Vane cheerfully. "We *know* who he is, of course. What we need is somebody to—oh, what's a nice term? To stop him, shall we say? To disconnect him. Did the major tell you, he went to a hanging once, too, Mr. Florry. In East Africa, wasn't it, sir? Before the Great War?"

"In 'eleven, actually," the major said. "Ghastly thing. One of the boys got drunk on honey wine on safari and actually attacked the mem-sahib with a panga. Cut her on the arm, left a scar. They had to make an example of the boy. Still, necessary as it was, it was horrid."

"What do you mean 'stop'?" Florry said. "I can tell you, I don't like the sound of that word."

"Play chess, Mr. Florry?"

"Some. A little. Not very well."

"Ever read *Sacrifice Theory* by E. I. Levitsky? Published in German in Leipzig in 1901?"

"Haven't read it, no."

"Written by a young Russian political exile who'd just won an important tournament. Don't play myself, although I ran into the author some years later under peculiar circumstances. They say sacrifice is what makes a chess genius a chess champion. The shrewd calculation of present loss against future gain. It's what Levitsky specializes in, the best part of his game. They call him the Devil Himself; that was his nickname as a chess player back at the turn of the century. Brilliant. Quite an opponent."

"Major Holly-Browning, I wonder if—"

But the major silenced him with a stout finger, as a prefect silences a particularly rambunctious sixth-former, and launched ahead. "Levitsky operated in this country during most of 1931, our information relates. He was at that time head of the Western European Bureau of Comintern, and a lieutenant colonel in the GRU, which is the Russian military intelligence department. Comintern is their apparatus for coordinating world propaganda and espionage. According to our source, early in that year Levitsky became acquainted with and began to cultivate a chap who was perfect for his purposes. Levitsky was talent hunting. He was on safari, one might say, hunting for that perfect young Englishman with a penchant for treason. At any rate—"

"Major Holly-Browning, I'm certain all of this is perfectly interesting to you but I can't quite—"

"Oh, he's just about there, assistant superintendent," said Vane sweetly.

"Yes, Florry. Another second has it. At any rate, this Levitsky, our source says, ultimately came in contact with a group of clever lads called—perhaps you've heard the name; it's a secret club, fashionable left-wing dons, that sort—called the Apostles."

So that was it. Florry sat back. He took a deep breath with some

difficulty. He felt the prickles of sweat begin to tingle in his hair.

"Interesting, eh, Vane? Speak the magic word and the impatient, thick-hided young writer instantly loses his color and begins to perspire."

"I shouldn't wonder," said Florry. "It isn't every day one is asked to inform on one's best friend."

"Yes, he's made the leap," said Vane. "You said he would, sir, and he did. But Mr. Florry, don't you think it would be more accurate to say 'former best friend'?"

Florry rose. "I think you are making a grave and foolish mistake. You are acting reprehensibly. We never treated the wogs this crassly out East, and you are talking about an Englishman of unimpeachable reputation and accomplishment."

The major stared at him quite placidly.

"Some more tea, sir?" said Vane. "Or a nice bun. They're very, very crisp, and I was able to find cinnamon."

"I do not want a bloody cinnamon bun. I want to leave, thanks."

"Florry, best to sit down."

"Julian Raines is a poet of distinction as well as a brilliant scholar. He graduated with starred double-first at Trinity College, Cambridge. His poem 'Achilles, Fool,' is one of the key texts in the modernist movement. His—"

"Yes, I've read it. 'In the end, it's all the same/In the end, it's all a game.' May I ask, do you agree with those sentiments, Florry?"

"He wouldn't spy for a batch of bloody Bolshies in overcoats twelve sizes too big. Good heavens, he wouldn't even have *tea* with them."

"He certainly treated *you* as if you were a figure in a game, wouldn't you say, Florry? You simply ceased to interest him and he cut you bloody dead. We've checked, Florry. You weren't worth much after that, eh? Went off and hid in the coppers in Burma, right? Couldn't face life without the great Julian at your side? Bit of a schoolboy crush. Happens all the time, Florry. Only with you, it cut to the bone."

"He wouldn't do it," said Florry. "Yes, Julian's a bastard. Yes, he likes to hurt people. But he wouldn't do anything like—"

"The facts are very clear. Of the Apostle Circle of the year 1931, Julian is certainly the boy who fits most perfectly with our source's description of Levitsky's recruit. As you say, he was brilliant. His mother is wealthy as well as well connected to the upper-strata political and artistic people of the country. She could get her dear Julian any position he wanted in a liberal or socialist government somewhere down the road. He would have access to the very most important circles."

"Julian is an artist, a writer. A _true_ artist. He's not interested in bloody politics."

"Julian Raines is many men. It simply won't do to fit him into an absolute category. He's a brilliant dabbler. At everything he tries he succeeds. And perhaps in this lofty sense of brilliance, he's come to see himself beyond the rest of us poor blokes. His analysis of history, for example, would be just that much keener. Who's to say he hasn't decided to have a dabble at the spy business, Florry, and make the success of it that he made of poetry and that he now makes of journalism?"

"Who is saying these awful things? Some ugly little man in a trench coat?"

"Mr. Florry," said Mr. Vane, "you were a copper. You know that we've got to use informants."

"A Russian. A secret policeman. Fleeing Stalin's executioners, that's all we can tell you," said the major.

"Some seedy little Johnny Red on the bloody run from his bosses. The bastard would say _anything_ to get himself into the country."

"Actually, he's not in the country. He's in the United States. He's told his story to the Americans and they believe him."

"The awful Yanks, yet! Good Christ, this gets seedier as it goes on."

"More tea, Mr. Florry?"

"I think it's necessary for me to leave."

"One last factor, Mr. Florry. Our Russian tattletale worked in Amsterdam. He said his last job for his employers involved opening a special, secret communications link to Barcelona. He concluded from the rush and risk involved that the link could only be to service a secret, most sensitively placed agent. This happened on five August; Julian Raines arrived in Barcelona on four August. And of the Apostle group, he and he alone is in Spain."

"You see, Mr. Florry, it *is* quite clear."

Florry shook his head.

"What we need is somebody to go out to Spain and establish an especially close relationship with Julian Raines. We need somebody to keep watch over him; we need reports on his whereabouts, his chums, his little jobs for the Russians. We need evidence."

"And then?"

"And then do the necessary. As the necessary has been done before, Mr. Florry, by brave young Englishmen."

"To kill him?"

"One stops one's enemies as one can or as one must."

"Good Christ."

"Were you in the war, Florry?"

"No, of course not."

"Well, I have been in several. One learns to do what one must."

Florry saw now that the whole thing was a sham: Sir Denis and *The Spectator* working in concert with His Majesty's government in the subtle, cozy, pleasant, particularly *English* way of doing such things. Offer Florry the life he wants; in exchange, take only his soul.

"No," Florry said. "You force me to be somewhat moralistic about this. It's simply wrong."

"But surely, Mr. Florry, one's *country* counts for more than—"

"One's friends are one's country; or rather, without them, one's country is meaningless."

He got up to leave. "I'm sure you will inform Sir Denis of my decision." He turned smartly and walked to the door. It wouldn't open.

"Mr. Florry," said Mr. Vane with some embarrassment, "there's a rather large constable from Special Branch out there at our request. It's his bulk that is blocking the doorway and he has his instructions."

"To arrest me, I suppose. On the charge of Refusal to Take Part in Ugly Plots."

"Mr. Florry, I must say, it's your sanctimony that I find the most difficult to bear," said the major at long last. "Vane, tell the moralistic Mr. Florry what the constable has in his pocket."

"It's a warrant. And it is for your arrest. But the charge is perjury."

"Perjury?"

"You do remember Benny Lal, do you not, Mr. Florry?" asked Vane.

Something ripped at Florry's chest.

"One would think so. You wrote about him quite eloquently. Although you left out certain details, assistant superintendent," said the major.

Florry looked at the man, hating and fearing him at once.

"Last year, another man confessed to the murder of U Bat. He was a member of the Burmese Po Ben Sien, or Freedom Party, a militant nationalist group that we believe to be controlled by Julian's friends at Comintern. The movement eliminated U Bat when they realized he was secretly reporting to one of our politicals in the area. They killed him and tried to place the blame on us."

"So you've got me. Some years ago, I made the mistake of telling less than the truth, and now you've got me."

"Well, the option is a term in the Scrubs. Four years, I believe, is the term for perjury in a capital case. And Mr. Florry, even in the Scrubs there are cell blocks that might be pleasant and cell blocks that might be dreadful for such a handsome chap as you. I might go so far as to use what little influence I've got to see you end up among nellie-boys and poofs of a particularly aggressive nature. Not a pretty fate for a public-school boy."

"I say, you are a bastard, aren't you?"

"As a writer, you enjoy irony, don't you, Florry? Here's one for your collection. I have no doubt you did exactly the *right* thing in the matter of U Bat. It was necessary to close that case swiftly. At the same time, I have absolutely no compunction against using it against you now, to force you, once again, into doing the right thing. Your duty. We are quite prepared to see charges placed."

"I'd go to the press."

"With Official Secrets, we can shut the press down."

Florry could only look off, through the window. He could see the London skyline, looking very much as it had looked in Dickens' day, a flat, neat vista of little houses and chimneys. It looked like a set of parcels laid out on the postman's table, and among the buildings crept, anonymous, huddled, bent, hustling, the citizens of the British Empire, faceless and nameless, in whose cause he had just been dragooned.

"I had no idea the British government could be so ruthless."

"The world has chosen to give us ruthless enemies, Florry."

"It really does have to be you, Mr. Florry," said Vane. "You are a writer and have cause to travel where he travels. You know him well. At a point, you knew him *very* well, in the ways that public-school boys can come to know each other. Those old school ties, Mr. Florry, they count for something. You know they do. Then, you are an ex-policeman, experienced in security matters. You do fit the ticket, Mr. Florry. And it is, sir, something of a duty."

"And one other thing, Florry," said the major. "You hate him. Or you should."

Julian, thought Florry, *why did you hurt me so?* He remembered the boy he'd loved and the boy who'd almost killed him.

Yes, I hate you. It was true. By some subtle alchemy of the emotions, his passion had turned abjectly to loathing. He could remember Julian cutting him for the sheer amusement of it all.

"We'll be in touch concerning details, Mr. Florry," said Mr.

Vane. "We'll provide everything, of course, No need to do this thing on a miser's scale."

Florry looked up to see that his two new employers had risen and put on their coats.

"Good day, then, Florry. Glad to have you aboard," said the major. Florry shut his eyes. He heard the door close and the quiet pad of feet down the hall. After a bit, he left, too.

2

THE LUX

B Y LATE 1936, THE MOST TERRIFYING SOUND IN ALL MOS-
cow—in all Russia, for that matter—was the sound of a
single knock. It always came at night—late. And it always meant but one thing.

The young men from the organ of state security, the NKVD,
were invariably polite, though a bit distant, as they stood there in
their green overcoats and their fur-muffled winter caps with their
hands on the Tula-Tokarev automatics in the holsters at their belts.
Mercifully, they kept the formalities to a minimum: they read the
charges, they allowed the accused a last word with his loved ones,
a chance to grab his coat, and then they removed him—forever.

It was the time of Yeshov—*Yeshovchina,* in the Russian—after
Nikolai Yeshov, the dwarfish chairman of state security. But the
process of purification represented by this massive wave of arrests
surely originated with the general secretary, whom most of the old
revolutionaries remembered as Koba. Koba sought to scour the
party clean, to make it a precise, scientific instrument, to do away
with the last remnants of bourgeois sentimentality so that the future
could be faced with strength and will and resolve. Koba most
certainly sought also to make certain *he* was never arrested.

In one Moscow building the arrests were greeted with something
beyond even fear and despair, something unique to the city: irony.
The building stood on Gorky Street, hard by Pushkin Park, not
three-quarters of a downhill mile from the Kremlin itself, in the
very center of the city. It was an ornate, Italianate construction,

rich in marble and brass, and its upper floors on the western side provided a grand panorama of the Kremlin's domes. The place bore the name HOTEL LUX, on a brass plate untouched since 1917. Once, in the early years after its construction in 1907, Russian and European nobility, American entrepreneurs, German adventurers, Jewish diamond merchants, and exceedingly expensive courtesans had occupied its stately rooms. These days, the Lux appealed to a different clientele.

It had degenerated into a dirty, dingy ruin, its marble pitted and brass unpolished, but the dreams dreamed in its bohemian corridors and cabbage-stinking rooms boasted as much scale and romance as any dreamed by capitalists. For the Lux served as the unofficial headquarters of Comintern, or the Communist International, which, while a direct apparatus of the GRU, was at the same time, since having been decreed into existence in 1919 by Vladimir Lenin, the coordinating organ of the World Revolution.

Its inhabitants now comprised almost a Party congress of famous, infamous, notorious, and violent European leftists, men who had lived their whole lives underground, in the swirl and fog and rat hunt of revolutionary conspiracy. The revolution achieved, it was seized from them; they became its victims. Thus the nighttime visits of the young policemen—they were frequent at the Lux— had a special bitterness.

And how the old revolutionaries talked of this! Their lives had become almost pure language. They argued endlessly, like old rabbis at yeshiva. It obsessed them. What was Koba doing? What was his vision? By what theoretical underpinnings did he justify the killings? How did *Yeshovchina* fit into the ultimate trajectory toward socialist victory? And who was taken last night?

But one man, in all that noise, said nothing.

He did not complain. He had no theories. He had no grudges or secret fears, or so it seemed. He did not mingle in the lobby or participate in the endless debate. Nor did he care to comment upon the justice of it or the pathology of Koba and his dwarf Yeshov.

Rather, he stayed behind his doors, emerging only for his afternoon constitutional. On those occasions, he strode briskly through the lobby with an aristocratic aloofness upon his face, as if any consideration beyond the ancient lift that would haul him to his rooms was utterly beneath him. He looked neither left nor right and issued no greetings to old comrades, nor, by his iciness, did he expect to receive any. He dressed as if a dandy in the last century, in spats, a velvet smoking jacket, well worn but beautifully fitted, a white silk scarf, and a lustrous mink coat. He acted as if, by special compact to the highest authority, he was invulnerable to the nighttime visits of Koba's killers.

He had been called many things in his interesting life, but one of them clung even to this day and to this circumstance. He was called, not only by his peers in the Lux and by his enemies in the Kremlin, but in the capitals of the West, the Devil Himself.

For a legend, he seemed rather vigorous. At fifty-nine, E. I. Levitsky still had a taut, lively face. His mouth retained its unusual thinness. It was a clever, prim mouth, as the eyes above it were also clever. They carried the electricity of conviction. He wore, after Lenin, a little goatee, purely an affectation. His head was glossily balding from the forehead back to the crown, though extravagant with bushy peppercorn hair beneath it, as if the black and gray individuals that comprised this mass were violently divided among themselves as to their ultimate direction and destiny. He had a lanky, surprisingly long body, wiry, and long, pale, exquisite fingers. He looked exceptionally refined, as if he'd spent his life in the higher realms of culture. He also looked hard in a peculiar way: hard, unmalleable, an alloy, not a base metal.

In his hand, he held a pawn. A blunt, smooth little soldier. It expects only death and in this humble aspiration is ever so frequently rewarded. Pawns are made for sacrifice; this is their function; this ennobles them.

As he gripped the ancient chess piece in his hand, a name came to him, a name whispered that afternoon in a hurried but not quite

accidental encounter in Pushkin Park, on a bench under the great trees.

"It's Tchiterine, Emmanuel Ivanovich. Your old comrade. Remember, he saved your life in the war?"

Yes, Levitsky remembered Tchiterine, another noble pawn.

It wasn't the sort of thing a man forgot: he lay out in the snow, thrown by his treacherous horse, the Maxim bullets clipping away at him. They struck close by with a stinging spray. He tried to shrink into the snow. All the while Kolchak's Death Battalion, with the eighteen-inch spike bayonets fixed to their rifles, advanced at the trot from the left, finishing the wounded as they came. No, one doesn't forget a memory such as that, or the moment when brawny Tchiterine had come slithering through the fire and with one strong hand taken him and pulled him into a ravine and safety.

"The old ones. Koba is taking the old ones. It's clear now." The rue in the mysterious comrade's voice had been almost operatic with passion.

"He can watch out for himself," Levitsky had said, concentrating on the lacy patterns the snow-heavy limbs formed against the bright blue sky. "He's no child. He's in Spain now, isn't he?"

"He'll never leave Spain. Koba is reaching into Spain now. Tchiterine has just been arrested in Spain. They say he'll be shot."

The comrade sighed. "Tchiterine, he was the best. You even took him to England with you. An inspiration."

"Yes, England," said Levitsky, aware that the fellow was well informed.

Then the man said, "Lemontov was the smart one."

"Lemontov was always smart. That's why he put a bullet in his head," Levitsky responded.

"No, haven't you heard? I just heard today. He's not dead, like they said he was. He went over. Can you believe it?" He shook his head as if in wonder.

Levitsky said nothing. However, he took a deep breath in acknowledgment that his life and fate had just altered radically. The

message had been well delivered. His breath came in quiet, harsh little spurts. He could feel his head begin to throb, as the comrade spoke.

It turned out that it hadn't been Lemontov's body, prune wrinkled and pulpy, they'd pulled out of the canal at all. It was a ruse, using some Dutchman's corpse. They say Lemontov had gone over to the Americans. He was the smart one. He was the only one to beat hungry old Koba. The Americans will give him lots of money and he will live in Hollywood and fuck Greta Garbo all night long.

No, Levitsky thought. He paid *them*. In information. Lemontov. Yes, Lemontov was the smart one.

Levitsky, in his room, set down the pawn. He went swiftly to the bottle, poured himself another brandy. Then, his nerves soothed, he walked back to the table and picked up the pawn again. It was from a German set, which he'd won in Karlsbad in 1901. He fingered the piece, clutching it tightly to his palm.

So soon.

Oh, Lemontov, you clever, treacherous bastard. Of them all, my brave boys whom I taught so well, I should have foreseen it would be you. Tchiterine was hard-working, dull, brave, a zealot. Another was nakedly ambitious, a stupid peasant boy dead set on rising above himself by sheer will. Still another was a coward, a schemer, a weakling. You, Lemontov, you were the brilliant one. A Jew like myself, of course. So smart, so full of ideas, so crackling with insight and enthusiasm.

If Lemontov had fled to the Americans, the Americans knew. And the Americans would tell the British. About the agent code-named Castle. Castle, Levitsky's lasting legacy to the revolution, the one thing not even a maniac like Koba could steal. His Castle at the center of the British establishment.

This meant the game had begun years earlier than it ought to have, and on the enemy's terms, and that, worse, it would have to be improvised in the middle of Koba's terror, thrown together with madcap dash. Somebody in the GRU saw that the buried Castle had suddenly become vulnerable, and knew that NKVD, crazy with

the bloodlust, didn't care. And somebody knew only the man who had recruited Castle could help. Thus by secret approach, a last mission for the Devil Himself.

Save Castle.

At once an impulse seized him. He rose, strode back across the carpet of his shabby room, and sat at the table before an empty chessboard. No emotion appeared on his studious, ascetic face. He stared at the glossy, checkered surface.

It seemed immense. Its sixty-four squares described a universe of possibility; an illusion, of course. There was, to begin with, a remote mathematical limit on possibility. More to the point, however, possibility was strictly a function of position: you could only go from where you were—that was Levitsky's first principle of reality, and it was more binding and absolute than any law in physics.

He therefore began to solve his problem by defining the positions.

What, for example, did Lemontov know? Did he know Castle's name, his identity? No, Levitsky had been exceedingly careful about the mechanism from the start, shielding Castle from his staff; only two men other than Levitsky and Castle himself knew of the arrangement: two high-ranking officers in the GRU, Red Army intelligence, men of unimpeachable honesty and honor, sworn only to reveal the information upon Levitsky's death. What Lemontov, therefore, could provide was only a description: a set of credentials and possibilities, a year (1931), a place (Cambridge), which would define perhaps more than several hundred young British men of a certain age and social standing and potential. It would be a British problem, then, to winnow these possibilities down to several specific candidates. And then, from among these, find the right one. Not an easy task, particularly in a democracy, where security services were notoriously hamstrung by sentimental notions of privacy and respect for individual rights.

He stared at the pattern on the board, absorbed. Was there time in the world to save Castle?

From far below on this still, late Moscow night, Levitsky heard the buzz of a motorcar. It pulled up to the hotel and halted. Doors opened, closed with a metallic slam. Men walked toward the hotel, their boots striking crisply on the pavement.

Levitsky looked at the clock on the mantel. It was 4 A.M., the hour of the NKVD.

He looked back to the board and, with an urgency that bordered on despair, reopened the leather-bound case. The figures were beautifully carved, with an ornate, quite possibly decadent skill that nothing in the Soviet Union could now equal. He plucked the pieces out and arranged them on the board, two white ranks, two red ranks.

From somewhere deep in the building, he heard the clang of the lift gate.

It's the time of sacrifice, he thought.

His fingers pushed a piece out from its rank. His humble rook's pawn, the red. Levitsky looked at the dowdy little thing, O hero pawn! Brave, willing to sacrifice yourself up in the furnace of the game for larger considerations.

Levitsky smiled, hearing the climb of the lift through the building. He remembered 1901. In that year, in the great hall at the Karlsbad Casino, against the best in the world, the humble pawn had been the key to Levitsky's greatest victory in the single master's tournament he had allowed himself before disappearing forever in the underground. And in the fortnight, the bespectacled young exile had become the mysterious Devil Himself, vanquisher of all . . .

He heard the lift stop at his floor. The gate opened. He heard the boots on the tile.

Schlecter, the German, suddenly sat across from him: a dandy, wordless little genius who wore carnations and plaid suits of English cut and had watery eyes and eczema and sported a flowery cologne and fought like a Cossack. Schlecter would not look at him. Schlecter preferred to avoid personalities. To him it was just the movement of pieces on the board.

Levitsky had the opening and pushed his queen's pawn into the fourth row and Schlecter matched him. Then he swiftly brought his knight into play, moving it to king's bishop three. Schlecter paused, a bit nonplussed, but not exactly near panic; then responded dramatically by moving his bishop forward to bishop's four. Strange: even Schlecter himself seemed controlled by some mysterious energy in the air then, as if strange forces, dybbuks, had been released to ride the currents of the vast space over their heads.

Levitsky was twenty-four; he was young and lean and furiously bright. He was only becoming gradually aware, however, of his gift.

He exploited the seam opening in the center of the board with that lone pawn, advancing him to bishop's four. Schlecter considered a long time—he was, after all, the drawmaster, more renowned for not losing than for winning—and ultimately shrank from the challenge with the conventional pawn to queen's bishop three.

Levitsky waited just a second, then reached down and shoved his queen through the gap he'd opened in his own ranks and pushed her out to knight's three; he heard the gasp and smiled, and felt himself almost blush as the gasp rose to a cheer.

Schlecter, of course, did not look up, as if to meet Levitsky's eyes would somehow be to submit to his power. He studied the pieces in perfect silence and then almost languidly brushed his blue-veined old hand across the table and yanked his own queen out to knight's three.

The tumult was enormous; neither player acknowledged it. Time for some blood, old man. Levitsky took a pawn, exposing his queen.

Schlecter quickly replaced Levitsky's queen with his own, and less than one second later, Levitsky had Schlecter's lady himself with a pawn; and he still had his lead pawn out there, achingly alone in center board.

Schlecter saw the open rank, and he hurled his bishop down the gap to take the suddenly defenseless knight; but it didn't matter, for Levitsky was able to spring the trap he had so ingeniously

engineered. He took Schlecter's solitary pawn and dared Schlecter to expose his king by taking the pawn out with his knight.

"Herr Levitsky," Schlecter asked in the quietest German, "do you wish me to play it out, or would you prefer that I resign now?"

"It is up to you."

"It was brilliant, young man."

"Thank you. I was very lucky."

"No, it was more than luck. I've played against enough luck in my time to know luck."

Schlecter took his pawn with a rook and Levitsky completed the action: he moved his lead pawn into the back rank, thereby castling it. In the back row it acquired extraordinary force; it was born again. It mated Herr Schlecter's poor king. The theme had been a variation on the idea of the brave pawn, an exceedingly unusual phenomenon in international play, where the odds against a single pawn surviving a charge into the enemy's last rank are forbiddingly rare. Yet Levitsky had brought it off because he had the hardness of spirit and the sheer guts to pay the price as the combinations developed, feeding his own pieces into the maw to advance the pawn.

That was it: the erratic, the brilliant fluctuation of it, the fascination of it—the humble pawn, suddenly castled in the back rank, suddenly made the most powerful piece on the board, planted in the soft underbelly. A humble pawn has become all powerful and any sacrifice, or any orchestration of sacrifice, is worth it.

Levitsky sat back. He had worked out his solution. It all turned then, on a single bright young Englishman. Levitsky remembered him with fondness, love even: bright, fair, gifted, pleasant, charming.

It's time. After all the years, it's time.

He heard the NKVD men knocking.

"I'm INNOCENT!" The scream pierced the narrow walls of the Lux.

A door slammed. Feet dragged and snapped in the hall. Levitsky heard the lift gate clank shut, and heard the machine descend.

Another for your hunger, old Koba.

The face of the young Englishman returned to his mind. He would be in Spain, of course, for Spain was all the fashion of his set. Spain would attract the golden lads of this world as a lamp attracts the moths.

Spain, then. The game of pawns and rooks and deaths must be played in Spain. It all turns on the position of the pieces, on the willingness, the nerve, for sacrifice.

3

BARCELONA, LATE 1936

COMRADE BOLODIN," INSTRUCTED COMRADE GLASANOV, "break his nose. But be careful of the mouth."

Comrade Bolodin walked to the naked old man who was bound to the chair. He studied the problem with dispassion while the old man looked up at him, as if he didn't seem too sure of what was happening. He looked dazed. Bolodin, who was exceedingly strong, drove a sharp, perfect blow into his face. The meaty thud filled the cell. He felt the nose crack and splinter in its flesh in the split second before the head snapped back.

"Well done, comrade," said Glasanov.

The old man's head lolled forward on his chest. Snot and blood ran from his face and spotted his white, scrawny body. Glasanov lifted the head gently and stared at it. The nose was crushed almost flat but the bruising and the swelling had not yet begun. Glasanov waited for the focus to come back into the eyes, and for the fear to appear.

"Listen, why do you make us hurt you?" he asked with genuine curiosity. "Why must we go through this? Can you not begin now to understand the gravity of these charges?"

"*Osysvorf,*" the old man cursed, but the language was unfamiliar to the Russian.

"He's delirious," he said. "He's praying in Hebrew."

"No," said Comrade Bolodin, "that's Yiddish. And it isn't a prayer. It's a curse. He said you were garbage."

Glasanov did not take the insult personally; he never did.

"You cannot win," he pointed out to the old man. "Surely you understand that. And not just in this room, where you are doomed, but in the larger sense, the historical sense."

Glasanov talked frequently of history; he loved history. Each night, when they were done or before they had begun, they sat in the Café Moka on the Ramblas sipping Pernod and *rijos* among English newsmen and fiery young Spanish Anarcho-Syndicalists and POUMistas and other assorted but quite colorful riffraff that an out-of-control revolution throws up. Glasanov would explain at great length to his assistant Bolodin about history.

"Fuck history," said the old man, in Russian.

"Hit him," said Glasanov. "In the body. The ribs. Hard. Several times, please, comrade."

Bolodin walked to the bound figure, feeling the old Yid's eyes on him the whole way. Jesus, they could be tough, these old birds. Without a great deal of emotional involvement, Comrade Bolodin threw a flurry of short, penetrating blows into his ribs and chest. He could hear the crack of his fists against the body as the old man jerked spastically in the ropes. But he would not scream.

"All right," said Glasanov. "It's very clear, Comrade Tchiterine. The charges are clear and they are obvious. You are a wrecker and an oppositionist. You have constantly worked to undermine the Party and betray the revolution. In England in 1931, you and Lemontov and Levitsky entered into an agreement with the British Secret Service, so you are also a spy. And all of this is under the control of your leader, the Jew Trotsky."

The old man raised his head slowly. His skin had gone almost the color of slate. Blood showed on his lips.

"Fuck your sister, you cowshit peasant. The Great Lenin himself gave Levitsky and me medals."

"And what if it's true, old Tchiterine? It's irrelevant to history. Hit him hard."

Comrade Bolodin hit him in the ear and the face. He hit him in

the mouth, smashing out his teeth. He hit him in the temple, then hit him again and again under the eye, in the face. The sound of the blows was slippery and wet and dense. He hit him in the—

"BOLODIN! Enough, Christ, enough. You forget yourself."

Bolodin stepped back. He sometimes had difficulty stopping.

"Tchiterine, it's pointless to resist. You'll sign the confession either here or in the Lubyanka. You'll go on trial. You'll be found guilty. You'll die. Your generation must pass on now. That's what history has written."

The old man's face had been greatly damaged by the punishment. It looked like a piece of mashed fruit, swollen and bruised and caked in blood. The blood was everywhere. He croaked something through his swollen lips.

"Eh?" asked Glasanov.

"Fuck Koba," said Tchiterine, somehow, and Comrade Bolodin hit him a cruel, powerful blow in the side. Of the many, this was perhaps the most devastating, for it ruptured the old man's appendix. In his bounds, Tchiterine commenced to struggle as the pain and numbness rocketed through him. In time he lapsed into a waxen coma. His breathing was imperceptible.

"You hit him too much. Your zeal gets the best of you. Discipline. Remember, above all, discipline. Strength, passion, commitment, they are all fine and absolutely necessary. The great Stalin, however, says that in discipline lies the key to the future."

"I apologize, comrade."

"You Americans," Comrade Glasanov said.

Comrade Bolodin's true name was Lenny Mink, and his last fixed address had been 1351 Cypress Avenue in the Williamsburgh section of Brooklyn, but he was to be found more frequently at Midnight Rose's, a candy store at Livonia and Saratoga streets, that served as the unofficial headquarters for his company, which went by the name Murder, Inc. He had left New York at the urging of certain parties, as police curiosity concerning his involvement with the deaths by shooting, bludgeoning, ice picking, and drowning of

several witnesses due to deliver evidence against Lepke Buchalter had reached embarrassing proportions. Lenny, like his peers Pittsburgh Phil, Gangy Cohen, Pretty Levine, Jack Drucker, and his bosses Mendy Weiss, Dandy Phil Kastel, and Bugsy Seigel, killed people for two reasons: because he was good at it and because he was paid for it.

"Well, he'll be out all night," said Glasanov. "Get him back to his cell. Wash him off, clean him up. Get him some brandy. We'll work on him some more tomorrow."

"Yes, comrade," said Lenny Mink, still in Russian.

"Tough old fellow," said Glasanov. "They had to be in those days. He's right, you know, what they did was extraordinary. Fighting the Okrana and the Cossacks and later the western armies and Kolchak. My God, they were tough."

Lenny looked at the old guy. Yeah, tough. Tougher than any nigger, and when he was young, Lenny had fought a nigger for almost an hour down by the docks until both men had been too exhausted to continue and nobody took the kitty. Later, some whore used a razor on the guy.

"Be careful with him, now. Comrade Koba wants him back in Moscow, understand?"

"Yes, comrade." Lenny kept his Russian simple and polite.

"I'll be in my office. Wake me if anything occurs."

Lenny, alone with the old man, reached into his pocket and removed a switchblade, popped it, and cut the bonds. The body fell; he caught it. Tchiterine had once been an important man, the Comintern agent in charge of imposing Party demands on the often unruly dockworkers' unions in the port of Barcelona. Now look at him.

Lenny, six-three and well over two hundred pounds, had no trouble getting the old guy up in his arms. The American had a blunt, sullen, nearly handsome face, though it was pocked. He seemed to carry his big bones slowly and had a kind of cold force to him—he liked to hurt people and people understood this of him almost instinctively, and tended to become uncomfortable in his

presence, an effect he enjoyed. He had always had it. In fact, in his youth, in the Diaspora before he had come to America, his shtetl nickname had been "Cossack," after the rumor that he'd been begotten, not by his nominal father, a butcher, but by a Russian raider in a pogrom.

He rarely spoke. He appeared to listen intently. People often considered him stupid, which was a mistake. He simply wasn't clever with words, although he spoke imperfect versions of English and Russian, having learned the latter during a two-thousand-mile walk from Minsk to Odessa when he was eleven years old, a remarkable journey. He had made the trip on his own, after another pogrom, the one in which his mother and father and all his brothers and sisters had been killed. His best language was Yiddish, the language of his boyhood, although he was picking up Spanish rapidly. When he had presented himself at the International Brigade clearinghouse in Paris, in hopes of finding suitable employment in the natural venue for a man of his profession—a war—the NKVD had scooped him up. The NKVD had plans for Barcelona, and Lenny looked to be the perfect instrument.

He took old Tchiterine's body into the harsh light of the newly wired bulbs and down the empty corridor of the prison, which at one time had been the novitiates' wing of the Convent of St. Ursula. The place had been vandalized, as had all Church properties in the first crazed days of the July Revolution, and rioters had smashed everything and painted slogans everywhere. Shards of broken glass still lay on the floor. Yet the place also had a sense of newness to it; recently occupied by elements of the NKVD, which clearly needed both privacy and security, it had been painted roughly, rewired for electricity, patched, and repaired. It smelled of paint and new wood and also of piss and despair.

Lenny reached Tchiterine's cell and set him on the bed. The old man breathed roughly. His swelling completely disfigured his face. Lenny covered his nakedness with a blanket. He went to a bucket, brought it over, and wet his handkerchief. He began to wipe the dried blood off the face. He'd really gone a little nuts there—a

problem of his. Sometimes he couldn't hold on to himself. He just liked the way it felt when he hit people. Discipline, this Russian boss was always saying. Discipline was the secret of history. He actually believed that shit.

The old man moaned suddenly.

Lenny jumped.

"Ya!" he yelped in Yiddish. "You scared me, old man."

One yellow eye came open. The other was swollen shut.

"Vasser," the old man begged through his ripened lips. "Please," he begged in Yiddish, "a little, please."

"You old *yentzer,"* Lenny laughed. He cupped some water in his big hand and let it dribble into the old man's mouth. The old man lapped it up greedily.

"I don't feel so good in my gut," he said.

"What'd you expect, from the smashing you got?"

"Help me," the old man said then. "I can pay you."

"Pay what? You got a treasure stuck up your old asshole? You're making me laugh, you old putz."

Lenny stood to leave. The old man looked like one of those bums you find on Seventh Avenue after the Harlem niggers got done rolling him: all beat to shit, beat to craziness, not good for nothing. Naked, shivering, in the straw, his face punched to shit. It made Lenny sick. He was so big once, this old man, and now look at him.

The old man fought to get a word out. It came in a whisper, racked and hoarse.

"Whaaaa?" said Lenny.

"G-g-g-g-gelt," the old man finally spat out. Money.

Lenny bent. Maybe the old guy had a stash somewhere.

The old man's feeble hand flew up to Lenny's shoulder. It felt like a perched bird.

"Save me, nu? Save an old Jew."

"How much? Talk a figure."

"Lots. Would I lie?"

"Everybody lies."

"*Gelt!* Lots and lots, I'm telling you."

"Where, up your asshole?"

"Gold, by the ton!"

"A ton of gold. In a mountain somewhere, no? Old putz, talking dreams."

Lenny had an urge to kill him. Put the thumb to his throat, press it in; he'd be history in a second.

"In 1931, me, Lemontov, Levitsky, we worked in England as spies."

"It's old business."

"Listen. Listen."

"So fucking talk."

"Levitsky found a student at a fancy university."

"Who's this Levitsky?"

"*Teuful.*"

"Devil?"

"*Shayner Yid.* The Devil Himself. The old revolutionary. The master spy. He was head of Comintern. A real important guy."

Lenny was growing interested. But what was the money angle?

"Go on, you old fuck," he said.

The old man told him swiftly, croaking the story out of his swollen lips in little bursts as he grabbed on to Lenny's arm with his tight hand, about the boy in England, the gentile boy who would rise, and yet was bound in special ways to old Levitsky, the spy.

"The Devil Himself owns the boy's soul," the old Jew said.

"What's this guy's name?" Lenny wanted to know.

"I don't know it. I only served Levitsky, the man is a genius. I never knew any of the real secrets. Lemontov didn't know. But I saw him once. This boychik, I saw him. When I was in a place I shouldn't have been."

"Where's the dough you're talking about?"

"He's in Spain, five years older, this boy, now grown to a man. Working for the Russians, nu? I've seen him with my own two eyes. I can point him out. He's in the cafés every night."

"So what's this talk of a ton of gold, old man. You pulling my putz?"

"Listen good. The Russians took gold off these Spaniards. To pay for guns, they said. It was shipped out, they said. And everybody thinks it's gone. But at the last minute, they got scared when the Italian submarines started sinking ships. I know, I found out in the harbor. Those ships they loaded up with gold, they were empty. They hid the stuff. Somewhere in this city. They're going to take it over land, through Europe. This Englishman, it's his job, I tell you. He's here to move the gold, because the Russians don't trust their own people. This Englishman, he knows where the gold is. When he moves, the ton of gold moves too."

Lenny looked at him, feeling something working in his head. A ton of gold. Moved secretly. An Englishman. Who would suspect an Englishman moving Spanish gold for the Russians?

Lenny thought it over. A ton of gold! Ripe for picking. With only an Englishman for a guard.

Lenny liked the idea of a lot of money; it meant you went to the clubs and everybody knew you and you had a swell dame and guys were always coming by and asking how you were, the way they did with Lepke.

"One thing. We got to protect Levitsky. He's family, nu? He's one of us. He's one of us. He's *shayner Yid,* and we don't give him away."

"Ah, he's off in Russia somewhere drinking vodka with his pals."

"No, I'm telling you. He'll check in on his boychik, he will. He's the smartest man in the world, a chess champion, a genius, not like us. Hah, he—"

He made a sudden strange, gurgling sound.

"I don't feel so good," the old man said. "When you hit me, the last time, in the side; my gut hurts."

"You're okay."

"No, get me a doctor. You gotta get me a doctor."

"There ain't any doctors in this joint. What, a stomach ache? In the morning, you'll be—"

But the old man had gone gray almost incredibly and he continued to choke and gurgle and tremble.

"Help me!" he said, his one eye opened wide. His hand flew to Lenny and grabbed his arm desperately. "Help me!"

"Fuck you," said Lenny, but he was talking to a corpse.

And fuck me, too, Lenny Mink thought, with his dream of a ton of gold as dead as the body before him.

A few days later, Lenny received a bit of unusual news. He was told to proceed, in daylight, to Glasanov's office in the Main Police Building on the Via Layetana, not far from the port. This was quite peculiar. Lenny had never been there before.

Some German drove him from the convent to the station. It was a big, square, white building in the middle of a busy city street, just a few blocks from the Ramblas. The revolutionary slogans and painted initials, the rippling banners, the huge posters of old men with goatees could not quite disguise the grandeur of the place, its link to a time when Spain had been ruled by about six guys who built everything to look like a wedding cake. It was maybe nine stories tall, and each window had a little balcony under it, all the way up. You went in through a main gate under a banner that said LET US GO FORWARD INTO THE MODERN AGE which took you into a courtyard and then you went in a set of double doors which took you into a big corridor and then you went up four flights to find Glasanov's office.

Glasanov, Lenny understood, was some kind of "adviser" to the Barcelona police department, which meant he ran it. He was helping them organize what they called the Servicio de Investigación Militar, the SIM; Lenny also understood that the SIM was a Spanish version of the NKVD; or, rather, that it *was* the NKVD. It was like gangs anywhere: one gang got control and they tried to take over everywhere. A tough gang stayed tough by squashing any gang that thought it was tougher.

Yet Glasanov's office turned out to be a modest arrangement at

the end of a hall. He walked in to find Glasanov standing. Glasanov looked a little like a German because he was so pale and blond. He was not smiling, but he never smiled, because he took his responsibilities so seriously. His cheeks had an almost artificial color to them, which the Russians called the "midnight look," because it seemed to show up on the faces of officials who spent the nights in their offices.

"Comrade Bolodin. Our Amerikanski."

Lenny had never liked the revolutionary pseudonym; he still had to think twice when one of the Russians called him by it.

"Comrade commissar," Lenny responded. He hated the comrade shit, the talk of history, the endless lectures on scientific Marxism and the necessity for building a better world. But when you worked for a boss, you played it his way. Until you got yours.

"A drink?"

"No thanks."

"Excellent. A man who controls his appetites. I like that."

"Is this about the old guy? Look, it wasn't my fault he croaked."

"No, no. An accident. A terrible accident. He was in ill health. Moscow understands."

Lenny waited. What *was* the story?

"Here. I have something for you. It's time, I think, for you to take a more active role in the processes of enforcing Party discipline here in Barcelona. This is why I asked you to come by."

He handed over a card.

Lenny realized it was an ID naming him a captain in the SIM—making him, in other words, an official secret policeman and giving him all the rights and responsibilities thereof, which included the right to make spot arrests and searches, to confiscate property and vehicles in the service of the state, to command units of the Asaltos, or assault police, to extract immediate cooperation, not to say obedience, from all civil authority.

"There's much work ahead," Glasanov went on. "There are traitors everywhere, do you understand? Even in Moscow in the heart

of government, among the oldest and most trusted of the revolutionary fighters. Every day, they confess their crimes in the dock, or flee."

"So I hear," said Lenny Mink.

"The late Comrade Tchiterine," said Glasanov, "for example, was under the control of a famous revolutionary fighter named Levitsky, who was the worst. Tchiterine, a man named Lemontov who has disappeared, and this Levitsky, they formed a terrorism center, working at espionage to betray us. Levitsky was second only to Trotsky. Did Tchiterine, by chance, mention Levitsky?"

"He didn't mention anybody. He just died."

"Umm. I had thought they might have been in contact. They seem to have been in some sort of plot together."

Lenny grunted, thinking *What plot, you fuck?*

"First Lemontov disappears—that should have been the tipoff. At least we were fast enough to nab Tchiterine."

"What about this guy Levitsky?"

"Ah. A wily old fox. They call him the Devil Himself, for certain colorful exploits. He's gone. He disappeared from Moscow even as the security people were coming to arrest him."

Lenny nodded. *The old fucker was out!*

"I tell you this to encourage your vigilance. We are preparing to move against our enemies here. The days of café sitting will soon be coming to an end."

"You can count on me," said Lenny.

"Of course. You are an extraordinarily valuable man."

Glasanov handed him a piece of paper. On it was written a name.

"An oppositionist. He leads the propaganda battle against us in his newspaper. His organization is powerful, and he is one of its leaders."

It was just like at Midnight Rose's. The word came, and you took somebody for a ride.

"You want him killed."

"Ah—"

"Believe me, he's gone."

"There will be others. Some to be arrested and interrogated, some to be liquidated. You must cut off the head of a beast before you dispose of its body. A period of great struggle is coming, and I am personally charged with commanding our forces."

But Lenny wasn't really listening, nor was he thinking about the man he would pop that night.

He was thinking of what old Tchiterine had told him.

He'll check in on his boychik.

Lenny smirked in triumph. He knew what none of them knew. He was ahead of this smart Russian, he was ahead of everybody in the world. He knew where this Levitsky, this *teuful,* would head. The Devil Himself, eh?

Well, the old guy was coming straight to Barcelona, to check up on his boychik. And he'd lead Lenny to him. He'd lead him to the *gelt.*

"Comrade," said Glasanov. "To the future." He handed him a small glass of vodka. "You must not refuse me."

"Let us go forward into the modern age," said Lenny, throwing the vodka down his throat.

He hated vodka.

4

MR. STERNE AND MR. WEBLEY

FLORRY MET HOLLY-BROWNING THE FOLLOWING TUESDAY on a bench in Hyde Park. The older officer had a bag of peanuts for the pigeons and a briefcase. Mr. Vane sat quietly three benches down the walk, looking blankly off through the trees.

The major sighed, his eyes settling on some obscure object in the far distance. He shelled a peanut, launched it to the walk, and a doddering, scabby old pigeon contemptuously gobbled it off the concrete.

"I wonder if this is quite necessary," said Florry impatiently.

"Oh, there's not much to say, Mr. Florry. The technical business is quite easily taken care of. We try to keep things simple. You'll find this is useful." He handed over a package, which Florry opened quickly. It was a thick, densely printed book.

"*Tristram Shandy*? I loathe it. I loathe Laurence Sterne. I never was able to finish it."

"I haven't met anybody who has. And that's the point. But it will do for an introduction to a chap in Barcelona called Sampson. David Harold Allen Sampson—"

"The *Times* writer?"

"Yes, indeed. You've seen his dispatches?"

"He's awfully dull, I think. Julian's stuff is much better."

"Sampson represents our interests there, and through him you'll keep us informed. He's got an office on the Ramblas, Number 114

Rambla San Jose. He can reach us quickly via the consulate wireless. Can you remember that?"

"Of course."

"Show him the book. It's a way of saying hullo, we're in the same firm. He'll guide you to Raines."

"I'm sure I'll have no trouble finding Julian."

"And there's this." From the briefcase he withdrew another bulky package, something heavy wrapped in oilskins. Florry took it in his lap and began to pull apart the rags.

"Not here. Good Christ, man, somebody might see—"

But Florry plunged ahead: he got enough of the material apart to penetrate to the center of the treasure. Wrapped in an elaborate leather rig there was a vaguely familiar object, and as his fingers flew across it, he recognized it immediately. He put his hand on the grip and pulled it out.

It was a well-oiled Webley Mark I, a big revolver with a short octagonal barrel.

"God, you're not joking about all this, are you?" Florry said.

"Put it away, Florry. Somebody could come along."

But Florry continued to look at it, fascinated. He experienced the weapon's heft and weight and perfect easy feel. He'd carried much the same thing in Burma, though in a slightly later model. With a dexterity from memory that surprised him, he hit the latch to break the action and the barrel obediently dropped to expose the cylinder. Six gleaming brass circles peeped out, like six coins on a pewter plate.

"Loaded," he said.

"The bloody things are useless without bullets. That's a shoulder holster, by the way. It'll hold the weapon neatly out of sight under a coat or cardigan. And as you know, the four-five-five will knock down anything on two feet at close range. Now put it away, Florry. Someone could come."

Julian? What would a monster like a Webley do to vivid, charming, cruel Julian? It would blow his guts in quarts across the landscape.

He shook his head, quickly replaced the pistol in the holster, wrapped it in the cloth, and put it back in the briefcase. Mr. Sterne and Mr. Webley were to be his companions in Spain.

"I suppose that's it, then?" he said. "A revolver and a code book. It *is* a game, isn't it?"

"It's not a game, Mr. Florry. Never think of it as a game. Think of it as life and death."

"I wonder if I could ever do the final thing."

"You'll do what's necessary. You'll see your duty."

"I suppose you're right. And that is what frightens me."

Florry turned and issued the major a look that was either stupidity or shock. The major had seen it before, but not since 1916. It was the look of men in the trenches, about to go over the top, who didn't believe their moment of destiny had finally arrived. Florry got up and walked away gloomily.

The major peeled another peanut and turned it over to the hungry pigeons. Soon Mr. Vane joined him.

"I trust it went well, sir?"

"It went as well as could be expected, Vane. Given the circumstances."

"Did you think he's up to it?"

"Not yet. That's Sampson's job."

"Yessir."

"We'll have to play Mr. Florry very carefully, won't we, Vane?"

"Yessir."

"Levitsky can make a traitor of anyone. Can I make a murderer so easily?"

They watched as Florry, now a small figure, disappeared in the traffic.

5

BARCELONA

MOST NIGHTS, IN OBEDIENCE TO HIS INSTRUCTIONS, Comrade Captain Bolodin of the SIM went out with his men and made arrests. The instructions were perfect: the addresses were always right, the criminal always available. Comrade Captain Bolodin and his men were always on time; they never had any trouble. Nothing worked well in Republican Spain except the NKVD and nothing worked better in the NKVD than Comrade Captain Bolodin.

Sometimes the criminals were imprisoned, sometimes merely liquidated. A libertarian lawyer, for example, author of a wickedly scatological anti-Russian poem for his four-page party newspaper, paid for this crime with a bullet in the neck; a Polish trade unionist also died, as did a French intellectual who wrote scathing editorials, and a German Social Democrat who had published an unkind article in a Norwegian socialist newspaper. A Cuban, however, was simply reeducated in the political realities of Barcelona by an administration of Comrade Captain Bolodin's fists for an excruciatingly long evening.

But under this political drama another one was running. Certain of the arrestees of a peculiar age and range of experience were spared the more furious applications of Koba's justice and—although this was quite unknown to Koba's official representatives, particularly the aggressively moral Glasanov—were escorted into an obscure cell for a private interview with Comrade Captain Bolodin. The subjects were always the same.

/ 55

The first was a certain shipment of gold, said to have left the Barcelona port in November of 1936 on four Russian steamers. Had this material actually been loaded on the ships and sent out to Odessa, as official records insisted? The answers varied, and the arrestees, mainly dockworkers and low-ranking Spanish port officials, were at great pains to please their interrogator. Some swore yes, they'd seen Russian tankers loading the material that the Spaniards had not been able to get near to. But others said the entire affair was quite odd, because the Russians had insisted on being so public about it; they wanted the world to know they were moving the gold. One man said the ships road awfully high in the water for all the weight they were said to be carrying. But if the gold remained hidden in Barcelona, where could it be? None of Lenny's many arrestees had an opinion.

For these men, the fate was always the same. They had learned, from their ordeal, of Mink's real interest. It was the most dangerous knowledge a man could have in Barcelona. They died, usually with a 7.62 mm slug from Lenny Mink's Tula-Tokarev in the back of their skulls.

The other subject that Lenny Mink examined at length was a certain category of arrestee's acquaintance with the legendary Levitsky, or "Devil Himself" as he was called in certain quarters.

These questions met with a variety of responses.

Some, for example, would not talk at all without severe assistance. It took Lenny the best part of one whole evening to pry out of one old man the story of Levitsky's youth, and how the Cossacks had, one bloody morning, liberated the boy from responsibility to parents and shtetl by slaying the former and burning the latter, all before his terrified twelve-year-old eyes, an event which forever propelled him to the revolutionary course. Lenny listened gravely to this account, having some familiarity with the materials himself.

Of Levitsky's early exploits in the underground of the nineties at a very young age, his first contests with the Okrana, and his eventual abandonment of anarchism for the tenets of Marx, no reliable witness could be found, though several alluded to it.

What they remembered most of Levitsky was the long period between the failed revolution of 1905 and the successful one of 1917 in which he roamed Europe making his legend as a cunning strategist and a fighter of great bravery. It was primarily his enemies from these days who remembered him and frequently hated him still and were ready, even eager, to speak. They remembered his ruthlessness, his cunning, and even his brilliant chess.

"He could have owned the world, it was said," one man informed Lenny. "Instead he chose to change it."

He planted bombs in Bucharest, he organized strikes in Turin, he robbed banks in Zagreb; wherever the Party needed him, he went; whatever price the Party demanded, he paid. He was arrested half a dozen times, usually escaping, most spectacularly from the terrible Constantinople Hall of Darkness. Three times, maybe four, the Okrana tried to kill him.

He surfaced, again briefly, in the incredibly hectic years of the revolution, from 1917 to 1921. In this period, an old veteran recalled, he was remembered mainly as a soldier: a great battlefield tactician who, unlike the cowardly Trotsky in his armored train, rode at the head of every charge and was once unhorsed three times in a single afternoon. He fought in all the battles around Kazan and was wounded twice; he was a brigade commander, a counter-intelligence officer, and a leader of cavalry. He rode with the Red Cossacks—he, whose parents had been butchered by Cossacks— out of the hills on June 3, 1919, in the battle that spelled the end for Kolchak. He fought against Yedenitch in the north and Denekin in the south. This was particularly impressive to all who remembered it because Levitsky hated horses as he hated nothing on earth. It was a sheer triumph of will.

After the war, he again passed from view as he returned to the secret life of the conspirator. Few facts were forthcoming on this period, though Comrade Captain Bolodin sought them with special fervor. At the point of death, an old Rumanian confessed that he had heard that Comrade Levitsky had arranged assignment to the Otdyel Mezhunarodnoi Svyazi, the International Liaison Section of

Comintern, where he could privately pursue his goal of world revolution and safely ignore Koba as he ransacked the revolution. Comintern, it was also stated, was really but an arm of the GRU, Red Army Intelligence, whose policies it pursued with an almost noble integrity. It was said that Levitsky carried a high, secret rank in the GRU. It was said that when the GRU lost favor to the NKVD, Levitsky's magic protection began to wither away, his freedom to say unkind things about Koba, his ability to shock at social gatherings with his imitation of Koba at the chessboard, all these disappeared. He was being watched. But they were, on the whole, mysterious years: no witnesses knew enough to tell Lenny more than he already knew.

The arrests began in 1934. Koba arrested him then, and again in 1935; he spent time in Siberia, six frozen months as a *zek* in one of the prison camps, before "rehabilitation," and returned from the East with his particularly forbidding dignity, which most interpreted as pessimism and which, most agreed, doomed him; his last days were spent in the Lux Hotel, waiting for something . . . or waiting for Koba's final justice. Whether he was affiliated still with GRU was unknown.

These shreds of fact and bits of legend Lenny accumulated over a few weeks; for them all, the payment was the same: the bullet in the skull. And from them, he determined where he might be able to find what he needed most in his quest.

It was a steelpoint etching from a quick sketch done in 1901 in the Great Hall of the Casino at Karlsbad of the champion of the chess tournament. It has been printed within the pages of *Deutsche Schach-zeitung,* the German chess magazine. It was a picture of a fierce young Jew, and the caption under had read, *Der Teuful Selbst, E. I. Levitsky.*

It took Lenny a week to find it in an antiquarian bookstore in the Gothic Quarter.

6

THE *AKIM*

LATE IN THE MORNING, A CALM FELL ON THE TIRED OLD SCOW. No breeze furled the flat sea; the sky was cloudless, but white and dull with oppressive radiance. It was a warm, almost tropical day.

Sylvia noticed it first.

"We seem to be dead in the water," she observed, looking up from her copy of *Signature*. "I hope nothing is wrong." She sat on a canvas chair on the *Akim*'s small passenger deck beneath its battered bridge and single stack with her two fellow passengers.

"Perhaps they wait for a clearance or something," said Count Witte, the Polish correspondent.

"Can we be that close to Barcelona?"

"I don't know, dear girl," he said.

"What do you make of it, Mr. Florry?" she asked.

It was another in the constant barrage of questions she had for him. She was a young Englishwoman of his own age and the middle class, who had, if he understood correctly, come into some money, picked up a taint of fashionable leftist politics, and was now headed to Barcelona for adventuring. Though her questions were generally stupid, it pleased him to be asked them. She had so many!

Florry, also sitting on a deck chair, put down *Tristram Shandy* and said, "With this lot of amateurs one can never tell. I suppose I ought to go check."

"If you can make yourself understood," said the count, an aris-

tocratic old man in a yellow panama hat and monocle. "These monkeys are hardly human."

The count had a point: the crew of the old steamer consisted largely of semicivilized Arabs, wily, barefoot primitives in burnooses and filthy whites who scuttled about her rusty chambers and funnels like athletes and spoke in gibberish. The officers were only slightly better: two smarmy Turks who always needed a shave and spoke in impenetrable platitudes in answer to any query. Tell them their hair was on fire or some fellow had stuck a knife between their shoulder blades and they'd have answered the same: All is well, all is well, and praise to Allah.

"I suppose I shall have to ask the bloody steward," Florry said. "At least he's European."

"Good heavens," said the count, "if you consider *that* chap European, Mr. Florry, you have extremely low standards." He made a face as if he'd just swallowed a lemon, and followed it with a quick wink.

"Keep the pirates off Miss Lilliford, will you, count?" Florry called, leaving them.

He set out in search of the steward, but of course the old fellow was not always that easy to find. He was a seedy but kindly chap officially charged with attending to their needs on this short voyage from Marseilles to Barcelona and, more important, charged with helping the cook. He was not the sort of man who took duty seriously, however; he spent his time affixed to a secret flask of peppermint schnapps, for he wore the odor of the liquor about him like a scarf.

Florry climbed down through the hatchway and made his way into the oily interior of the craft. Twice, he stopped to let jabbering Arabs by. They salaamed obsequiously, but he could see the mockery in their bright eyes. He pressed on, and the temperature rose and the atmosphere seemed to thicken with moisture; it was actually steamy.

He finally found the old man in the galley, where he sat hunched in his filthy uniform, slicing onions into a large pot and weeping

copiously. As Florry approached he realized Gruenwald had really been on a toot this morning, for he smelled like a peppermint factory. He also gleamed with sweat, for the temperature in this room was even more grotesque than in the passageways. Florry mopped his face with a handkerchief, which came away transparent.

"I say, Mr. Gruenwald. The ship is no longer moving. Do you know why?"

"Hah?" replied old Gruenwald, scrunching up his face like a clown's. "No can I quite hear."

"We've stopped," Florry shouted over the clamor of the engines. "In the water. No propeller. No move. Understand?"

"Stopped? *Wir halten, ja?*"

"Yes. It's upsetting. Is anything wrong?"

"Ach. Nothing is. Is nothing. *Nein,* is nothing."

Old Herr Gruenwald leaped out of the galley—the Arab cook cursed him to Allah as he rose, but he paid no attention—and pulled Florry out through a hatchway onto a rusty lower deck—ah, fresh blast of salt air!—where he settled into the lee of a rotting lifeboat and bade Florry collapse beside him.

"Hah. You some schnapps want, *ja,* Englischman?"

"No, I think not. Awfully nice of you though," Florry said. Take a swig of *that?* Revolting!

"Ach. You should relax, no? Relax. Old Gruenwald, he take care." He reached into his back pocket, pulled out his flask, swiftly unscrewed the lid, and took a swallow. His bony old Adam's apple flexed like a fist as it worked. He handed the flask to Florry. "Go on. Is *gut.*"

Florry looked at the thing with great reluctance but in the end didn't want to seem an utter prig, and so took a swift gulp. It was awful. He coughed gaspingly and handed it back.

"Good, *nein?*"

"Delicious," Florry said.

"We stop because the Fascists sometime bomb docks in daylight. We stop here until five, *ja.* Then we go in in dark. So? Is okay?"

"Yes, I see." Florry looked out across the flat, still water.

"Not so long to wait, eh, Herr Florry?"

"Not if safety's the issue. I'd hate to think of what a bomb would do to this old tub."

"Boom! No more tub, *ja?*" The old man laughed merrily, took another swig from his flask. "The *Queen Mary, nein*, eh, Herr Florry?" he said conspiratorially, gesturing down to the paint-flecked, rust-pitted deck.

"Nor, I trust, the *Lusitania.*"

The old man laughed.

"I had a brother killed in the *Unterseeboots. Ja.* 1917."

"I'm sorry to hear that."

"Ach. No matter. He vas bastard, anyhow. Hah!"

Florry nodded sweetly, seeming to pay attention, and then said, "Come on, now, old fellow. The true reason. Don't let's play games."

Gruenwald professed indignation and shock at the accusation.

"Hah. Gruenwald tell truth. *Ja, Ich*—"

"Now, now, don't get excited. Perhaps you are. On the other hand, I can't imagine the owners of this wonderful oceangoing paradise would be too pleased to have it inspected terribly closely, would they? Unless my nose deceives me—and I've got a very good nose—I think I make out the undertang of tobacco amid the general welter of odors available below decks. Tobacco's contraband, I believe, in Spain. That, I believe, is the reason for our delay. So that we can sneak in under cover of darkness. Damned interesting." Florry gave the old man a sly look.

Gruenwald was gravely offended. "Herr Florry, you must zay nothing of zis! You keep your nose clean. *Ja?* You are at risk if you go about—"

"Don't worry, old fellow. I personally don't care what's done with the stuff, just so it doesn't inconvenience me unduly. All right?"

"Herr Florry, you be careful. Barcelona is very dangerous."

"Why, there's no fighting there any more."

"You listen *gut,* Herr Florry, I like Englisch peoples, even if they

kill my brother in 1917. Hah! You be careful. The man who own zis boat, he is very powerful. He would not like young Englisch gentleman go around town talk about tobacco. *Ja*! Bad trouble for someone who do this. There are many vays to die in Barcelona."

"Well, that's a fair warning given, and I shall take it to heart. Thank you, Herr Gruenwald."

"*Ja,* Gruenwald not zo zmart these days. I vas vunce real zmart. But in here, now, ist—how you say?"—he tapped his head and leaned close to Florry, his pepperminty breath flooding all over the Englishman—"*luftmensch*. Ah—"

"Crazy, we would say."

"*Ja*! *Ja*! Crazy, I got blown up by the Frenchies in the great war. In here metal *ist*. A big plate. Like as you would *haben die zup*—eat your dinner off. *Ja,* metal in the head, *ja*!"

"Good heavens," said Florry.

"In the war. The war was very bad."

"Yes, I know."

"How would you know, Herr Florry? You are too young for zuch things."

"Yes, I suppose I am," said Florry.

The old man took another swig on his flask and then another. His eyes seemed dead.

"Mr. Florry, where on earth have you *been?*" she asked, as he at last returned.

"I *am* sorry," he said.

She lounged on a chaise in the pale sun. Count Witte, his jacket off and folded, a pair of circular sunglasses perched comically across his face, lay beside her. He was reading a book in Polish.

Florry quickly explained. "And so we sit," he concluded. "I suppose if you choose a vessel that asks *you* no questions, then you must not ask questions of *it*."

"A good principle, Mr. Florry," called Count Witte. "It's as true of political parties as well. And also"—he added with another wink —"of women."

"Count Witte, you are such an old charmer," said Sylvia.

"Miss Lilliford, you make me wish I were a *young* charmer."

"Well," said Sylvia, "at least it will give me a chance to get all this read by landfall." She meant her pile of magazines. "At least then I shall have some understanding of things."

"It is exactly when one thinks one understands a revolution," said the count, "that the revolution changes into something that cannot be understood."

"I certainly understand the basic principles," boasted Florry. "They are threefold. If there's shooting you duck and if there's yelling you listen and if there's singing you pretend you know the words."

"Exactly," said the count. "Mr. Florry, we shall make an international correspondent of you yet."

The girl laughed. Florry pretended not to notice, as he'd been pretending not to notice since he came aboard three days earlier and discovered her on the deck. She was as slender as a blade, with a neck like a cocktail-glass stem. She had a mass of tawny, curled hair. She was about his own age, with gray green eyes. He did not think her terribly attractive. but nevertheless found himself taking great pleasure in the sound of her laughter or the sense of her attention when he talked politics with the sardonic old Witte.

"Oh, Mr. Florry," she had said, boldly speaking first, "you know so *much*."

Florry knew it not to be true, but found himself smiling again.

By five, the *Akim* had begun to move again, and shortly before nightfall, the passengers could see the long, thin line of the Spanish coastline.

"Look, Mr. Florry," Sylvia called from the rail. "There it is. At last."

Florry went to her.

"Hmm, just looks like the other side of the Thames to me. One supposes one should feel some sense of a great adventure beginning. I'd rather spend a night in a bed that doesn't rock quite as much as this one."

She laughed. "You're such a cynic"—and she gave him a slightly oblique look from her oddly powerful eyes—"except that you *aren't*."

"I tend to put my own comforts first, I suppose. Before politics and before history. And before long, I hope."

She laughed again, which pleased him. Then she said, "I don't feel the adventure, either, to tell the truth. What I feel is a sense of confusion. This war is a terrible mess. Only this fellow Julian Raines, the poet, can seem to make any sense of it. Did you read his piece on Barcelona?"

The name struck him uneasily.

"Brilliant fellow," he said uncomfortably, hoping to be done with the subject.

"His explanations are the clearest," she said with what seemed to be a kind of admiration. "What an extraordinary place it must be. On the occasion of the army rebellion, the armed workers beat them down. Then they refused to turn the guns over to the government and established a revolutionary society and are preparing for the next step. Which would be the establishment of a true classless society."

"God, what a nauseating prospect," said the count. "No, my dear, you'll see. The tension will mount between the Russian Communists and the libertarian, anti-Stalinist Anarchists and Socialists, and there'll be an explosion."

"In which case," Florry said, "we all obey Florry's First Rule of Revolution, which is: when the bombs go bang, find a deep hole."

They both laughed.

"You make it sound like a war, Mr. Florry. You have been reading your Julian Raines, too. He's very pessimistic about the Popular Front. He feels that—"

"Yes, I know, Sylvia. I *have* read all of Julian's pieces. He's awfully good, I admit it."

"It's a surprise, actually. I loathe his poetry. I loathe 'Achilles, Fool,' the poem about his poor father on the wire. My father also died in the Great War, and I don't see it as a game at all."

"Julian inspires passions," said Florry, looking out across the sea at the dark jut of land, profoundly aware that he himself did not.

"Oh, do you know him, Mr. Florry?" She squealed with delight, vivid animation coming into her eyes. Florry stared at the life on her face, hating it.

"We were at school together," he said. "Rather close, at one time, actually."

"He must be the most brilliant writer of his generation," she said. "Oh, could you possibly *introduce* me. He could teach me so much."

"Yes, I suppose. One never knows, of course, how these things will work out, but I suppose I might be able to. He'll be quite busy, of course. As will I."

"Oh, of course. As will I." She laughed. "To imagine, learning from *both* Robert Florry and Julian Raines. What an unusually lucky chance. The correspondent from *The Spectator* and from *Signature*." She laughed again. "I feel so lucky."

Florry looked at her. There was something about her slim neck that attracted him enormously. I'm the lucky one, he thought and watched her go back to her cabin.

Florry stood at the railing, nursing his vague feeling of unease, and was there still several minutes later when Count Witte approached.

"Mr. Florry, I must say I envy you. That's a lovely young woman."

"Yes, she's quite special, I agree."

"I envy you her feelings for you."

"Well, it's not gone to that. She seems to be drawn to adventure. She's evidently got some money for travel. She says she wants to be a writer."

"Whatever it is, I must say I can think of better spots to take a beautiful young woman than a volatile city like Barcelona. Perhaps she is the sort who feels most alive in danger. Still, I'd be careful if I were you."

"Thanks for the advice."

With that comment, the old count went to his cabin.

Florry turned back to the sea. It was almost dark now; the sun had left a vivid smear where it had disappeared into the ocean; the Spanish coast looked much closer now. Florry knew he ought to go to his cabin and pack.

But he looked at it one more time. Spain. Red Spain, in the year 1937.

What the devil, he thought, am I doing here?

Then he went back to his cabin to pack for the arrival.

Florry gathered his tweed jacket about him, wishing he had a scarf. He could feel the ludicrous revolver hanging in the ludicrous holster under his arm. He lit a cigarette. The night was cool and calm, full of moon which reflected off the sea in a gleam that was incandescent, fluttering, almost mesmerizing. It was absurdly beautiful, almost as bright as day. Before him, he could see the land mass, looming larger. He could see the light of the harbor and make out in the light what appeared to be the hulk of a low mountain off on one side, Monjuich it would be called. There was another mountain, one behind the city, called Tibidabo, but he could not see it.

He leaned forward on the railing, wondering how in the world he'd handle it with Julian.

Julian, old man.

Robert, good God, it's been bloody *ages*.

Been reading your stuff in *Signature*. Damned good. I'm out for *The Spectator* myself.

Oh, and how's bloody awful Denis Mason? Hated that man.

Been absolutely topping with me, old sport—

No, that wouldn't work. So much between them. Julian, once I loved you and then you hurt me and now they've sent me out here to betray you. How on earth can I ever look upon your face? He took a deep breath, happy at least for the solitude. He flipped the cigarette out into the dark, wondering if he had the force to deal with Julian. Something powerful about Julian: it almost frightened

him. The city, a few miles beyond, looked serene and peaceful in the moonlight. It looked like some sort of silly, romantic painting.

"Mr. Florry. Staring into the future?"

He turned. It was the girl.

"Yes, well, you've caught me at it."

"How long now until we dock?"

"Well, not a goodly while. You can make out the quay. We slip through the breakwater, then wherever these Arab monkeys choose to tie up, and we'll be on dry land."

The moon touched her oval face and made it shine. She smiled and the moon turned her teeth blinding white, small perfect little pearls, little replicas of itself. Had she ever really smiled at him quite like this before? He didn't think so. The radiance of her look overwhelmed him.

"You've changed your clothes." She now had on some sort of purple dress.

"Yes. The adventure begins, that kind of silly nonsense."

"It's quite appropriate, I assure you."

He could see her hand on the rail, her fair face in the white moonlight. He could smell her. It was lovely, something musky and rather dense. He wanted to reach out and touch her, but felt incapable of even commencing such a move. A squawking of Arabic rose from the bridge—two sailors cursing each other.

"I'm actually glad I caught you here alone," she said. "You've been awfully kind to me. I wanted to thank you for it."

"Believe me, Miss Lilliford, it doesn't take much effort to be kind to you."

"No, you're just one of the decent chaps of the world. I can tell. Fewer and fewer of them around, and you're one."

"You exaggerate my decency, Miss Lilliford. Scratch my surface and you'll find the same brute underneath in any man."

"I can't begin to believe it."

It occurred to him he ought to kiss her. He had, actually, never kissed a white woman before.

"*There* you are," said Count Witte, coming out onto the deck.

"Good heavens, I've just had the most terrible altercation with that awful old Gruenwald. The man is completely drunk. He smells as if he's bathed in peppermint. He was trying to get my trunk up and banging it around terribly. It was most upsetting."

Florry turned.

"Oh, he's a harmless old fellow. Worthless, I suppose, but harmless," said Florry tightly.

"Oh, I say—am I disturbing you or something? I didn't mean to intrude."

"Oh, no," said Florry, "it's nothing—"

"But it is. I can tell from the startled look on Miss Lilliford's face. I shall beat a hasty retreat."

"Please, Count Witte. Our conversation can wait. Mr. Florry and I have plenty of time ahead. Come out and watch the ship sail into the harbor."

"Yes, do come on, Count Witte."

"Well, you English are so wonderfully polite I don't know if you mean it or not, but I will come. Yes. Do you know, we must get together for dinner in the week to come. There used to be some wonderful restaurants in Barcelona, though I shouldn't be surprised if the revolutionaries have closed them all down in the spirit of equality. But—"

Amazingly, it had begun to rain!

Florry had the distinct impression that the air itself had suddenly liquefied and then, oddly, all sound had vanished from the earth: the slosh of the prow through the water, the clank and groan of the old engine, the chatter of Arabic from deep inside the ship.

Or no: there *was* sound. There was, in fact, *nothing* but sound, huge in his ears. Sound and liquid—sound and water—sound and chaos.

A shock seemed to slither through the guts of the ship. Its very relationship to the shiny sea began to alter crazily; the deck, which had until this second seemed as secure as the surface of the earth, issued a great animal shudder; Florry, in his mind, thought of a dying elephant he'd once seen, that moment when the bullet

plunges home and every line is somehow terribly changed as the consciousness of doom suddenly imprints itself upon the beast. He stood bolted to the rail, trying to make sense of it all: water and roar, everywhere; Sylvia's dress plastered with hideous immodesty against her body as the shock spread from the ship to her own face, in the form of total panic, which flashed whitely in the wet moonlight; old Witte, gobbling in terror like an ancient bird before the ax, his jowls heavy and flopping, his wet hair curled, his monocle fluttering about. And suddenly also a tide of demented, howling voices, a guttural mix of Arabic and Turkish and all the dialects of the Mediterranean.

And Florry, attempting in the first second, with what he felt was icy calm but was in fact the beginning of bone-deep panic, to sort all this out, became aware of yet another and perhaps more frightening phenomenon. That is, the angle of the deck to the horizon had begun to shift radically. We're sinking, he realized. We're sinking.

7

MI-6, LONDON

MAJOR HOLLY-BROWNING TOOK TEA LATE AT HIS HEAD-quarters that same night. He sat in his little fifth-floor office in the Broadway Building off a corridor that led only to a rear stairwell. Perhaps it looked a bit more like a publisher's cubicle than a spy's: he was surrounded by an almost endless collection of books and pamphlets of poetry, clipped newspaper reviews, glossy and not-so-glossy literary quarterlies, reproductions of paintings, tutors' reports, the minutes of meetings of long-abandoned undergraduate political committees, broadsides, handbills, and the like. It all dated from the year 1931 at Cambridge University.

Where another, more sympathetic mind might have divined from the rubble a new generation of promising voices attempting to define and make itself heard, Major Holly-Browning saw most of it as infernal gibberish, a bloody Playfair cipher without a key, whose maze was therefore sealed off forever from his entrance. It represented a private language, a chattering of pansy aesthetes; it filled him, also, with melancholy.

He'd seen so many of these young fools' fathers die in the '14–'18 show, cut down by the German Maxims, or blown to shreds by Krupp explosives, or choked, their lungs browned and shriveled in the mustard, or mutilated by the serrated upper edges of the ghastly Hun bayonets. And for what? For this? For "In Excelsior Pale Grows the Mould"? For "Nocturne in Shades of Gray"? For "A

New Theory of Spanish Radicalism"? For "The Pacifist's Litany"?
For Julian's hated "Achilles, Fool"?

The poem, originally published in the February 1931 number of
Denis Mason's foolish rag *The Spectator* and later the title of Julian's
sole collection of verse, from Heinemann in November of the same
year, was never far from the major's consciousness. He could recite
it.

> *Achilles, fool, on your wire,*
> *the scream lost in your ripped lungs,*
> *Achilles, fool, they took your lips,*
> *Achilles, fool, you let them have your tongue.*
>
> *We are the tendentious generation, Achilles,*
> *Fool. No wires for us; our lips will stay*
> *Our own. We know the final truth:*
> In the end, it's all the same.
> In the end, it's all a game.

Julian's father had died on the Somme, hung up on a wire for a
long day's dying. The major had heard Capt. Basil Raines over the
artillery barrage that day. He screamed for hours. But not to be
rescued. He screamed at his men to stay away, because he knew
they would die if they came for him. The major touched the bridge
of his nose, which was tender with pain.

"May I get you something, sir?"

"Vane, are you still here? Perhaps you could go on down to
Signals and see if Florry's ship has reached Barcelona yet. Sampson
said he'd inform us."

Vane darted out. Major Holly-Browning turned back to the sea
of paper before him. He had mastered with sheer, dogged persis-
tence nearly everything the pile contained. It was not a happy
experience. He had become a kind of reluctant expert on the culture
of 1931, its torrents and enthusiasms and excesses, its pacifism, its

ideologies, its brilliances, its ugly insistence on secret conformism. And most of all, running beneath it like a hidden current, its spies.

Yes, there were spies. The climate almost demanded it. The postwar euphoria had long since worn off, and with the coming of economic hard times, a certain sensibility flourished, a sensibility of doubt. Despair seemed somehow fashionable. Peculiar sexual styles became smart. And the brightest lads were the worst: dandy boys, cleverboots, know-it-alls, fellow travelers; they climbed aboard the Soviet Russian bandwagon, toot-toot-tooting all the way. They *loathed* their own country. They simply, in their glib and fancy way, *hated* it, as had no other generation in English history. They hated it for its smugness and complacency. They hated it for being English and they hated it for making them comfortable while it was unable to feed its own poor. They regarded the very presence of the poor as *a priori* evidence of the corruption of the society. And they loved what little Koba, the red butcher, was doing in his worker's paradise. It was this, finally, that so infuriated the major: their willed, forced, self-induced self-deception.

Major Holly-Browning touched the pile. It was there. He had dug it out, assembled it, bit by painful bit, as an Etruscan artist must have assembled a mosaic, in which no one piece has any meaning, but the pattern was everything!

The evidence was irrefutable. The dates, the places, the reports: they meshed so perfectly. It seemed that Levitsky, who nowhere else in his career had behaved with anything but utmost care, had been utterly sloppy around Cambridge in 1931, so contemptuous was he of our lazy security, our comforting veil of illusion, our pious stupidity.

Levitsky's prime blunder had been a botched come-on to a clerk in the F.O. in February of '31; from that time on, he'd been identified as a Bolshevik agent, though it had been assumed from the clumsiness of his approach that he was a low-ranking, incompetent one. He had been routinely surveilled on a weekly basis for the next seven months by Section V, until he left the country for

parts unknown. His special watering hole, the MI-6 investigators noted, was Cambridge. He made trips there nearly every weekend for the entire seven months. He was hunting for talent, it was clear. But what talent? Who did he see? Where did he go? One investigator could have supplied the answers in a weekend at Cambridge.

He was never followed. In those days, Section V never worked weekends!

But twice Levitsky had not gone when he had been scheduled to. On April 12–15 and May 11–13; and both weekends, Julian Raines had appeared at prominent London society parties as part of a set of bright young things that so caught the public's eye that year!

Then there was the matter of the arrest. Levitsky had been picked up by the Cambridge constabulary late on a Saturday night in March. The copper, mistrusting his foreign accent and his peculiar ways, had hauled him off to jail. And who had, the next morning, bailed him out? The copper, five years later, had recognized the picture.

It was the famous poet, Julian Raines.

And then there was the holiday. In June, Julian had taken off a week to rusticate in the south of France, Cap d'Antibes, to be exact. That same week, Levitsky, according to Passport Control (which kept impeccable records) left the country, too; his stated destination was . . . southern France.

Julian's face seemed suddenly to appear in front of Holly-Browning: that smug, handsome face that seemed to be sweet reason and aesthetician's grandeur. How he hated that face!

You little bastard. You smirk at your own father hanging on the wire, trapped in his own guts, too far to reach, his screams louder in the sulfurous vapors of the attack than the sound of the Maxims or the Krupps. The major closed his eyes. He could hear those screams still.

Your father died to give you everything and you in turn give us to the Russians.

Julian. Julian in 1931.

Yes. In discreet interview after discreet interview, they all agreed. Some time during 1931, Julian _changed,_ his friends said. He became graver, odder, more private, more profligate, sloppier. His own easy brilliance seemed undercut with what one of his oh-so-sympathetic chums called "tragic self-awareness." His gaiety was "forced."

What had happened to dear Julian?

Holly-Browning knew. It'll weigh a man down, deciding to betray his country.

The dates told the rest of the story. Julian had gone out to Spain on August 4, 1936, three weeks after the outbreak of rebellion. According to the defector Lemontov, an urgent flash had come to him from Moscow, graded Priority One, the highest, which ordered him to establish a radio hookup in a safe house with a transmitter in Barcelona, and to service it with a code expert, to use the Orange Cipher, the GRU's most private, most impenetrable, most highly graded secret language. He was then to prepare to funnel the same information almost immediately back to Moscow via a second radio link. He was _not to_ decode the information himself. That's how secret it was. The date of the flash? August 5, 1936.

Lemontov had buckled. Making such arrangements was not only expensive and time consuming but risky. And this one seemed utterly unnecessary. After all, there were already enough OGPU and GRU operatives in Spain to—

Lemontov was curtly ordered to return to Moscow. The implication was clear. Someone very high was running a special, sensitively placed agent and trusted (wisely) none of the usual security arrangements. It had to mean that a long-term asset was involved, and who but his old master Levitsky would run long-term assets on a private channel through Amsterdam to Moscow?

Lemontov realized that Levitsky was running the agent he'd recruited five years earlier, in England, and that the job was very important. And Lemontov realized that to return with this information was to die in Koba's purge.

Julian Raines, you bloody bastard. A stooge for the GRU, for

old Levitsky. You've sold us out. But now we know. And now we can stop you.

"Sir."

It was Vane, silhouetted in the doorway. Something in his voice immediately unsettled Holly-Browning.

"Yes, Vane. What is it?"

"Sir, I'm afraid the news isn't good."

Holly-Browning sighed. He waited a heartbeat and said, "Go ahead, please."

"The ship is evidently overdue."

"Is that all? Does he send details?"

"No, sir. But there is another bit of news. Signals also monitored a communication between the Italian diesel submarine D-11 and its home port at the naval station at Palma on Majorca."

"Yes, Vane?"

"The D-11 claims a kill off Barcelona."

8

THE WATER

W E'RE SINKING," HE ANNOUNCED, TRYING TO SORT out what the bloody hell *to do.* "We're sinking," he repeated, as if to convince himself, but at that moment a sailor leaped off the bridge down to them, bounded by, and launched himself into the darkness.

"Robert, oh God," Sylvia screamed. He held her tightly. Steam had added itself to the spectacle and curled up everywhere from the decks and out of hatchways. One of the Turks hollered at them from the bridge but it was all gibberish. Above, the stars reeled and whirled through the rising steam.

Florry found himself yelling, "Lifeboat! Lifeboat aft." Yes, he'd seen it with old Gruenwald that afternoon. "It's this way, come on."

He pointed in the darkness, aware suddenly that the destination his finger described also seemed to be the destination of the ship as it slid into the sea.

He grabbed Sylvia and they began to wobble down the slanting deck, the old count close behind. The *Akim*'s relationship to the surface had grown exceedingly tentative. She lurched under their feet as she fought for some leverage against the sucking waves and the hole in her own guts that dragged her down. She'd begun not merely to slant but to tilt, corkscrewing into the sea.

As they moved they found themselves not walking on the deck proper, but on the juncture between deck and bulkhead, one foot

on each, with the awkwardness of working their way down a gutter. A garish fire blazed up ahead. It was almost purple in the dark. Florry felt the heat pressing up from the boards beneath his feet. Smoke and steam mingled in the atmosphere. He breathed, getting smoke, and coughed. He pulled her hand along.

"Just a little farther."

"We're going to die."

"Not if we keep our heads."

A sudden BOOM blew a gout of flame out of the hatchway just ahead of them.

The count screamed.

Chairs and crates plunged about the deck like missiles. Steam continued to gush from the blown-out hatchway and suddenly a man crab-walked out in scalded agony, pulled his way to the rail uttering the name of God—or blaspheming with it—and hurled himself over. The boiler had ruptured and the live steam was cooking the engine-room crew. Another man groped in the steam's murk and Florry grabbed for him, but he fell back and was gone. Florry could hear the screams from inside.

"Come on, damn it," Florry yelled, for Sylvia had seemed to settle back, and behind her poor old Witte looked numb with shock. The ship, meanwhile, was steadily rising behind them, seeming to encourage their progress. Florry yanked her past the hatch, which, as they fled by, made them wince for the heat it poured out.

"Come on, count," Florry called. "Come on." The old man managed to get by the opening and the energy seemed to liberate him; now he led them on their plunge through the smoke and steam.

"No. No. Nooooooo."

He stopped and fell to his knees.

"It's ruined. God, it's ruined," and he lapsed into Polish.

And so it was: just ahead, the empty lifeboat hung limply off one davit, enmeshed in a tangle of ropes. At least a dozen Arabs squawked and fought and scampered about it, some beating inef-

fectually on the jammed pulley, others simply howling insanely against their fates.

"Oh God, we're finished," said Sylvia.

"No," shouted Florry, but even as he insisted, a new burst of steam ripped up from the decks, and the ship seemed to groan once again in pain and slipped farther into the water.

"It's no use," sobbed Witte.

Suddenly, with a freakish crack, the second davit broke and the lifeboat plunged toward the sea. It struck the water with great force in a roar of foam and flailing lines. Yet even as the foam subsided, it seemed to emerge intact and afloat and squirt across the surface.

"Can you swim? Sylvia, listen, can you swim?"

"Yes," she muttered through trembling lips.

"Swim for the boat. You'll be safe in the boat."

"Come on, Robert."

"You go. I'll get this old man out."

"Good-bye then."

She lunged to the railing, and with a dive that was almost a jump, she disappeared over the side.

Florry tugged the old man to the railing.

"Can you swim?"

The old man clung to him tenaciously.

"No," he gulped. "No, I can't."

"Look, you'll die here for certain. Don't you see? The water is your only hope."

"Ah, God. To end like this. I—ah, God, it's so—"

"Look, when you hit the water, look about for wreckage. Perhaps you can thrash your way to it. Now take off your coat, Count Witte, and get going. I'll be over next and I'll help you."

"God bless you, Florry."

"Hurry. We'll both be gone if you don't move."

The water was littered with planks and bobbing heads in the purple flicker of the flames.

"Good luck, old man," Florry said, and rolled him off. He fell screaming and hit the water with a crash.

The ship yielded further still, and Florry felt it begin to gather momentum as it descended. He took a last look around and could see that the stern had broken off and was low in the sea about fifty yards off, amid hissing bubbles and steam. The stench of petroleum lingered everywhere and fire moved across the water itself.

Florry shucked his own jacket, kicked off his shoes, and leaped. He seemed to hang in the air for an eternity, until finally the sea's green calm claimed him. Utter quiet assailed him after the chaos above. In the cold thick murk, bubbles surrounded him. He fought against the water, but was not entirely sure which way was up. His legs cramped and knit. His clothes became leaden, pulling him down. His lungs filled with panic, which spread to his brain, arriving with an urge to surrender. But instead, in a spasm of clawing, he broke the surface. He could see a dozen other bobbing heads and the lifeboat, as yet tantalizingly empty, just ahead.

He looked about for the girl but saw nothing.

"Sylvia!"

"I'm all right! Where's the old man?"

"Make for the boat! Hurry!"

"Yes. Yes."

Florry looked back toward the ship, which had become nothing but a low silhouette lit by spurting flames and rising vapor; it had settled almost entirely into the water. A few small oil fires burned on the surface, amid crates and chairs and other wreckage. The ship gave a final shudder and slid under the water. It went in backward, its prow last, as if with infinite regret. From all about, there rose shouts and screams.

"Count Witte!" he shouted. "Count!"

There was no answer.

Florry paddled about a bit. It seemed to have gotten calm suddenly.

"Count Witte!"

There was still no answer. He looked about. The old man was gone. Damn the luck, he thought bitterly. Gone, gone, gone.

Something brushed against Florry's face in the water. He reached out to touch it with his finger: it was a rotting cigarette. He looked about in the flickering light: the surface of the water was jammed with millions of the things, forming a kind of tobacco scum.

"Ahhh."

It was the old man, clinging to a floating portion of the railing. Florry thrashed over to him. His face, covered with oil, kept flopping forward in the water.

"I have you. I have you. It's just a little ways. You're going to be all right."

But the old man slipped away. Florry got to him in the water and struggled oafishly with the limp body; both kept going under. He could feel his will ebbing. Dump him, he thought. Dump the old fool and save yourself. But at last he seemed to get the old count properly situated, with his arm under the man's oily neck, and he began to pull himself with a long stroke through the water toward the lifeboat.

He thought bitterly of Julian, for whom it was always so easy. Lucky Julian. *Julian, why did you hurt me?*

He shook his head at the idiocy of it all and continued to plunge ahead. It seemed to take forever, the long passage through the salty, ever-colder, ever-heavier sea, which grew soupy and finally mushy as his arms weakened in their thrashing. Twice the salt water flooded his lungs and he broke stroke, coughing and gagging and spitting, the snot running from his nose. The old man groaned at one point and tried to fight away.

"Stop it, damn you," Florry shrieked, tasting sea water.

The old man gargled in agony but seemed to settle down. Florry pressed on, growing more numb and more insane; at last, nothing seemed left of the whole universe except the rotten-ripe heaviness of his arms, the ache in his chest, and the sea water leaking into his nose and throat. His eyes stung themselves blind and his muscles seemed loose, unconnected to his bones, which nevertheless continued in their mechanical clawing. Yet when he at last allowed him-

self to look, the surprise was mighty: he had made it. The lifeboat bobbed in the water, looking immense, a mountain, against the dark horizon.

He got one weary hand up to the gunwale while holding the old man close to him, and gasped, "Christ, help us."

Quickly, a strong set of hands had him, and then they were pulling Witte aboard. Florry was slipping away; he was beginning to see things in his head, odd spangles of lights, patches of colors, whirling patterns of sparks and flashes. Then the hands had him too, and up he went.

He came to rest with an awkward bang on the floor of the boat, and was aware of bodies all about him.

"Praise to Allah, all is well," said the man who'd rescued him, who turned out to be the captain.

"Robert!"

"Sylvia, thank God—I got him. Christ, I got him."

He pulled himself up to a sitting position.

"Is he all right? Is the count all right?"

Two Arabs were working on the old man, slapping him about rather roughly to get him back to life. Florry saw the old oil-soaked body stir into a convulsion and he heard the sound of wretching and gagging and then a cry.

"He's alive," said Sylvia. "You saved him, oh, Robert, he's *alive!*"

The count sat up.

"Ohhh," he groaned.

And then Florry smelled something so peculiar it made him wince: peppermint.

He had saved Gruenwald.

As they huddled together in the flickering light they could see bobbing heads, which gradually disappeared; perhaps some of the Arabs had managed to cling to floating wreckage, perhaps not. They could not steer into the flotsam to save the occasional scream-

ers because they had no oars and the rudder of the lifeboat had rotted away.

Florry sat in numb exhaustion among the perhaps ten or fifteen others who had made it to the boat; he wanted to die or curl up and surrender to sleep. He could not seem to get his mind working properly. Sylvia sat very close to him. It seemed he was shaking and she was holding him, or perhaps she was shaking and he was holding her.

"God," she said. "My mother insisted that I take swimming lessons. I always hated her for it. Oh, Mother, you were so wrong about so much, but you were so right about the bloody swimming. She's dead, you know, the poor idiot."

Florry could hardly understand her. Meanwhile, of them all, it was Gruenwald who recovered with the most amazing speed. He scuttled perkily through the craft, hopping over the survivors like the lead in a Gilbert and Sullivan operetta, shouting orders, bellowing crazily to the stars, commenting acidly on Arab seamanship. The captain cursed him in Turkish but the old man only laughed at him and at one point a sailor made a lunge, and Gruenwald squirted away.

"Hah! *Nein* catchen Gruenwald!"

"A madman," said Florry. "Poor Count Witte."

"Hah. Herr Florry, in za var, much worse. *Ja,* pretty Englisch lady. Boats mit *kinder,* kiddies, go down. Men die in war. Torpedo kill."

"Oh, Lord," said Sylvia wanly. "Mr. Gruenwald, do you think you could spare us the history lesson."

"Yes, please shut up. We all feel rather terrible."

"Hah. Should feel *gut.* Ve ist alive, *nein?* Hah!"

The first boats to arrive were fishing vessels, and it occurred to Florry, in watching the fleet spread out across the water, that the fishermen were more interested in salvage than survivors. The captain hailed them, but they ignored the call. Soon, however, a large official boat reached the scene and made straight for the lifeboat. It

only took seconds before they were hauled aboard and wrapped quickly in blankets.

The trip into the harbor was largely anticlimactic. By the time they arrived, the sun had begun to rise. Florry's first glimpse of Barcelona was disappointing: he could see the city on the low hills and the port beginning to come alive in the early light. He could see palm trees but it was still cold and he shivered.

"If I don't get some sleep," said Sylvia, "I think I shall die. They can't expect much of us when we get there, can they?"

"I hope not," said Florry, unsure of what exactly awaited them.

It turned out not to be much. There were some policemen at the dock and some officials from the Maritime Commission with a brief to talk to the officers and some first-aid attendants. Florry found himself explaining in the Maritime Commission Building, to which they had been removed, who and what he was to a largely uninterested Spanish youth who gradually ceased taking notes. It occurred to Florry that they were done with him.

"Where should I go?" Florry asked him.

"Find a party," said the boy. "Barcelona, many parties. Parties everywhere. Then you can march in our parades."

Florry wasn't sure what this meant—party as in *political* or party as in *celebration,* or, possibly, both—but before he could seek an explanation, he was summarily dismissed and found himself escorted to the street and abandoned under a palm tree, with only a pair of ill-fitting plimsoles in place of his lost shoes to prepare him for the ordeal ahead. By this time, his clothes had largely dried on his body, even though the breeze still brought the goose pimples to his skin.

He was standing there with Sylvia, discussing their next move, when it occurred to him that he still had the silly revolver in the shoulder holster under his sweater. It had hung there through the ordeal!

"Good heavens," he said to her, "can you believe I still have my pistol! Isn't that amazing?"

But she was suddenly not listening. Florry looked and saw that

she was watching as first-aid workers were applying bandages to Mr. Gruenwald.

"Well, it's off to the hospital for him," said Florry, yet something was particularly odd about it all. For one thing, Gruenwald had been unhurt, and for that reason it seemed unnecessary to bandage him, particularly about the eyes. His hands were bandaged too, but behind his back.

"I wonder if that's necessary," said Florry.

"You'd best stay out of it," said Sylvia. "I don't like the way it looks."

The head doctor, an enormous man in a black leather coat with cold eyes and pitted skin, had just thrown the old man against the side of the ambulance, which, Florry now realized, was no ambulance at all.

It said POLICIA.

9

THE INTERROGATION

GLASANOV HAD A PREDICTION. HE WAS IN A JAUNTY mood, close to humor. His life was filled with good cheer and possibility and with something as close to amusement as Lenny had ever seen on his face. They were walking through the prison toward the old man's cell.

"He won't sign a thing," predicted Glasanov. "Not a thing. He'll be intractable. You'll pound your fists to pulp on his skull, Bolodin, before he confesses." He was almost giddy.

"No," he continued in his lecture-hall manner, "we shall have to break him down. Assault his illusions, dismantle his vanities, force him to see reality as it is. Brick by brick, we must disassemble his brain. Oh, it'll be a test. It'll be a struggle, Bolodin, as you've never seen. But what fun! Imagine, the old dog himself here, in our humble jail."

Lenny nodded dumbly, as if he were the moron Glasanov clearly believed him to be, and then issued a grunt of imprecise meaning that Glasanov took to be stupefied agreement and enthusiasm. Yet, looking at Glasanov, he recognized a man caught in some vision of higher glory, some scheme of higher ambition: you saw it in Brooklyn all the time. A dreamer, full of fancy ideas of what tomorrow would bring.

"I want him sent back to Moscow split," said Glasanov. "I want him confessed and repentant, not merely captured. Eh, Bolodin, how's that for a challenge? It's not old Comintern unionists we're

dealing with here, but the GRU's best, a man of iron will, a legend."

They had now reached the corridor that led to Levitsky's cell.

"Get some water. It's time to wake our charge from his baby sleep."

Lenny fitted a bucket under a faucet set in the wall and filled it brimful with icy water.

It was dark and damp down here, as in fairy tales, all old cobwebs and ancient stone. The walls showed cruciforms where religious icons had been smashed down in the first crazed days of the July victory; a number of grotesque revolutionary admonitions had been painted on the stone and they stood out like wounds in the harsh glare of electric bulbs that hung crudely jerry-rigged from the ceiling. Glasanov produced a key, an ancient thing, and with some effort got the stiff old tumblers of the massive door open. Inside, the old man slept under a thin blanket on a straw mat under another raw cruciform denoting a smashed symbol of the untrue faith. The old man wheezed thinly. He looked vulnerable and pale and in the bad light his skin seemed like old parchment.

Glasanov studied the man for a second without emotion, then nodded to Lenny, who dashed the water on him. Levitsky sat up instantly with a howl of pain and a massive, marrow-deep shiver, all naked animal hurt and outrage. His eyes snapped instantly alert, displaying confusion and panic for just a second, but the man quickly controlled them, and as Lenny, standing just behind Glasanov, watched, they seemed to dilate down into something tightly focused.

"Stand up, old man," Glasanov said with theatrical heartiness miles outside his character, "we've got work to do."

The old man stood next to the bed, soaked, staring straight ahead. His eyes were fixed and blank.

"We'll get you singing before long," Glasanov said. "We'll have you singing like a bird. We'll have all the crimes out on the table."

Levitsky looked up at his tormentor.

"Glasanov, isn't it?" he asked.

"I'll ask the questions, comrade," said Glasanov.

"Nevertheless, it *is* Glasanov. Nikolai Illyich, if I'm not wrong. I remember you from the Baku Conference in 'twenty-seven. You were on Glitzky's staff. They said you were bright."

"Old man, I'll run things here. This comrade here is quite brutal and I haven't time for you to impress me with your memory. I'll have him beat you to turnip mash if you give me cause."

"We both know how absurd that would be. Beat me to turnip mash and you'll have nothing to ship back to Moscow—except turnip mash."

Lenny, watching the two Russians pick at each other, heard a sigh, perhaps even involuntary, escape from Glasanov's lips.

"They said you'd be sly. The Devil Himself."

"I'm not sly at all, Comrade Glasanov. I'm an old man without much in the way of strength or guile. I simply adhere to my beliefs exactly, and they give me a foundation that careerist scum can never shatter."

"Oh, I'll break you, Comrade Levitsky. I'll split you for Moscow, don't doubt it. Time, after all, is all on my side. Time, and the considerable skills of Comrade Bolodin here."

"Your vanity, Glasanov, will kill you sooner than my idealism will kill me."

"The ribs," said Glasanov. "But not too bad yet."

Lenny went to the old man, hit him hard, once, in the ribs, sending a spasm through him. As he twisted, Lenny put two more swift right hands into his solar plexus. He shrieked, falling. Trying to halt himself, he clung to Lenny, who brought his knee up quickly, catching him between the legs. The old man slipped loose and went to the floor. He lay there, wet and trembling. His lips were white. He coughed and heaved wordlessly, his face drawn in the pain.

"See how quickly the mighty Levitsky is reduced to nothingness," said Glasanov. "Bolodin exposes you for what you are, Le-

vitsky: pathetic. With your feeble, ancient disguise, which Comrade Bolodin penetrated with comical ease. Your pretend accent. You stink of the peppermint schnapps even now, you pitiful old fool." Glasanov shook his head, as if in great disappointment. "I had expected so much more from the Devil Himself. Instead I get an obsolete comic actor from a nineteenth-century operetta. It actually disgusts me."

He bent over Levitsky and spoke quickly into his ear.

"Now. I ask the questions and you give the answers. If I like the answer, we go on. If not, Comrade Bolodin here, with his American efficiency, will hit you in the ribs. He is inexhaustible and indefatigable and without a brain in his muscular head. Do you see, old man, how it is to be?"

Levitsky rolled over. His face was gray. His eyes would not focus on anything in the cell. Glasanov leaned close.

"Now, *der Teuful Selbst,* tell me, to begin with. Why Spain?"

Levitsky spat in his face.

In the evening, he lay against the gray cobbles of the cell floor, breathing raspily. He had been beaten expertly. The ribs were not broken yet the pain was extraordinary. Bolodin knew how to take him to the very edge, then bring him back. Bolodin knew how to inspire the thought that the future would forever and ever be pain.

He concentrated on not trembling. He tried to will the pain from the center of his body, tried to drive it out.

Come on, old Devil.

He laughed bitterly. Some devil. Old, infirm, lying beaten in a Spanish cell, attended by rats. And so this was how the great adventure ended; thus it was with all vain and foolish crusades. His plot came to an end as did his odd, perhaps senile quest, doomed from the beginning, he now saw, to play in life, in history, in flesh, what he had once played on the chessboard. The march of folly! the pyre of vanity! the absurdity of ego!

Too many enemies. You, Koba. And you, Glasanov, Koba's

minion. You, dreadful Amerikanski, with your thunderous fists and your murderous eyes. And you the English spy-catchers, somewhere lurking in the distance.

You all want me. You all want Castle.

Castle was doomed. He saw it now. In check. They were closing on him and would dog him down. Like me, he will cease to exist.

He felt the sweat running down his body, leaving icy tracks. He tried to sit up but the pain came instantly, seizing him. He tried again and managed to get himself up against the wall. A victory, a giant victory!

Why fight them? You'll confess in the end, everybody does. Why not give Glasanov his moment of glory, his tiny triumph? He, too, is doomed, if not this year then the next. Koba will have him because he stinks of ambition. The better he does, the more arrests and executions, the more efficiency with which he routs Koba's enemies, the more completely he dooms himself. So smart in so many things, Glasanov, can you not see this one thing?

Then he heard the approach of steps on the stones outside, the click of the old lock. The door swung open in the dark.

Beyond surprise, Levitsky at least had the capacity for stupefaction. The figure silhouetted in the harsh corridor light filled the frame.

For a big man, he moved with a rare grace. He moved swiftly, hauling the door shut behind him, and came to Levitsky. The old man watched him come, not scared but awed. What? What could —? The Amerikanski bent and with his strong hands he lifted Levitsky's skull from the stones and turned it this way and that, a queer gentleness in his fingers.

"You still stink of the shtetl after all these years," the American said, and it occurred suddenly to Levitsky that he was speaking in Yiddish. The language flooded back upon him; it had once been his only language, years ago, ages ago, in the time before there was time.

"*Jud,* nu?" asked Levitsky.

"Yes. One of the chosen. Raised in a little shit-smelling village. And, like you, old fuck, I remember the day when Cossacks came."

So long ago: Ural Cossacks, Levitsky remembered, in fur hats and upturned boots, with curved sabers, on great black steaming stallions. They came out of the trees at daybreak, after a night's drinking. He remembered the bright blood, the smells of huts burning, the screams, the heat of the flames, his brother's sobs. He remembered his mother, butchered, his father, hacked, the bright blood, the woodsmoke, the heat, the screams. He remembered the horses, brutes that stank of death and would smash you to nothingness . . .

"So we changed all that," Levitsky said. "We made a revolution."

"Fuck the revolution."

Levitsky stared at the huge shape above him. Had he been sent to kill him? He could do it easily, with his thumbs. But why now, in the dark? Why not with the pistol?

"So what do you want, comrade? A confession? You should fuck goats."

"To help you."

"Excuse me, I'm hearing things, no?"

"To help you. I help you, you help me. A deal. Between two Jews."

"So talk. I'm not going anywhere."

"A certain name, old man. Give the name, and I'll get your ass out of here."

"What name?" said Levitsky.

"The name that no one speaks. The English boy, whose soul you own, old devil."

"What boy?"

"You call him Castle, after a chess thing. Surprised? You didn't think *anybody* knew. But I knew!"

Levitsky felt the closeness of the huge man. He let the moment linger. He felt an awful stillness settling through him. A new player on the board.

"What bo—"

"Don't play with me. I can kill you in a second. Or in a second you can walk out of here to America. You can be a writer for the *Daily Forward,* huh? And sit in the park with all the other East Side dreamers and talk revolution. Give the name!"

Levitsky tried to concentrate, to calculate the chain of possibilities. How could he know? What had he learned? Who told him? Who sent him?

"I have no names."

"You have a bellyful of names. In England in 'thirty-one, with Tchiterine and Lemontov. Lemontov's gone and Tchiterine's in the ground a few hundred feet from here. Give me the name of this English boy, or so help me I'll put you in the ground alive and you can die by slow degrees you never dreamed of in this world."

And so Levitsky saw his chance. The big American Bolodin had made his mistake. He had revealed exactly how important the information was to him.

"Kill me, and you'll never know anything. But give me a night to think and maybe there's this deal you keep telling me about."

"After tomorrow, there may not be enough to *give* an answer."

"I may surprise you, Bolodin. I may surprise you."

The American snorted.

"I'll go easy. But I'll come back at night for the answer, and if it isn't the right answer, then I'll go so hard you'll pray for death. And God doesn't work this neighborhood."

At dawn, Levitsky lay on his pallet. He knew he had two simple choices: suicide or escape.

Consider: a locked cell in some sort of Spanish monastery. In a few hours, Glasanov would arrive and the beatings would begin anew. Another day's torture would leave him just that much weaker and less able to escape or resist, and the Amerikanski would be back at night for his answer. But there really was no answer: if he told, the Amerikanski would kill him quickly. If he didn't, the

Amerikanski would kill him slowly. Either way, Levitsky perished, and with Levitsky gone Castle was open to assault.

It occurred to Levitsky that he had reached the climax of his life. The chess master, designer of elegant combinations and strategems, now faced his greatest test, and it was a simple puzzle. He looked about, as if to study. This puzzle might not have a solution. The cell was vaulted; it had one barred window; it was, at least, at ground level. Levitsky ran his fingers painfully over the mortar of the old stones. No, it was solid, undisturbed except by tears for centuries. He turned his attention to the window. The iron of the bars felt ancient and cold, tempered in medieval fires and set in the stone to last until the arrival of God the Father on earth. His hands locked about and tested each. They had no give at all. Next, the door. It, too, seemed ancient, a collection of polished oak slats, massively thick and heavy, held together with iron bands. The hinges were on the outside, beyond reach. The lock only remained. He bent to it. Hmmmmm. It was not at least a dead bolt, but a tumbler mechanism, old iron, black and hard. Well-oiled. It could be picked, perhaps, with a pick. But he had no pick.

His examination of the physical possibilities of the cell had exhausted him. His bruised ribs hurt furiously. He closed his eyes: sleep came toward him. He fought it off—or did he? For an instant he was back in the water after the ship had gone down, knowing he would die, until the Englishman's strong hands had pulled him back to life.

For this?

I should have died, nu?

He blinked awake: the same cell. How much time had passed, how much time had he lost?

He went to the window: the sun was coming up. He could see they were on a hill on the outskirts of the city: he could see across the way a chapel, now abandoned, desecrated, the doors blasted off, the interior blackened by flame, all the windows shattered. It was a dead building. The Church, enemy of the people, enemy of the

masses, at last feeling the full brunt of their wrath. The nuns raped and beaten, perhaps shot; the processes of history were never pleasant and only made sense in the longer view.

Another cracked smile passed over Levitsky's face. Old nuns, old mother superior, facing the workers' bayonets and the hour of your death, how just you'd see it that a man like Levitsky should perish on the same blasphemed ground. You'd cackle at the perfection of it—an old revolutionary professional, me, *der Teuful Selbst,* devoured by the very forces he'd thought to understand and master and that he'd liberated.

He turned away from the window and stared at the scab left in the stone where an old cross had been beaten down from the wall. It was, he now saw, a room of death. What was a cross except a way to kill a man in slow, horrible agony, a long day's dying. Maybe that's why the Jews could never make sense of it: worship an execution device. Strange, these Christians.

He might not be the first Jew in this cell. Others, four hundred years ago, may have been held here, facing the same choice he would face: renounce your faith or die. Which was really, renounce your faith *and* die. They would have been men like his father, men of decency but without weapons. What would they, having squandered their gifts for analysis and dialectic on the Talmud in five thousand years of hushed, devotional study, have made of their torturers?

Levitsky felt it sliding away. He had trained himself so hard over the years to a certain pitch of revolutionary toughness: to see only what was real, what was important. Always to move to the heart of the issue. Always to be without illusion. Never to waste time in pointless bourgeois memory, nostalgia, and sentiment. To be, after the Great Lenin, a hard man. Now, when he needed them most, these difficultly acquired disciplines had simply vanished.

He sat down, under the mocking cruciform. The crucifiers were coming. It was another *memento mori,* teasing him, a monument to the dead—

✦ ✦ ✦

"The sleep will have done him some good," said Comrade Commissar Glasanov. "He'll see the hopelessness of his situation. He'll see the inevitability of surrender, the rightness of it. You know, Bolodin, I'm somewhat disappointed. I had expected something more impressive."

Lenny nodded as if a stupid man.

"These old Bolsheviki, at least they were realists. They understood what was required."

They reached the end of the corridor in the yellow morning light. The door, solid and massive, lay before them.

"Open it," said Glasanov.

Lenny took the big brass key and inserted it into the hole and felt the tumblers yield to his strength. He pulled the door open. They entered.

"Well, Comrade Levitsky, I hope—" began Glasanov, halting only when he realized Levitsky was gone.

10

ON THE RAMBLAS

FLORRY SLEPT FOR A DAY AND A HALF IN A ROOM ON THE sixth floor of the Hotel Falcon, which he and Sylvia chose, in their delirium, on the strength of one of Julian's pieces, which had described it as the "hotel of the young and bold."

When he finally stirred from his dreamless sleep, it was night. Someone was with him in the room.

"Who's there?" he asked, but he knew her smell.

"It's me," she said.

"How long have I been out?"

"Quite some time. I've been watching you."

"God, how boring. I'm ravenous."

"There's a curfew. You'll have to wait for morning."

"Oh."

"How do you feel?"

"I feel fine, Sylvia. I'm rather pleased to be alive, come to think of it."

"I am too. Robert, you saved my life. Do you recall?"

"Oh, that. Good heavens, what a terrible mess. I think I was saving *my* life and you just happened to be there."

She sat on the bed.

"We're all alone."

She was very near.

"Do you know, Sylvia," he said, "I'm rather glad I met you." Then, surprised at his own boldness, he took her to him and kissed her. It felt like he always knew it would, only better. She stood up.

"What are you doing?"

"I'm undressing," she said.

He could see her in the dark, a blur. She was quickly shedding her garments with a kind of athletic simplicity.

She stepped out of her chemise and he could see her breasts in the dark and sense their weight. They were very small and pear-shaped and lovely. Her hips were slim, her belly flat and tight. She walked to him and he could smell her sweetness. She had his hand.

"Touch me," she said, moving it to her breast. "*Here*. Feel it. Hold it."

It was warm and full. Beneath it, her heart beat. She was so close. There was nothing else in the world except Sylvia.

"I've wanted you for so long," he could hear himself saying.

Their mouths crushed together; Florry felt himself losing contact with the conscious world and entering a new zone of sensation. Sylvia was tawny, sinewy, and athletic—very strong, surprisingly strong as she pulled him to the bed. Florry was surprised that in his fumbling rush in the moon-vivid room and among the thunder of images and feelings and experiences that raced across him he didn't want to miss anything, anything at all. Her breasts, for example, upon which he suddenly felt as if he could spend a life-time. They were a marvel of economy and grace. He wanted, strangely, to eat them, and he tried eagerly.

"Oh, God," she moaned, sprawled beneath him. "Oh, God, Florry, that feels so good."

She became increasingly lyric yet increasingly abstract: he was astonished that she had enough sense to talk—for she continued, in a froggy voice, to comment upon events—when language had been banished from his mind.

He put his hand into her cleft, feeling the moist surrender, the eagerness, and it was quite something, the extent to which she'd become smooth and open and liquefied to him; her whole body had liquefied and then began to tense and arch and crack like a whip.

And then there came a time to shut her up at last with a kiss and it felt as if he were at the center of an explosion, so plummy and sweet, so crammed-full, so bloody perfect, like a line of poetry against his skull.

"Hurry, darling," she whispered. "I can't wait. God, Florry, hurry."

He raced on to the act's finale, entering her and falling through into a different universe.

"Do it," she commanded, and he completed the exchange, sinking in further, rising to gather strength to sink again. It had become a thing of rising and sinking: high, off, and distant followed by the giddy plunge, the surrender to the gravity of pleasure, and then climbing back up again.

"Yes, yes, yes," she was saying and the last bond of restraint snapped and the whole universe seemed to transmute into a phenomenon of optics: lights, lights, lights, lights. He felt a screeching moment in which he seemed at last to slide beneath the surface, while at the same time exactly clinging to her as she was to him, as if in recognition that each had only the other in protection against the world.

"Do you know what's odd?" Sylvia asked the next morning. "It's the history. It's everywhere. Can you feel it? One is actually at the *center* of history."

Florry nodded dreamily, although at the moment he would have preferred to find the center of his overalls. They were roomy, Spanish things of one huge piece, rather like an aviator's or a mechanic's suit. They were of worn, rough, blue cotton, and they had been donated to the cause of his depleted wardrobe by the POUM, which turned out to control the Hotel Falcon.

POUM stood for the Party of Marxist Unification, in the Spanish, which was more colloquially and less tendentiously translated into English as the Spanish Worker's Party; its initials were everywhere in the city, as it was one of the largest and most enthusiastic

of the several contending revolutionary bodies within Barcelona proper, but it did not quite control the city. It did not even control itself; it did not control anything. It was something more than a splinter group but perhaps not quite a mass movement on the scale of the gigantic union organizations that had dominated Barcelona for so long. In a sense it simply *was,* in the way that a mountain is *there.* It was more a monument to a certain pitch of feeling than an actual political movement: it stood for how things would be, as opposed to how they had been. Florry understood it to be loosely affiliated with the Anarcho-Syndicalists, another large, dreamy, semipowerful group, equally enthusiastic, equally long on vision for the next century while short on vision for the next day. In fact if the POUM and the Anarchists stood for anything beyond a set of vague words like *victory* and *equality* and *freedom,* they seemed to stand for having a smashing time while trampling the rubble of the old.

Down with what was; what would come simply *had* to be better, even if nobody had any good idea what that was. The POUMistas, nevertheless, had taken control of the Falcon, here on the Ramblas. What was more, they sponsored the largest of the militias, the Lenin Division, now entrenched outside of Huesca two hundred fifty miles to the east in the foothills of the Pyrenees, the closest authentic "war" to Barcelona.

But Florry, still sluggish after the business of the night, understood what she meant.

"Yes, it is odd," he replied. There was something particular in the air, and to come to it, straight out from tidy England, was to feel its power in a particularly undiluted dosage. They'd heard the theories all these years, the fashionable arguments, the intellectual fancies spun in cigarette-smoke-filled rooms, the shouted dreams, the fevered visions. The optimism of it was like a virus, the hope like a fantasy. Yet here it was, or at least one early model, clearly clunky, a wheezing, puffing, whirling gizmo, but the thing itself: the classless society.

"It fills one with hope," Sylvia said. "It's how things *could* be; it's how they *should* be."

Florry nodded, unsure of the feelings in his own heart just then, but somehow in agreement with her. They sat in the sunlight at a table at the Café Moka, which occupied the ground-floor corner of the Hotel Falcon, surprised at the warmth and sunlight of January, which in its way was oddly appropriate. They sipped *café con leche* and watched the parade. For the revolution *was* a parade.

Down the Ramblas, a wide thoroughfare that ran a mile from the Plaza de Catalunya to the port, in never-ending columns, the revolutionary masses tramped. To watch it, one felt, was almost a privilege; it was quite a moment for the tired old world.

"God, look at them," Sylvia said, her face flushed, her eyes vivid.

"It's the biggest parade there ever was," said Florry, speaking the truth, but leaving unsaid and unanswered the question of ultimate destinations.

And for this parade, Barcelona had tarted herself up in a new garb, as if part of the joy were in the costumes; the whole population had become workers, it seemed. It was, for the first time in the history of the world, *fashionable* to be a worker. Everybody wore the blue monos of the working class, or the khaki of the fighting militias. Even the prosaic public transportation contrivances wore costumes: the trams up and down the Ramblas moved like vast floats, pulling their cargo through the crowds; all wore a gaudy red-and-black scheme and all of them sported the giant initials of their particular political affiliations. At the same time the autos and trucks had been liberated to political purpose and they, too, wore their allegiances as proudly as old guardsman's chevrons. It was a Mardi Gras of revolutions, a reveler's revolution. The air was full of confetti and music and history. Festive banners flapped from the balconies of the buildings to the leafless trunks of the trees of the Ramblas or were strung in crudely painted, sagging, dripping majesty from balcony to lamp pole, offering a cheerful variety of exhortations to the duties that still lay ahead.

THEY SHALL NOT PASS
FASCISM WILL BE BURIED HERE
TO HUESCA! TO HUESCA!
UNITE, WORKERS
IN UNION, LIBERTY
DEATH TO THE BOURGEOISIE!

Huge portraits from the revolutionary pantheon hung everywhere, heroic, kind, knowing faces, the faces of saints. Florry knew the key figures: Marx and Lenin, the woman called La Passionaria, an intense intellectual fellow named Nin, head of POUM; and some other Spaniards whom he didn't recognize. Only the Soviet Man of Steel, Stalin, was missing, unwelcome down here among the unruly libertarians; but he held great sway not half a mile away at the vast Plaza de Catalunya, where the PSUC, the Communist Party of Catalonia, under Russian guidance, had taken over the Hotel Colon and turned that ceremonial space into a small block of downtown Moscow.

There was noise, too, on the Ramblas, noise everywhere: a din of singing and gramophone recordings, the clash of a dozen different tongues, Spanish and Catalonian the most popular only by a narrow margin, the others being English, French, German, and Russian. The air had filled with sunlight and the dust and the noise and the smell of flowers and petrol and horses and sweets. Sensation piled atop sensation, sight atop sight.

"It's like a new world," Sylvia said. "It's like a different world altogether. It's like some year in the future."

Florry didn't know what to say. The extent of her passion somewhat astonished him. She had not referred to last night.

"I want to believe in it so much," Sylvia said. "It explains so many things to me."

She was quite right, of course. So pure was the sense of revolution, the ether of justice deferred for so long but arriving at last, that to breathe it was to endorse it: the joyous madness of Starting Over, of Doing Right, of the Just State. To be in the birthing

room of history, as a new age attempted to wrench itself into life! Florry, sitting there, could feel the sentiment move through his bones.

Yet even now, in the blooming ardor, with the mood of purpose as heavy as perfume all about him, Florry could not prevent the coming of doubts. How much, one could ask, of all this was simple illusion. Parades, speeches, leaping peasants: the future?

Or was the future old Gruenwald removed by the police for reasons unknown? What about poor, drowned Witte, lost in the night, and the hundred unknown Arab crewmen sucked under the black water?

"Your face is so long, Robert."

"I was thinking of Count Witte."

"Dead and gone," she said. "The poor man."

"Yes." He reached over and took her hand.

"I was also thinking of us, Sylvia. Not of history, not of progress or justice. No, *us*. Is that fair, Sylvia? Do I have that right?"

"I like it when you touch me," she said. "I like it very much."

"Here we sit, Sylvia, in the brave new world. And you tell me you like it when I touch you. Are you part of my illusion, Sylvia? Tell me, please. Am I misreading you? Am I weak and sentimental and seeing things that aren't there?"

Her face clouded in the sunlight. There was a particular burst of music from somewhere, so loud it made him wince. A haunted look came to her face.

"I just wonder if there's time for us," she said. "In all this."

A troop of khaki cavalry was moving down the Ramblas, the horses' hooves clattering on the cobblestones. From this distance, they looked fierce and proud, a conceit of glory and destiny.

"I like you so very, very much. I just want time for this. Not the revolution really, but the experience of it. I've never been anyplace so exciting, I've never been so close to history. I never will again. I want some time to . . . to have my experiences. That is what I came for, for my experiences. Do you see what I'm saying?"

"Well, Sylvia, I suppose I do. Still, the truth is—God help me for finding the courage to face it at last—I suppose the truth is that I love you. Comical, isn't it? Well, let's do be grown up about the whole thing. Yes, let's do be friends."

"Last night was wonderful. Do you see? But there's so much more to it than just the simple business of how we *feel*."

"I suppose there is."

"There's so much to do still."

Florry said nothing. Yes, he had things to do, too.

"Your friend Julian has joined up. I talked to some of the party members. He no longer represents his little magazine. Now he represents the People. With a capital *P*, one supposes. He's joined the POUMista Lenin Division. He's out in the trenches at Huesca. He's in the war. God, Robert, now there's a man."

The admiration in her voice almost killed him.

"Well, Sylvia," he heard himself saying, "well, then you may get your introduction to the great Julian after all. Because I shall be there, also."

"Yes," said David Harold Allen Sampson, "yes, I suppose you *are* Florry, even if you don't have the item."

Sampson turned out to be a youngish, gray chap with flat eyes and a vaguely chilly manner, though handsome in a certain pampered way. He had a toneless, measured BBC announcer's voice and when he talked he tended to look away, into space, as if fixed on the stars. He looked as if he'd seen nearly everything there was to see in the world, even if he was only thirty.

"I say, Sampson, with the ship sinking and people dying all about, one would hardly have headed down to one's cabin to dig up *Tristram Shandy*."

"It's your rudeness that convinces me. Only Eton could teach it and the bloody Bolshies haven't got good enough yet to turn out bogus Etonians. Yes, I suppose I must believe you are Florry."

He took a sip of his whiskey. They sat on hard chairs at a marble-

topped table in the dark and smoky interior of the Café de las Ramblas, an old-fashioned place of high Mediterranean style much favored by the English press in the wearying heat of the afternoon when the Spaniards laid aside their furious revolution for the age-old custom of siesta.

"And now you propose to go off to the front. As a common soldier, no less. God, Florry, one would think after that awful experience with that damned boat, you'd want nothing but two weeks in hospital."

"That's not important. What's important is Julian."

"Good heavens, they didn't tell me you were cut of such *heroic* stuff," Sampson said, manfully restraining his excess enthusiasm.

"I simply want to get the business over."

"I shall so inform them. We shall see what they say."

"I certainly am not going to wait about," said Florry, "for the major and his fruity assistant to make up their minds. I'm going to the Lenin barracks first thing tomorrow. Is that understood?"

"Florry, you needn't be bloody *shirty* in this matter."

"You see, I'm anxious to be on with it. Do you know why?"

"I suppose I cannot prevent you from telling me."

"Because I am sick of the whole thing. I want to do what must be done and get on with it."

"Good," Sampson said. "You should know that we believe that Julian's signup is another step in the proof, so to speak. Another whiskey? *Boy!* Good heavens, I'm supposed to call him 'comrade,' as if he's an old school chum. Comrade! Another round, please."

The sounds of gaiety had suddenly begun to pick up from the out-of-doors. Florry could hear a snatch of music, the rush of many voices. The afternoon sing had begun.

> *Arise, ye prisoners of starvation*
> *Arise, ye wretched of the earth*
> *For Justice thunders condemnation*
> *A better world's in birth.*

"Wonderful sentiments, eh?" said Sampson, with his tight, prim, fishy smile. "It's a pity they go about murdering chaps, isn't it?"

"Get on with it, Sampson. The game isn't amusing any more."

Sampson smiled. He was enjoying the game immensely.

"We have been aware for some time that the Russian secret police's intelligence on its factional rivals—the POUM, the Anarchists, the trade unions, the bloody parade marchers—has been exceedingly good. In fact, there seems to be a secret war going on. Key people in the opposition disappear in the dead of night; they turn up dead, or they never turn up at all, they simply vanish. It's just a racket, isn't it? One mob of gangsters rubbing out another. But the Russians have got to know who to take, eh? Can't just take anybody. And so who better to go among the enemy than a seemingly innocent British journalist with a brilliant, wondrous, easy charm? It fits with what we know. He wouldn't report to anybody here, except some control fellow, who would send his information straight back to Moscow via the Amsterdam route that was so important to them. Then the orders go out from Moscow; there's no direct contact between Julian and the local goons. He's never compromised. It's quite clever."

Florry stared at him.

"So it's murder, then? Yet another level of debauchery."

"In for a penny, in for a pound. Now it appears this secret war may be moving into another, perhaps ultimate, phase. What better way, really, to get to the inner workings of POUM than to place their best agent among its militia, near to its military headquarters at La Granja? And, for the record, it doesn't appear that he's in any great danger. The real fighting's still around Madrid. Out near Huesca, it's mostly potting about in the mud. If one keeps one's bum down, one has an excellent chance at surviving. The only thing he's *really* given up is his abundant corps of female admirers. Still, one has to do what one must for the wonderful revolution, eh?"

"You're as cynical as a whore."

"The profession inclines one thus. And it is, come to think of it, rather a brothel. And I must say I take the cynic's pleasure in another's discomfort: the idea of Julian Raines potting about in the mud is quite amusing. At university, he and his lot were such dandies."

"You knew him?"

"Everybody knew him. He has a gift for getting known, quite apart from other gifts."

Florry took a drink of the whiskey.

"So if you must go off and be a hero for that lovely girl, then, go," said Sampson. "Perhaps it may even work out for the best."

It suddenly dawned on Florry how much Sampson had thought about all this. "I've made it easy on you, haven't I?" he said.

Sampson smiled. Florry hated him.

"I suppose you have. You rather conveniently started where I had hoped to finish. The major's most recent communication reached me last night. He said it was imperative that you join the Lenin Division. He left it to me to engineer a way. You spared me that, old man."

"You *are* a whore, Sampson."

"Of course I am. But one likes to think of oneself as a *good* whore. But let's not part enemies, old man, even if we did go to different public schools. If you've a mind, do drop in, and bring that girl. I've rented a villa out in the Sarrea district. Big, damned drafty place, rather nice. They go for a song these days. I'll have my man do up a nice meal. We'll have a bash."

Florry got up to leave. "Er, it sounds fine. Let me give you a ring on it or something."

"Splendid. By the way, there's one other interesting little tidbit that might be of some help to you," Sampson said.

He turned back.

"Yes. There's a rumor afoot that Julian's old friend Levitsky is in Barcelona. You might keep your eye open."

"And how would I know Levitsky? Do you think me a mind reader?"

"Good God, no. But you would know him because you arrived with him. He traveled undercover on that ship. He survived the sinking too, evidently."

Florry looked at the fishy young Englishman who smirked up at him. Yet what he suddenly felt was the memory of an odor.

Peppermint.

11

IGENKO

LEVITSKY, FROM THE WINDOW, WATCHED IGENKO APproach.

The man was prissy, a bit pudgy. His white suit wore immense, dark crescents under the armpits. He needed a shave. He looked desperately uncomfortable.

Come, little one, Levitsky thought.

The man wandered with not a small amount of trepidation the winding, evil-smelling, narrow streets of the Barrio Chino, which was just beginning to fill with customers as the night began. Even the revolution had not halted the practice of certain ancient professions and in the Barrio Chino, in the warren of overhanging buildings, balconies bright with wash, amid the smell of garbage and piss, amid the little bars where Spanish men stood and ate and talked the nights away, the tarts had come out, mingling with sailors, soldiers, politicians, and revolutionaries; a hundred little nightclubs had half-open doors that promised certain otherwise unavailable delights inside.

As Levitsky watched, prim, chubby Igenko tried to melt into the cosmopolitan crowd, evidently terrified first that he was under observation by the NKVD and second that he might be stopped by an Anarchist patrol. For the Anarchists controlled the Barrio Chino, which is why it was able to flourish, but the Anarchists were not terribly fond of Russians.

But the man was stopped by no one, fortunately, and after a time consulted a watch. He seemed to take a deep breath, as if in search

of his courage, and, with a last glance at the world around him, ducked out of sight.

Levitsky waited. He could imagine poor Igenko's ordeal as he negotiated the protocols of the brothel. In time, Levitsky knew he approached: he could hear the girls cooing.

"Hey, sugar tits, come see me, I'll make a man out of you."

"Put your little thing in a woman's hole, princess."

"Lick my titties and I'll show you things you never saw in your life, dolly."

Poor Igenko, pretending to stoicism. Teenage boys frequently yelled things at him and the whores knew, too. Levitsky wondered —how did they know? So surely, how did they know? How did *everybody* know?

Outside the door, they stopped.

"In here," Levitsky heard the girl say. "Now give me the money."

There was a pause, as Igenko dug through his wallet.

"You Russians," she said. "Through the eyes and the nose, you all look the same. Fat or thin, you all look the same." She left him.

Igenko opened the door and stepped into the darkness.

"Ivanch? Ivanch, are you there?" he called, using the most intimate abridgment of Levitsky's middle name.

"Were you seen?"

"Ivanch, thank God you're all right."

"Close the door!" Levitsky hissed.

Igenko closed the door. There were another few seconds of silence and then the light came on.

"God, Ivanch. You look dreadful."

"God had nothing to do with it, I assure you," said Levitsky. He held himself with grave care, because the pain was still intense. His face was pinched and drawn.

Yet it was Igenko who seemed close to coming apart. He sat on the bed, heaving and breathing wretchedly, struggling for his breath, his pallid skin becoming chalkier. "It's so terrible. They beat you?"

"Of course they beat me. They're serious about their work."

Igenko began to weep. He covered his eyes with his dainty handkerchief and made sniveling sounds.

"Is it really that awful?" said Levitsky.

"You were such a handsome man. To see you like this is almost more than one can take."

"Don't concern yourself. It's nothing I won't recover from."

"We heard that you were here. There were rumors. That the NKVD had—"

"What about my escape?"

"Nothing. Nothing at all. That is why I was so stunned when your note reached me."

Levitsky laughed harshly, through pain.

"Glasanov has gotten himself into a terrible mess. He can't let anybody know I'm gone or he's on his way back to Moscow for a bullet in his neck. So he must catch me without officially admitting I've flown. Let's see him bluff his way out of this!" He enjoyed it immensely.

"Ivanch, how did you manage to—"

Levitsky laughed again.

"Don't concern yourself. One simply does what one must."

But it had been quite simple. Levitsky laughed at the memory. They are so stupid, these new fellows. Some inheritors! He looked about the cell in his hour of need and noted by the variation of color on the stone that for centuries a crucifix had been hung above the pallet. He reasoned that surely such a device must have been affixed to the stone in some fashion or other. It didn't take much cunning to find a nail sunk in the crevices of the stone—an ancient thing, there for centuries. A strong tug and it was his.

He felt his trophy in his pocket now—a wicked lance of black iron, perhaps four inches long.

He used it to pick the lock. Then, reasoning he had no chance to escape in full daylight, he simply slipped into the cell next door, where his hardest problem was to stifle his laughter during the great Commissar Glasanov's rage. When he and his Amerikanski

finally left, Levitsky went back to his original cell, figuring that it would be the safest place. He waited there until nightfall, then made his way out.

"I suspected that an Anarchist neighborhood would offer the least chance of NKVD observation, and so here I am. Safe, if not quite sound," he told Igenko.

"You are brilliant, Emmanuel. As usual. You always were." Igenko's little eyes shone with respect and admiration.

He reached and touched Levitsky on the knee, with a weak, hopeful smile. "I've always been your staunchest supporter. Your greatest admirer. You know that."

"I need help, Ivan Alexyovich. I need it badly."

"I understand. You can trust me. I owe you so much. I will do anything for you."

"Yes."

"Anything. Use me in any way to advance your plan."

"All right. All right, Alexyovich."

Igenko began to weep. He put his head down on the bed and cried. Levitsky stroked the back of his fat neck and crooned to him gently.

"It's been so long," Igenko said.

"So many years. Since 1919. Come on, wipe your tears, old Ivan Alexyovich. Stop whimpering."

"I'll be all right, now that you're here."

"Of course you will."

"I know I can help. I'm a clerk in the Maritime Commission. I know people in the port. People owe me things. I've done favors. I can get you out. I can get you on a ship. To Africa maybe, to America, even."

"No."

"Emmanuel, they'll kill you. Glasanov and his monster Bolodin. They're feared everywhere in Barcelona. The Comintern people dread them. The radicals and the Anarchists are terrified of them."

His voice rose in pitch; he was verging on hysteria.

"Listen, Ivan Alexyovich, please. Calm yourself, and listen. I need money. And I need a place to go to earth for a while. It's only a question of a few days before they begin to run down the brothels, even in the Anarchist neighborhoods."

"Glasanov controls the SIM, and the SIM is everywhere."

"I know. That's why time is so desperate. But mostly I need papers. Above all, I need papers. I need to *be* somebody."

"I can give you money. I have twenty pieces of gold. I've had them for years. I can sell them. And I can find a place where you can hide. And as for the papers—well, it's not my line, but I can certainly try."

"And one last thing. That watch. The watch is important to me."

"Why, yes. Of course. You gave it to me, of course. I give it back."

"Thanks, old friend."

Levitsky took the thing from Igenko, quickly strapped it to his wrist.

"Here. Take what little money I have now," Igenko said. He pushed over a wad of pesetas. "I'll get you the gold tomorrow."

"Are you observed?"

"Everybody is observed. The NKVD is everywhere, just like the SIM."

"They are the same, one supposes."

"I am not observed *regularly*. I've some freedom."

"All right. I'll move to another bordello tonight. Can you get back to me tomorrow?"

"I-I think."

"On the Ramblas, across from the Plaza Real. Among the stalls in the center. There's one where an old lady sells chicken on a spit. Do you know it?"

"I'll find it."

"Meet me there at seven. Carry a briefcase. You have a briefcase?"

"Yes."

"If you think you've been followed, carry it in your right hand. If you know it's safe, carry it in your left. Do you understand?"

"Yes. Right, danger; left, safe."

"As it once was in politics."

"Please be careful, Ivanch. Please." He touched Levitsky's thigh in an absentminded way.

"Ivan Alexyovich, if you help me, we can both get away. You and me, we'll get out, in just a few days. We'll go to America together."

"Yes."

"Go now. Hurry, so that you aren't missed at the Colon."

Igenko stood to leave, but paused. "Ivanch, it's wonderful that you're here."

The fat man smiled. "And I want you to know, whatever you do. *Whatever.* It's all right. Do what you must. Do you understand?"

Levitsky looked at him. "I'll do what I have to, Ivan Alexyovich."

Igenko hurried out.

Levitsky stood up slowly, feeling the ache in his ribs. You are an old man. You are nearly sixty, much too old for this.

He turned and saw himself in the mirror. He snapped the light out quickly, for he could not look upon his own face.

It was a question of timing, of careful calibration. Levitsky had decided that six was the ideal hour; an hour later and they would have too much time to think, to plot out the various possibilities, to counterplan against his game. An hour earlier and they might not be able to bring it off: the system would break down somewhere and he'd pay his dear price for nothing.

Accordingly, he left the barrio at five the next afternoon, at last reaching the crowded Ramblas and turning up it, toward the Plaza de Catalunya. Oh, the cafés were jammed this bright late afternoon, beginning to fill up for another evening of celebration. All revolu-

tions alway love themselves first; it is a rule. As he climbed along the central strip, walking among the trees and benches and stalls and street lamps, the busy density of the place momentarily dizzied him. The hunted man is safest in crowds, and here the masses were a torrent. Bright banners, heroic proclamations, bold portraits flapped off the buildings. Several of the cafés had been reconsecrated to political usage, as well as alcoholic: the UGT had one, and so did the FAI and the POUM; it was like a bazaar of crazed political ideas. He continued, until he reached the splurge of freedom of the open space of the plaza itself, where the last of the great battles of July had been fought and students and workers and slum boys had overwhelmed the army's final position at great loss. He traversed the martyred ground, avoiding the Hotel Colon on one side, with its PSUC banner and its huge picture of the great Koba and its smart NKVD troops at their machine-gun nests behind the sandbags and the barbed wire. He headed instead to another key building in the fighting, the Telefonica, whose façade was still pocked with bullet marks from the battle. It was the central telephone exchange, and who controlled it, controlled all communications in Barcelona. But before he reached it, Levitsky stopped to check Igenko's watch: quarter to six. He was early. He sat on a bench. A parade started up as Levitsky waited. He looked at it with some contempt.

Parades!

He watched as the ragtag Spanish cavalry marched down the street. The beasts were not well-trained, and the troopers had difficulty holding them in the formation. He could see them scuffle and pull at their reins. A shiver passed through him. Horses were such terrible creatures.

At precisely six o'clock, he crossed the wide street and entered the exchange. He found himself in a vast central office. A man came up in the uniform of one of the crazy anarchist groups. Anarchists running a telephone exchange? It was madness.

"Business, comrade?"

"Of the most urgent kind," Levitsky said.

"You are foreign. Come to help our revolution or to loot it?"

"Does this answer?" said Levitsky, and he rolled up his right sleeve to show a tattoo on his biceps. It was the tattoo of a black fist.

"You are one of us, then. Salud, brother. It looks as if it's been there a few years."

"Almost as long as the arm itself. From the time before there was time."

"What business have you?"

'To place a call."

"Go on, then. While it's there. When at last we tear down the government we will also tear down the telephone lines, and then all men will be free."

"And so they will," said Levitsky. God: the Anarchists. They were still the same dreamers!

He went to the counter.

A girl came up.

"How much?" he asked her. "Rather, how much, *comrade?*"

She smiled, so young and pretty.

"Ten pesetas."

"The Anarchists have not yet outlawed money?"

"Perhaps tomorrow, comrade."

He paid her.

"Number six." She pointed to a wall where twenty-five or so numbered phones were mounted, most of them in use. He went to number six, picked up the earpiece—still warm—and hit the receiver several times. As in Moscow, the connection was terrible, but after a time a voice came on the line.

"*¿Número, por favor?*"

"*Policía,*" he said into the speaker.

"*Gracias,*" came the reply; there were clicks and buzzes and then another voice arrived.

"*¡Policía! ¡Viva la Revolución!*"

Levitsky cursed him in Russian.

There was confusion and chatter from the other end, as the speaker

demanded in Spanish to know what was going on. Levitsky cursed again and again, and after a time and some confusion, at last a Russian speaker came on.

"Hello, Who is this?"

"Never mind, who is this?"

"*I* ask the questions, comrade."

"What is your name, comrade? To whom do I speak?"

"Speshnev," the man said. He sounded very young.

"The Speshnev who works for Glasanov? Of NKVD?"

"Identify yourself."

"Listen, Speshnev, and listen good. I'm only going to say it once. I wish to denounce a traitor. A secret Trotsky pig and a wrecker."

"Most interesting."

"He's third assistant secretary in the Maritime Commission. One Igenko. But he's a fat cocksucking rat. He's sold us out to the Jews."

"And you have proof of these charges?"

"Of course. This Igenko was a comrade of the traitor Levitsky. Do you know of this Levitsky, Speshnev of the NKVD? You should. Second only to Trotsky."

"Keep talking."

"Igenko's trying to get papers together so he and his loverboy Levitsky can take off. They'll fly the coop tonight. They're going to meet on the Ramblas across from the Plaza Real tonight, near the stall of the lady who sells chicken on a spit. Don't ask me how I know. It'll be at seven. Just show up and nail the two butt-fuckers yourself."

"Who—"

Levitsky hung up. He felt as if he were going to vomit.

"There," said the second undersecretary, wiping the sweat off his face. It was excruciatingly hot in the tailor's shop, on the Ramblas, overlooking the entrance to the Plaza Real, and the steam from the presses in the back room hung heavy and moist in the air. "The fat

one, with the sour look, in the mottled white suit, comrade commissar."

"Yes," said Glasanov. "Do you see, Bolodin?"

Lenny Mink, standing next to him, nodded. He could see the fat guy through the window and down across the street, standing in the crowded thoroughfare with a nervous tightness, an aching discomfort on his mug. He was obviously a nellie, too, with his mincing walk, and his big ass stuck out like a girl's. His face was milky and unshaven.

"He was exceedingly distracted today, comrade commissar," said the second undersecretary. "So much so that had not your phone call come when it did, I would myself have most certainly reported it. One can tell when a man is guilty, even if one—"

"Yes, that's fine," said Glasanov. "I'll note it in your record. Your record will reflect your service to Security, you may rest assured. Now the driver will take you back. And I think you'd best tell your staff the workload is going to increase."

"Of course, comrade commissar. We are only too happy to make any sacrifice for the good of—"

"No shooting, Bolodin," said Glasanov. "Tell your people. I want Levitsky alive. Anybody who harms Levitsky is to be severely disciplined. Is that understood?"

The fifteen other men in the room nodded.

"Bolodin, do you think you can get down and into that stall? Stay back. We don't want Levitsky to see you. But when he approaches, you can knock him to earth. You knock him down, do you understand, and pin him to the street. The others will be there in seconds. But he's a clever old wolf; he will have found a weapon by this time, perhaps even a revolver. He will not hesitate to use it."

Lenny nodded again. He'd like to see that old guy try something smart with him. He took off his leather overcoat. He wore the blue overalls of a POUMista, and he pulled out a black beret and put it on his head.

"I'll be here, of course. Watching it, you understand."

"What if he bolts?" asked Speshnev, the young Russian. "These jobs can go all to hell if the rabbit bolts. Why, in Moscow—"

"If he bolts, I'll catch him and snap his legs," said Lenny Mink, and nobody disagreed with him.

"All right. Now go, go quickly. This may be our best chance, our only chance."

They began to file out, and just as he left for the stairway, Lenny felt Glasanov's hand on his shoulder and felt his breath warm and quick in his ear. He turned, to see the man's eyes almost aflame with urgency.

"Comrade Bolodin, for God's sake, don't fail."

Lenny grinned and proceeded to walk on his way.

He came out of the stairway onto the sidewalk, waited for a break in the traffic, then darted across to the broad center strip of the Ramblas. Keeping his face low, he pushed his way through the throngs, past somebody selling birds and somebody selling flowers and somebody selling militia hats, sliding through soldiers and revolutionary women and young intellectuals, and approached the old lady's chicken stall on the oblique, maintaining it between himself and Igenko.

He ducked into it.

"Eh, señor?" The old lady looked at him. "What is—?"

"Beat it," Lenny Mink said. "Take a hike."

"Ahhh. Who—"

"Here, take this, old one," said Ugarte, Lenny's best boy, who had discreetly slid in behind Lenny. He handed the woman a hundred-peseta note. He told her to have a nice cool drink at a café for a while.

"You take the counter," said Lenny, and Ugarte moved past him, throwing on an apron lying on the table. Lenny drew back, into the shadows. He could see the fat man in the white suit real good. The distance was about thirty feet. The fat man had a briefcase in his left hand.

Come on, old devil, he told himself, looking around nervously. Come *on*.

✦ ✦ ✦

Just inside the main police station courtyard, Levitsky encountered two Asaltos with German machine pistols who demanded abruptly and impolitely to know who he was and where he thought he was going. They insisted on papers. Levitsky let them carry on for a few seconds in Spanish, full of their own toughness and importance, then halted them with a Russian curse.

"NKVD, comrade," he said, fixing his eyes on the eyes of the bigger of the two, who immediately melted like a chocolate soldier in the sun.

"Comrade *Russki?*"

"*Da. Sí,*" said Levitsky. "*De Madrid, no?* Comrade Glasanov?"

"*Russkis?*"

"*Sí, Russkis.* Glasanov, NKVD?"

"Ah, *sí, sí. Primo Russki.*"

"*Da,*" said Levitsky in a dead voice.

The man pointed up the building to the fourth floor. He showed four fingers.

"*Gracias,* comrade," said Levitsky. He turned, went into the building through a set of double doors under one of the porticos, found some stairs, and walked swiftly up them. He passed several policemen, but nobody challenged him.

At the fourth floor, he turned down the dank hall until at last he found a huge poster of Stalin and a desk. The air was thick, where men had been smoking, but now only a single woman sat at her desk, and near her a hulking Spanish youth lounged proudly with his machine pistol, an American Thompson.

He walked to the woman, whose eyes rose as he approached.

"Comrade," he announced in a clear, commanding, humorless voice, "I'm Maximov. From Madrid. You have my wire. Where is Comrade Commissar Glasanov? Let's get going. I've had a long and dusty drive. I have come to take possession of the criminal Levitsky."

He watched a great range of emotions play across her face in what seemed to be a very short time. Finding at last her breath and her

way out of her shock to some kind of coherence, she leaped up and shouted, "Comrade! It's a pleasure to meet you and—"

"Comrade, I asked a question. I did not come by for meaningless chitchat of a social nature. Where the bloody devil is Glasanov? Didn't he receive the wire?"

"No, comrade," she stammered. "We received no wire. Comrade Commissar Glasanov is off to arrest—" And she halted, terrified.

"Arrest whom?"

The woman could not begin to tell Levitsky that Levitsky had escaped.

"No, it's—"

"It doesn't matter. Please arrange to have me taken to Levitsky at once. I have explicit orders."

"I-I-I-"

"Can it be, comrade, that Levitsky is gone? Has Levitsky escaped from Glasanov? Comrade, tell me."

The girl was almost white with terror.

"I have my sources," said Levitsky coldly, staring furiously at her. "I can tell you, comrade, that Madrid—and Moscow—don't appreciate being made to look silly by an old man. It sounds like wrecking, deviation, and oppositionism."

"I can assure you, Comrade Maximov—"

"What is your name, comrade?"

"I am Comrade Levin, comrade."

"Comrade Levin, it is most urgent that I speak with Comrade Commissar Glasanov on this matter of Levitsky. This is not a playful request, I assure you, comrade. I have a report to file. I am under extreme pressure from Moscow myself. I would hate to have to tell the committee secretary that in Barcelona our representatives are sluggish and inefficient, given to Spanish ways. It almost makes me think—"

"Comrade, accept my apologies, please. You must understand how hard we work here, how difficult the problems are."

"And let me tell you, comrade, that in other areas of Spain our

policies are pursued with much greater Party discipline and control. Our detention houses are everywhere. There are no Trotskyite columns, no open denunciations of the general secretary, no Anarchist organizations patrolling the streets, no opposition newspapers. Moscow has noticed the comic opera here in Barcelona. We have our sources. We are not surprised."

"But comrade, the problems are so different here. Only here, in the early days—"

"The problems are no different, but perhaps the quality of the personnel is different."

"Comrade, I can assure you the arrest is imminent. Even now, the commissar is—"

"This would seem his only arrest."

"Oh, no. No, comrade, begging your pardon. No, we have been very diligent. Our commissar works like the very devil himself. Night after night. Look, Comrade Maximov, I'll show you. Come, please."

She took a key from her desk and led him back into Glasanov's inner office.

"I'll prove it to you," she said. "I'll show you the records."

Lenny Mink watched the fat man shift the briefcase back and forth. He kept asking people for the time. He was a mess. Lenny could almost smell the fear. It was five past.

Come on, _Teuful_. You're dead in Spain without papers. Without papers, the Asaltos shoot you. Come on, old devil, come to me. This is your only hope. Now, when it's crowded, when the soldiers move down the street, when you think it's safest.

There was a sudden pop in the air.

Lenny, startled, looked about. Pop, pop, pop. His eyes shot back to the fat Igenko, who stood on the verge of panic amid the suddenly frozen crowd, peculiarly reddish, as if—

Flares. The twilight sky had filled with red flares, like small pink suns that hung, floating, against the dusk. Music rose tumultuously in the weird spectacle; it was the Internationale.

"Boss—" It was Ugarte.

"Shut up," Lenny said, shooting his eyes back to the frightened Igenko, afraid he'd fled. No, he was still there.

Soldiers. One of the militias must have been heading out to the front. Igenko stood in the pink night as the soldiers swept along the Ramblas, on either side of him, and the crowd surged toward them to line the way, and Igenko, against his will, was caught in the human tide.

"Fuck it," said Lenny, just as Igenko was hurled out of sight in the masses. Trust the devil Levitsky to pull something like this.

He vaulted the counter smoothly and his long, powerful strides took him through the running people. He bowled a man over, shoved others aside, knocked a woman down.

Someone grabbed him.

"Hey, comrade—"

"SIM," he barked. The grabber fell back instantly. Lenny pulled the automatic from his mono and pushed on. He hated the idea of failure. Rage filled him. Where was the fat man?

There, yes. He'd had a glimpse, through the troops and beyond the crowd on the sidewalk on the other side. He was right at the Arco de Teatro, about to disappear through the arch and vanish in the winding, messy old streets of the Barrio Chino, which the Anarchists controlled.

Lenny dashed across the way, pushing through the mob of soldiers.

He could hear them yelling sporting things at him.

"Hey, come to war with us, comrade, if you're so eager."

"Come and kill the Fascists with us, brother."

"He can't wait. Come on, the POUM needs fighters like you."

But Lenny pushed through their ranks and on to the other side, ducked through the Arco himself, and ran down the narrow street. The buildings loomed over him: the road seemed to split and split again into a maze, but a maze jammed with human riffraff. He halted, breathing hard. There was no illumination, though up ahead, here and there, red lights shone on the sides of the buildings.

But then he saw him. Just a glimpse of heft and mince, darting ahead in utter fright. Lenny didn't stop to consider the fragility of the connection: he had looked down the right street at the right moment.

He caught him in a lonely pool of red light.

"Ivanch . . . ?" The fat man turned, his face warm with expectation. But when he saw Lenny, his expression fell apart into something ugly with terror.

"Swine," Lenny said, hitting him in the fat mouth with the pistol. Igenko fell into a mewling heap.

"Hey. Hey, what are you doing, comrade?"

Lenny looked up; three Anarchist patrolmen were unslinging their rifles and heading over.

"SIM," barked Lenny.

"Fuck the SIM, comrade," yelled the first. "Russian swine had better stay out of—"

Lenny threw the slide on his Tokarev, jacking the hammer back, and said in English, "Another step, motherfucker, and you're dead meat."

Igenko was crying.

Ugarte was next to him, pistol out, and then another man arrived and another and another, and then Glasanov himself. The Anarchists began to back off.

"These are simply records," said Levitsky. "A list of names. This means nothing."

The woman's eyes fell.

"I assure you, Comrade Maximov," she began, "each name on that list is an enemy of the state and each has been dealt with by Comrade Glasanov. We are moving even closer to—"

"You show me a list of names on a paper and you say, here, here is your revolution, this paper. Meanwhile, opposition newspapers are published condemning the general secretary, slandering him, and armed dissenters swagger in the streets and drink wine in the cafés, laughing at him."

"Look," she said, opening a drawer. "Look! Do you see! This is not a list! These are our enemies' lives!"

She pulled the pouch out.

"All these passports. They each represent an arrest. And they will be sent back to Moscow Center by diplomatic pouches. Our agents will be able to use them to penetrate the Western democracies in the years to come. Look, see for yourself."

She handed the pouch over to Levitsky; he rifled it quickly. Passports and plenty more: official papers, work records, confiscated identification cards, the remains of the Tomas W.'s and the Carlos M.'s, and the Vladimir N.'s of Glasanov's assiduous underground campaign against oppositionism.

"Yes," he said. "Yes, it appears to be impressive. One must not judge too hastily, however."

"Examine them, comrade. They are our evidence. We are tireless in our efforts. We broach no treason. Comrade Glasanov is a gifted, inspirational leader. He is a Party worker who doesn't know the meaning of fatigue."

Levitsky studied the matter gravely.

At that moment a flare popped outside filling, the office with pink light. Another detonated, then another. They looked to the window and could see the spangled patterns of the starbursts glossy and spectacular against the night sky, dwarfing even the moon.

"A parade," she said. "Men are going off to fight at the front. But we fight here, too, comrade. We have no interest in parades."

Levitsky realized that the stupid girl was in love with Glasanov. He was probably fucking her every night.

"Perhaps the matter deserves more study," he said. "I shall return to my quarters at the Colon. Tell Glasanov to expect me tomorrow at nine A.M. Sharp. He had better have the criminal Levitsky by then. In the meantime, I'll review these documents tonight so as to better understand the situation here and the difficulties Comrade Commissar Glasanov faces."

"Yes. Yes, I'll tell him. Oh, listen. Listen."

Music. It was the Internationale.

"It's quite beautiful," he said. "Truly inspirational sentiments. Good day, comrade. You serve your superior well. I shall keep my eye on you. Perhaps the right word in the right ear."

"Thank you, Comrade Maximov, but my work is pleasure enough. I have no desires except to serve my nation and my party."

He left quickly.

In the street, he melted into the crowd and departed the area, heading into an Anarchist neighborhood, his cache of identities under his arm in the stocky leather pouch. The extent of the triumph was stunning, far greater than he had hoped for: he had wanted out of his sortie some sort of identity card, and he had come away with an encyclopedia of personalities. He could easily sell half of them on the black market, where genuine papers were a prized item, and the others would give him extraordinary operating latitude, made more deliciously useful by Glasanov's inability to acknowledge the loss of the documents.

In the revolutionary mob he hurried along, the sound of music ringing in his ears, the sky behind him still pink and hot with light. He tried not to think of Igenko.

When Igenko died at 4:05 A.M. that morning in the prison at the Convent of St. Ursula, after sustaining the inevitable massive internal injuries, it was greeted by his captors as something less than a tragedy. He died badly, screaming. He had told them, as much as he could, everything. But he didn't make a lot of sense.

"He knew nothing," said Glasanov. "That raving, that terror. He was worthless."

But Lenny was thinking that Igenko was a clerk in the Maritime Commission, which handled shipping. And he was thinking of Igenko's dying words, the ones that had confused poor Glasanov.

"The gold," he had screamed, "Emmanuel came for the gold and he betrayed me for the gold."

12

THE PARADE

BY GOD, THOUGHT FLORRY, IF I LIVE ANOTHER FIFTY years, I'll never forget this night. He shifted the lumpy hulk of the Moisin-Nagent rifle from one shoulder to another—in a POUM formation, it made no difference which shoulder one braced one's rifle against, just as it made no difference whether one marched in step or in uniform; all that mattered was mass and direction. Around him, men churned ahead. In the sky above, flares burst and hung, hissing. Each was a small sun, burning its image into the retina, bleeding its color into the sky behind it. It was the red night, *el noche rojo,* and he was part of it.

It seemed that all Barcelona had either wedged itself onto the Ramblas to cheer the soldiers or had found space on the balconies above, and half the musicians of Spain had been conscripted to provide music by which to send the soldiers off to war. Flowers and confetti fell upon them; petals drifted pinkly in the illuminated air. It was a theater of light. Shafts rose and flashed against the sky like saber blades; fireworks burst and crackled as the parade swept down the Ramblas.

"To Huesca! To Huesca!" came the cry from the crowds.

"Long live the World Revolution!" somebody up ahead yelled in exuberant English.

A wineskin, circulating among the militiamen, finally arrived at Florry.

"Here, *inglés,*" said a boy, handing it over.

Florry took the warm thing and held it close to his mouth and squirted in a brief, pulsing jet of wine. *Blanco.* A little bitter, yet vivid all the same. Yes. He swallowed and passed it on. He noticed that the rifles had spouted roses and that women had come among them.

"Hey, *inglés,* not so bad, eh?" someone yelled to him.

"Yes, bravo," shouted Florry back, feeling excited and cynical at once. He'd spent two crude weeks tramping about in the mud with broomsticks with these boys—the rifles were only issued recently —and yet he felt a part of it. What a jolly show! What a spiffy send-up! It was like '14, wasn't it, everybody off on a bloody crusade. Pip, pip, do one's best, and all that.

At the bottom of the Ramblas, the parade wheeled to the left in an unending torrent under the watchful, cool eye of Christopher Columbus at the top of his pedestal, and headed along the broad boulevard at the lip of the port until it arrived at the station, a grand Spanish building, all monument and stern purpose and majestic self-importance.

Within its sooty portals, however, the Spanish talent for disorganization reasserted itself aggressively after the relative precision of the parade. Florry found himself stalled under a vast double-vaulted ceiling filled up with steam and noise. Half the lights in the big cavern were off and searchlights prowled about, illuminating rising columns of steam theatrically. It was a near riot. Suddenly, the queue began to move. Florry advanced to the train and then the movement broke down again, abandoning him in the throng right at the portal of the car. He stood, one boot up on the step, his heavy rifle over his shoulder, his kit on his back and a water bottle at his belt, like a 1914 victory poster. He felt absurd. Could not the Spaniards do one thing efficiently?

It seemed to take forever. Good Christ, how can they hope to win a war and finish a revolution if they cannot even fill up a train in an orderly fashion?

"Robert! Oh, Robert. Thank God!"

Her hair was pulled back severely under a black beret and she

still wore the sexless mono and plimsoles, but her eyes had that special, sleepy grace, and when she smiled as she fought her way through the soldiers to him, he felt a burst of pleasure scalding as steam and thought he'd faint. Yet he also felt himself pulled up short and breathless with anger. Sylvia, off to watch her little hero do his bit.

"Hello, Sylvia," he said, unsure what else to say, possessing no opinion as to what would happen next.

"I had to see you. I hated the way you just went off."

He was surprised at the anger he felt.

"God, Sylvia, is this scene really necessary?"

"*¡Vámanos, inglés!*" a sergeant yelled from the car. He was holding up the line. He stepped out to let the others file by.

"I have to go," he said gruffly. "They're getting ready to go out."

"Robert, I had to see you one last time."

"What nonsense! You were the one who pushed *me* away. You were the one who wanted some room. You were the one who had to have experiences. You paid your debt, Sylvia. Florry had his fun, bloody good fun it was, too. You owe me nothing."

"I owe you everything," she said. "I want you to know how much I respect you for this. Like Julian, you'll write history rather than *about* it."

"What rubbish! You've been reading too many posters. Nothing's happened up there in months. The only attacks are launched by the lice. It'll simply be a time without bathing, that's all. Just like Eton, actually."

"Robert—"

"*¡Vámanos, inglés, amigo!*" the sergeant called again. "*Es la hora. El tren sale. ¿No quieres ser ejecutado?*" The train whistle rang through the air, echoing against the stones of the station.

"Stop that damned crying and let me shake your hand," Florry said. "You shall have your adventures and I shall have mine."

She tried to smile but it was wrecked by the intensity of her emotion. Florry took her hand and meant to shake it primly and

ironically and angrily after their sweet night together. But he surprised himself by pulling her to him. Eveybody on the train was cheering and making suggestions of what to do with a lovely young girl and he didn't give a damn. He could see her eyes widen in surprise as he brought her close and he brought her closer, feeling all the war gear on his back encumbering him, but he didn't care about that, either. He crushed her body in his arms, taking pleasure in it, feeling the give and yield of her slight bones, smelling the soft sweetness of her, and he kissed her, hard, on the mouth.

"There," he said, speaking quite brutally. "Now that's a proper send-off for a soldier boy, eh? Now smile. Show Florry some teeth, darling."

She looked at him, shocked.

The train whistled and began to move.

"Good-bye, Sylvia. I'll put in a good word for you to Julian. Perhaps you and he can have tea when this is finished." He jumped up on the doorstep of the train as it pulled out of the station. He hung there until he could see her no longer, and then they pulled him aboard, cheering and happy for the romantic Englishman.

He hated her. He loved her.

Damn the woman!

13

THE MAJOR

I N LONDON, IT WAS WELL AFTER MIDNIGHT. HOLLY-BROWNING had become almost a vampire: he lived by night, as if the sun's touch were lethal. He sat, isolated, chalky complected, his eyes black-ringed, working with furious concentration on the message Vane had so recently brought up from Signals.

The major had a gift for codes, or at least an enthusiasm for them. The message was encrypted in the standard Playfair cipher of the British army, and he had no difficulty pulling its meaning from the nonsense of the letter groups that faced him. He merely compared them against a square formation—five letters by five letters—from the key group and extracted, off the diagonal, the bigram of each two-letter unit. The key group, curiously enough, was always drawn from a verse of standard English poetry; the code was made secure by changing the key—the verse—each week, by prearranged schedule. That week's verse happened to be from one of the major's favorites, Rupert Brooke. "If I should die, think only this of me," it went, "there's some foreign field that's forever England."

Sampson's dispatch yielded its secrets and its purposes swiftly and cleanly as the letter groups tumbled into words, the words into sentences. When the major was done, he sat back. It was a longish document, nicely crafted, tightly constructed, succinctly covering recent developments.

Yet it struck the major with a peculiar, cold authority. He looked to the fire, which had burned low, and felt the shame come across him like a shudder.

A soft noise sounded in the darkness and he looked up to see Vane standing silhouetted against the illumination of the open door.

"Yes, Vane?"

"Sir, I wondered if there's a reply?"

"No, I think not," said the major, and as effortlessly as he had arrived, Vane began to slip away.

"Vane, stop. Do come in."

"Sir, I—"

"No, I insist."

Vane padded vaguely through the darkness and took the leather chair opposite Holly-Browning's desk.

"Drink, Vane?"

"No, sir."

"I've got some very fine brandy. I've some whiskey. I've got a bottle of scotch barley somewhere and I've—"

"Thank you, sir, but—"

"No, that's fine. Suit yourself." He removed the bottle and a glass from his desk, poured himself a finger of brandy, brought it up, and swallowed it quickly. He remembered the stuff from 1916, when extra rations had been issued before the big jump-off at the Somme. It had certainly came in handy *that* day.

"It's very good, Vane. Are you sure you won't have any?"

"No, sir."

"As you wish. Good heavens, these have been long days, haven't they?" He had no idea how to make conversation.

"Yessir. If I may say, sir, you really are working too hard. Wouldn't want to damage one's health."

"Working?" the major said, pouring himself another finger of the brandy. "Actually, I'm not working at all. Sampson's doing the work. Sampson and poor Florry."

"Perhaps you should take a holiday, sir."

"Er, perhaps I should. Perhaps I will, too. Vane, tell me. Have you ever been to Moscow?"

"No, I haven't, sir."

"All right. Come with me. I'll show you something."

The major rose and walked from behind his desk to the window, a journey of just a few paces. There, he threw the heavy curtain. They looked from MI-6's old Broadway offices just a few blocks toward the Thames and the gaudy, crenellated buildings of Parliament. It was utterly peaceful, a serene composition off a Yule card. The moon, a bright half circle, shone in the sky at the center of a blur of radiance and its cold chill touched everything, especially a sheath of new-dusted snow that lay upon the roof of Westminster Abbey.

"Vane, what do you see?"

"Nothing, sir. Silent London. That's all."

"Look over at Whitehall."

"One can hardly see it, sir. All the lights are out."

"They are, indeed. Think of it, Vane, all those empty offices, locked and silent. All those chaps gone home, now in bed or reading or working at their hobbies or off to the theater, what have you. But the truth is, at this precise moment, so certain is the British government of its place in the world and the stability of its empire, it can actually afford to cease to exist for a full twelve hours. Every day, the British government disappears for twelve hours. Extraordinary, isn't it? A daylight government."

Vane said nothing, as if the thought had never occurred to him.

"Vane, in Moscow in the winter of 'nineteen and again in 'twenty-three, the lights were never out. They blazed away each evening until dawn. Those chaps were figuring out ways to beat us. They were, Vane. Stratagems, ploys, plots, subversions. They were like Wells's Martian intelligences, cool and implacable. It used to haunt me, those burning lights. Our people in Moscow with the embassy, they tell me that the lights burn brighter than ever these nights."

"Surely, sir, they are merely attempting to figure out ways to get their electric plants to cease from conking out every two weeks or learning how to get their harvests in on time under that terrible—"

"No, Vane. They are burning with fury, with fire, to destroy us. To have what we have. Or, rather, to take what we have from us. It obsesses them. It obsesses this man Levitsky, the master spy."

"I'm sure you are his match, sir."

The major issued something very like a chuckle. Levitsky's match? How rich!

"If I am very lucky," he said, "and if my people perform up to their very, very best, then yes, perhaps I have a chance against Levitsky."

"You knew him well, sir?"

Another jest. Poor Vane had no idea how inadvertently droll he had become.

"Levitsky and I had quite a few sessions in the cellar of the Lubyanka in 1923," said the major, remembering. "A number of highly interesting conversations."

"I'm sure you taught him a thing or two, sir."

The major looked at the moonstruck landscape. Oh, yes, he'd taught Levitsky a thing or two! He shook his head. A set of memories unspooled in his skull and he remembered the passionate conviction in the Jew's eyes, the emotional contact, the intensity, the glittering intelligence.

"May I ask, sir, what brings Levitsky to mind?"

"He's in Spain," said the major. "He's in Barcelona, or so Sampson reports."

"Yessir."

"Yes, you see how it all fits, how I said it would fit. His agent goes to Spain and communicates with home base via Amsterdam. But there comes a time when communication isn't quite enough; the campaign has become more complex, the plans more intricate, the possibilities more numerous. And thus does Levitsky travel undercover to Barcelona to confer with Julian Raines. God, Vane, if Florry could catch the two together! That'd be it. No one in government could deny Raines's complicity. And we could take Florry the last step. We'd then be done with it altogether!"

"Yessir."

The major was trembling with repressed wanting. He felt himself so terribly, terribly close.

"Let me tell you, Vane, what sort of a man this Levitsky is. So you have some idea as to what it is we're up against. Within days after his arrival to take over the NKVD operations, he claimed his first victim. He ordered the arrest of a Soviet clerk named Igenko. Igenko was picked up, interrogated, and is surely dead by this time."

"Yessir."

"It sounds quite mundane, doesn't it, Vane, the Soviet Russian system in normal operation. A clerk is suspected of vague 'crimes,' and in days he's dead."

"It's revolting, sir."

"Actually, it's quite a bit more than revolting, Vane. You still don't know the half of it. I remember Igenko, too, from 1919. It was so long ago."

"This Igenko and Levitsky: they were connected?"

"Yes. And surely that was Igenko's 'crime.' He knew Levitsky, and thus he was a risk to Levitsky's operation. Levitsky is so important he must be protected at all costs."

"Could they have been comrades, sir?"

"More than that, Vane."

"Lovers, perhaps, sir? Would they be poofs?"

"More again, Vane," said Major Holly-Browning, looking out at the dark halls of government, the sleeping city under its lacy snow, its bone-cold, moonstruck radiance. "They were brothers."

Part II
JULIAN

14

HUESCA

I N THE COLD REAR OF A TRUCK HAULING HIM FROM THE RAIL-
head at Barbastros to the firing line, and amid a crew of largely
drunken militiamen, Florry remembered the last time he had
seen Julian Raines. It had been in June of 1928, nine years
earlier, Honors Day at Eton, a June afternoon. The sixth-formers,
liberated that morning at matriculation from the rigors of the college, had gathered with their parents on the lawn of one of the
yards, near the famous Wall, for a last mingle or whatever before
commencing with the lives to follow. These lives usually meant
university or something promising in the City or at Sandhurst;
however, not for Florry. He knew by then he'd spend the summer
boning up on engineering and math at a place that tutored dim
boys just furiously enough to get them by the India service exam.
He knew, in other words, he'd wasted it all.

A bright and lovely day it had been, too, a touch warm, under a
sky of English blue and a breeze as sweet as a perfect lyric—or was
this his wretched memory playing its wretched trick on him, in the
way a generation insisted that the summer of '14, wet and hot and
muggy, had been a rare masterpiece of temperate beauty? Florry
didn't know. What he remembered was the misery and shame he
felt, in counterpoint to a gathering so full of hope and ambition
and confidence—the earth's natural heirs pausing for just a second
before assuming their rightful place—and had stood off, the failed
scholarship boy, with his mousy mother and his uncomfortable

clerk of a dad while glossier types laughed merrily and quaffed great quantities of champagne on the lawn and told school stories.

"Robert, can't you introduce us to your friends?" his mother had said, but before he could answer, his dad—surprisingly sensitive, in retrospect—had replied, "There, it isn't necessary."

"Well, now he's all fancy Eton, you'd think he knew dukes and the like," his mum said. "He talks like one."

"Sir, maybe the three of us could go off and get a pint," he'd said. "They've a nice pub in the town."

"Robert, can't say as I have a thirst," his dad said. "But if you'd like. Just the three of us, to celebrate our Eton chap."

Florry then led them on an awkward pilgrimage through the crowd with an excuse-me here and a beg-pardon there, his eyes down, his face hot and drawn. He was exceedingly worried that his hated nickname—"Stinky," from a bad spell of bed wetting when first he'd arrived—would come up at him within his parents' earshot.

But something far worse happened.

"Good heavens, Robert, can these be your parents?"

It was the first time that Julian had spoken to him in six months, and Florry looked up in weird, passionate misery. Julian stood before him, having appeared from God knows where, having suddenly, magically materialized—it was a gift for dramatic entrances, uniquely Julian's—blocking the way. Julian's skin was flushed pink and his fair hair hung lankly across his forehead, nonchalant in a way that many younger boys imitated, from under an Eton boater worn atilt on his head. He had on one of those absurd, smug little Eton jackets, too, with its white piping, and it looked dashing and perfect.

It had been most peculiar. Julian, the form's swankiest boy, had taken up Florry abruptly, been his closest and most trusting friend for nearly three years, then six months earlier had just as abruptly dropped him. It still hurt; in fact, it absolutely crushed Florry and he'd watched helplessly as his studies disintegrated and his chances at a university scholarship, once so close, had simply vanished.

Thus Julian's sudden appearance was at once wonderful and terrifying. Was this to be a sort of reconciliation, a readmission to
favor? Florry's knees began to shake and his breath came sharp as a
knife.

"I say, Mr. and Mrs. Florry?" Julian bent forward, past Florry,
and Florry was yet unable to identify the tone and did not know
what course the next moment or so would take. "I'm Robert's
friend, Julian Raines."

He paused, as if to tighten the suspense.

"I wanted to say hello to you. It's an honor to meet you."

Julian bowed, shook dad's slack hand and kissed mum on hers.
Florry could see the poor woman's eyelashes flutter: a gent like
Julian had never paid any attention to her.

"I must say," said Julian, "it's a shame Robert mussed his opportunity here. It's not often that a chap from your class has the
chance. We'd all so hoped Robert would prove out. But alas, he
hasn't. Off to India, Stink?" Julian smiled in the excruciating
silence of the moment. "Well, it's probably better that way. You
won't be dogged by it, old man. Well, best of luck."

And with that little masterpiece of destruction, he was off. He
had not looked at Florry after the first second, yet in less than a
minute he had transformed Florry's failure from a general one to a
specific one, given it special shape and meaning and inserted it
forever into his parents' memories.

But Florry surprised himself by not crying. He simply swallowed
and led his parents onward.

"You're lucky to have such fancy friends," his mum said. "Did
you see how he kissed my hand? There, nobody's ever done such a
thing."

"A bit cheeky, you ask me," said his father. "Robert did graduate, did he not? First of our lot to get even half so far. Well,
Robert, there's still India. You'll get your chance yet. What's that
he called you?"

"It's nothing, Dad," Florry said. "Just a schoolboy name."

"Damned silly," his father said.

Florry managed a dry heroic smile, but—and later he hated himself for this last weakness—looked past him back into the mob one last time: into Eton through the gates and the crowd of boys and their parents—and he'd seen Julian amid the form's handsomest youths, laughing, sipping champagne . . . and then lost sight of him, and that was the end of it.

Thus when the truck halted and the driver came back and shouted, *"Inglés. Sí, inglés. ¡Vámonos!"* and he'd climbed down to find himself hard by a seedy, battered old country house, he discovered in himself a curious mixture of apprehension and loathing. He knew he was at La Granja, near the English section of the line around Huesca. Somewhere hereabouts he would find his friend and enemy, the man he was sent to stop.

Mobs of soldiers loafed about in the sun, most of them scruffier looking than hobos. In the yard, a dozen different languages filled the air. The largest crowd had formed up about a fire, where a cook was ladling out huge helpings of some sort of rice dish. Near the great house, a tent had been set up with a huge red cross painted on its roof, and Florry could make out wounded soldiers lying on cots. The house itself bore the marks of battle: one wing was smashed to rubble and most of the windows had been broken out. The ubiquitous POUM initials had been inscribed across its façade in garish red paint, in a spidery, gargantuan penmanship. Yet for all the noise and the numbers of men, the scene was strangely pastoral: it had no sense of particular urgency or design. It was as so much of the Spanish revolution, that is, primarily improvised and quite ragtag. No sentry questioned him or challenged him and there seemed to be no office for new arrivals. He simply asked the first several men he saw about the English, and after a time, someone pointed him in more or less the right direction.

He was directed beyond the house, through an orchard, and across a meadow, perhaps a mile's walk in all. At last he came to a dour little redhead sitting on an appropriated dining-room chair in the middle of a field, sucking on a pipe, and hacking at what proved to be an ancient Colt machine gun.

"I say," Florry called, "seen a chap about calling himself Julian Raines? Tall fellow, rather fine-boned. Blond."

The man didn't bother to look up.

After a time, Florry said, "Er, I was addressing you, sir."

The man at last raised his face, fixing Florry with shrewd, dirty-gray eyes.

"Wouldn't have a spare potato-digger bolt on you, mate? This one's about to bleedin' snap."

"I assume 'potato digger' is slang for the weapon?"

"You got it, chum. They said they'd send one up."

"No, they didn't say anything about that."

"Public-school man, eh?"

"Yes. My bloody accent, is it? Afraid I can't much help it."

"Your pal's up top the hill, chum. Just go on up."

"Oh. Thanks. Thanks awfully."

"Think nothing of it, chum."

Florry marched up the hill, dragging his rifle with him. At the crest, he saw before him a broad brown plain and beyond that a range of glorious white mountains and halfway between himself and the mountains there lay a doll's city of brown structures crouching behind a wall from which there issued, lazily, a few columns of smoke. Huesca itself, the enemy city.

Florry looked down the hill where a group of men huddled around a cooking fire behind a rude trench, and cupped his hand to his mouth and—

The tackle sent him hurling down, rolling with bone-crunching racket, over rocks and bushes and branches. He came to a rest against a stunted tree, all tangled up in his equipment, hurting and scraped in a half dozen places. There seemed to be a flock of birds fluttering through the trees.

"You bloody idiot," someone nearby was shouting at him.

Florry blinked in shock.

"What on earth—"

"Them's bullets whippin' about, you bloody fool," screamed his assailant, no less than the redheaded runt of the other side of the

hill. "Blimey, mate, don't you know a bloody prank? Don't they have bloody humor at that awful school of yours? Christ, 'e goes and stands against the crestline!"

"Eh?"

"Come on, then."

Florry, in his confusion and embarrassment, became aware of a circle of faces above him.

"Billy, you awful toad, playing games with some innocent swot," came a voice of piercing familiarity. "Good heavens, fellow, don't just lie there like the fallen Christ awaiting resurrection. Get your scrawny bones up and give us some account of yourself."

A lovely apparition in mud and pale whiskers stood above him. He wore a small automatic pistol at his waist and some kind of many-buckled leather Burberry. He looked like a Great War aviator, all dash and style, more than any kind of infantryman, even to the scarf—silk, naturally—and the puttees and the hollow, noble sunburned face. His hair was almost white-blond from the outdoor living, the eyes still their fabled opaque blue.

"Hullo, Julian," said Florry, in spite of himself excited. And a little nervous.

"Good God, it's Stinky Florry of the old school. Stinky, can it really be you?"

" 'E said 'e was a chum of yours, Julian," said the runty redhead. "If I'd known it for a fact, I wouldn't have knocked 'im down before Bob the Nailer invited him to tea."

"Had Bob the Nailer known he was an Eton man, Billy, I'm *sure* he would have shown a degree more politeness," said Julian with what Florry began to see was a kind of mock snootiness that must have been his style up here. "Robert, you've already met the disgusting Billy Mowry, who actually calls himself a commissar. He's the only man I've ever known who's actually read *Das Kapital,* which is less impressive than it seems because it's the *only* book he's read. He's not read *my* book, for example. He's not even *heard* of me, or so he claims."

"Comrade," said this Commissar Billy to Florry, "if you can

work out a way to keep your fancy chum's mouth glued tight, you'll have served the revolution heroically. Anyhows, glad to have you here. We need all the fighters we can find, whatever the class. I reckon you'll bleed just as red as any of us. I'm boss fellow, or so it says somewhere. Don't ask me why; these foolish fellows elected me." There was something like warmth—though not much of it —in his voice.

"Only to shut him up about Karl Bloody Marx, his patron saint. Come on, dear boy, to my quarters. You can meet these other fellows later; they'll be the first to admit they're not important enough to waste our time now."

There was much laughter, and Florry saw that part of Julian's job here in the trenches was to make the boys laugh.

"Now," said Julian, drawing him off, "tell Julian why on earth you've come halfway across Europe to die in mud among louts and lice. I thought one fool in our form was enough. God, Stinky, you can't have turned into a bloody Communist, can you? You don't believe all their nonsense, do you?"

"Christ, Julian, it's good to see you," Florry surprised himself in suddenly blurting. He could feel Julian's charm like a tide sweeping in to engulf him.

You hate him, he told himself. You'll destroy him, he told himself.

"Look at me, Stink. Yes, by God, it _is_ you. And what a present from God you are. Let me tell you, old man, this bloody giving oneself to the revolution is a good bit of trouble. It's a picnic in the mud among Java men. Good fellows, but the blokes haven't even read _Housman,_ for God's sake. And with your usual flair for the dramatic, you've managed to come upon something unique in history: it's the only time a _city_ has besieged an _army._ Why, it's—"

"Julian, before we go any farther, I must tell you something."

"Oh, God, I do hate it when someone says they must _tell_ me something. From the look on your face, you're about to tell me you've managed to get yourself listed ahead of me in Mother's will. I can forgive you anything, Stinky, except that. Now keep low

here. First rule: never stand against a crestline. Bang, Bob the Nailer has potted you. Now, what was it you were going to tell me. Can it wait at least until—"

"Please, no. I must get this out. You must know."

"Lord, you're not still ticked at me for the awful thing I said on Honors Day. Stink, I'd just had a rare turn-down from a bloody trollop—Jack Tantivy's sister, as I recall, awful girl—and I was drunk and looking for somebody to hurt. Lord, Stink, how I've often regretted that. You're not out here for revenge, lo these many years later? Here—"

He pulled out the little pistol, snapped it prime, and handed it to Florry.

"Go on then," he said dramatically, closing his eyes. "Do the deed. I deserve it. I can be such a cad. I hurt people all the time, Stink. Pull the trigger and rid the world of the awful Julian."

"You bloody idiot."

"Ah, Stink, that's the spirit. Give as good as you get."

Florry saw that the pistol was the little Webley automatic, in .25 caliber.

"Here. Take the bloody toy. I've a Webley myself. The big revolver. When it comes to shooting, I could blast the moon out of the sky."

"A four-five-five! Topping! Now *that* I envy you. A bloody big four-five-five! Christ, I'd love to turn it on a Moorish sergeant. Or pot a Jerry or an Eyetye captain. What fun! War's great fun, Stink. Better than school . . . better even than poetry."

Florry exploded. "Julian, I hate your poetry! I hate 'Achilles, Fool.' You've destroyed the talent you had at Eton with debauchery and sloth. You haven't written a good verse in years."

Julian's blue eyes held his for the longest time. Then he smiled.

"Well spoken, Stink. Hate it myself. It's no bloody game when it's your own rump they're shooting at. Yes, as a poet I'm finished, I agree. I'm halfway through an awful poem called 'Pons,' and I've no end at all for it. It'll remain forever undone. Come on, we'll

have a tot and I'll show it to you and we can have a good laugh over its utter dreadfulness. And some day we'll go back to Barbastros to the whorehouse. Now *that's* a pleasure you'll have to experience. These revolutionary tarts, Stink, they're utterly enchanting. They take your shooter in their bloody *mouths!* Extraordinary!"

"Julian." Florry idiotically, wearily, repeated.

"Now, Stink, there is one thing I absolutely have to know." He paused. "How *is* Mother?"

Some days, Bob the Nailer was more active than others; like so many things Spanish, it seemed to depend entirely upon the whim of the sniper himself. If he awoke in an indifferent mood, he might prang away indiscriminately, manufacturing only enough noise to keep his own *sargento* and priest off his back. If he awakened with the fire of zealotry moving in his bones, he might crawl close enough to do some real damage, and make things in the English section's crude trench at least interesting.

Curiously Florry soon came to hope for interesting days. For Bob the Nailer was like a morale officer; he made the time in the trenches bearable, because when you are ducking bullets, you may be risking death but you are also blissfully unaware of rain, cold, mud, and all the other disgusting elements of the life of static warfare.

It was '14–'18, again, the cold, wet living in mud hovels scooped from the earth, with only the occasional scurrying patrol into no-man's-land to liven things up, the occasional calling card from Bob to keep you honest. It was as if the tank hadn't yet been invented, and in a certain way it hadn't. Jerry couldn't get his PzKpfw IIs down here, Billy Mowry allowed, because the Spanish stone bridges were too old; the rumbling of a heavy vehicle upon them would bring them crashing down, dumping Jerry and his tin toy in the drink. And of course bloody Joe Stalin wouldn't allow any T-26s up here where it was largely a POUMista show. But Florry almost wished for a tank or two; like Bob the Nailer, they'd

make things more interesting—and boredom was almost as dangerous as the Fascists.

There was only one cure for boredom. It was Julian, who, whatever his horrors of the past, his history of cruelty, would not allow himself to be hated any more than he would allow anyone about him, particularly Florry, to appear put out.

His flamboyance and natural outrageousness seemed to cloak him in special grace and he was always happy, happier even than Billy Mowry, a true believer.

"I say, Billy, do you know why I joined this POUM thing of yours?" Julian baited on a day so like every other day it would have no place within a week or on a calendar.

Billy Mowry, sucking on a pipe while filling sandbags, delivered up the sour face of a man about to face an execution, paused, and finally sprang Julian for the pounce.

"No, comrade. Pray tell us."

"Ah. You see, it happened like this. I saw the bloody great initials POUM on the banners outside this hotel on the Ramblas where I was rusticating one summer's day, and I said to myself, why, these silly buggers cannot even properly spell the word POEM, and as our century's fifth greatest living poet, I went in to correct them and the next thing I knew, here I was picking lice as big as hobnails off my balls."

Everybody laughed. God, Julian.

Julian's true enemy, however, wasn't fascism or party politics or even war in general: it was time. Julian was the only one of them who could vanquish time. He could turn the months into weeks, the weeks to days, the days to hours. He could rip through the numbers on the clock and the pages of the calendar; he could make them forget where they were and how long they'd been there and how long they *would* be there. That was his special, most lovely gift. And as Florry settled into the troglodyte life it was Julian who freed him from his bondage to the calendar: and when Florry looked at such a document in what seemed to be his third or fourth week on the line he was stunned to discover that not only had January

turned to February but February had turned to March and that March was soon to turn to April. It was, however, still 1937.

"Ain't we low on wood?" Commissar Billy asked, part of the ritual of the sameness of days. "Whose bloody turn is it to scrounge some up?"

"I'll go," said Julian, shucking his blanket.

"Here, I'll come along," said Florry, grasping his first chance to confront Julian alone.

"Stink, you do have a use then, don't you?"

But it wasn't a joke. The night was coming and without wood there'd be no fires and no warmth. But by this time there was damned little wood. The ground behind the trenches had been picked clean for hundreds of yards.

With their comrades' best hopes along as baggage, and a godsend from Bob the Nailer—sprang! the bullet rattled off the rocks a goodly distance away—the two clambered out of the trench and began to wander about the thickets and over the hills that lay behind them.

Florry steeled himself toward the hatred he felt he properly ought to feel and set out to trap Julian into some sort of acknowledgment of his treason.

"I say, Julian, I hope when the revolution's secure here, it'll move to England. Chance to set things right at last."

"You do?" said Julian. "That's a bit lefty, isn't it, old man? I think it's a revolting idea. I mean, Billy Mowry is a natural-born leader but if he tries to take my mother's coal mine from her and give it to some committee, I'm afraid I'd have him hanged from the nearest willow."

"But justice is—"

"Justice is ten thousand a year, free and clear, and lots of pretty, idiotic young ladies with whom to do nasty, lascivious things. That's justice, old man. No, inside this revolutionary, there's a Tory who'll inherit a nice little chunk of England some day."

"Well, why on earth are you here, then?"

"Why, I just wanted to _count,_ thank you very much."

"You always counted, Julian. If anyone counted, Brilliant Julian did."

Julian drew a great charge out of that!

"Hah!" he laughed. "Yes, that's what everybody always *said,* which just goes to prove how bloody little everybody *knew*! Bloody Brilliant Julian, everybody's favorite cleverboots. Lord, Stinky, how I hated that boy. That's why this war is such a godsend. I wasn't the young beauty any more, except of course to Mother. But to the rest of the world, I'd become an adult with little crinkles on my pretty face. How awful. I kept expecting to do something great— great beyond my little book of absurdly famous verses—and the others kept expecting it too. Yet it somehow never *happened.*"

"But, Julian, everybody loves you," Florry found himself saying, half in admiration and half in hate.

"Oh, not *everybody,* Stink. Even Brilliant Julian's picked up his enemies. If you only knew."

"What enemies?" Florry pressed. "Who could hate Julian?"

"I'll never tell," Julian said coyly.

"Unburden yourself, old man. Bob the Nailer could prong you at any mom—"

"I say, Stink, speaking of unburdening, have you had a woman recently?"

"Julian!"

"I thought not. Your type never does. Too bloody noble or decent, or some such. Listen, chum, take it when it's offered, that's my advice. You can sort it all out later. Take it when it's offered. That's all you owe anybody."

"Actually," said Florry, feeling that Julian had somehow maneuvered him into spilling *his* secrets, but unable to stop himself nevertheless, "yes, I did. I met a young woman on the boat. We had an adventure together. We ended up . . . well, in the—"

"In the sack. Stink, boy, that's the way! And what's this lovely creature's name? I may look her up myself, you wouldn't mind, would you?"

"Sylvia. Sylvia Lilliford," Florry confessed uneasily. "I'm actually

rather gone on her. I thought I might even *marry* her if it all works—"

"Marry her! Good heavens, you can't be serious. Why, I absolutely forbid it, not until I've had my way with her. I shall steal her from you, Stink. I'll make her mine, you'll see. Tell me, does she have nice fat titties? Which way do they point? When she scrunches them together for you do they seem somehow *bigger*? I've noticed that—"

"Stop it, damn you." Florry was surprised to discover the passion in himself. "You're being quite unpleasant."

"Oh, look what I've gone and done. I've made the poor lovesick bastard angry with me. Florry, mate, your Julian's only jesting, surely you can see that, can't you?"

"You shouldn't speak of her that way."

"Ah, Stink, you've more Eton in you than even a prig like me, who was born to it. God, I envy you your illusions. Listen, here's a smashing idea. Suppose we all go on furlough together. That is, the three of us. To some little seaside place. We can have a nice holiday. I'll pay for it. I swear to you I'll not touch the lady. I may even bring one along for myself, a dusky dark Spanish girl with a mustache and titties the size of cabooses. And she and I will drill ourselves dizzy while you and your Sylvia have tea and discuss Auden. It will be delightfully civil—Hello, what's this?" He had stopped suddenly and pointed off, and Florry followed his finger into a mass of brambles where there seemed to be a kind of bundle or something.

It was a statue of a saint—and it was wood.

"A saint. The Lord has sent us a saint to rescue us our trespasses," Julian preached.

"It looks old," said Florry. "It could be worth a fortune."

"Up here, it is worth more than a fortune," said Julian, in theatrical reverence. "It's worth a night in front of a warm fire, which is as rich as a trench rat ever gets. A saint has brought us the gift of fire. We thank thee, O Lord, in your munificence."

And Florry felt his chance to pin down Julian slither away.

✦ ✦ ✦

There was to be an execution. It seemed that a patrol had captured three Fascist soldiers and their officer digging potatoes in no-man's-land. The soldiers, peasant louts without politics, were rapidly converted to the Republican cause. The officer, after interrogation, was to be shot.

"Oh, won't it be fun. We'll actually see one of them die. Oh splendid," sang Julian. And as it happened, the shooting was to occur on a day after Julian and Florry had undergone sentry-go and so they were free to watch the fun. Uneasily, Florry acceded to Julian's demand. The next morning, after a few hours of sleep, they followed a path through untended orchards, unplucked rows of corn, fields of hypertrophied mangoes and sugar beets, now pulpy beyond use. The war had come just before harvest and the fruit and vegetables lay everywhere, rotting and corpulent. It was something Florry hadn't noticed before, and now, a little bleary from fatigue, he saw the unharvested bounty as a sort of curse on their enterprise. He was surprised to discover how nervous he was.

When they at last reached the great house, it was almost too late. Crowds of soldiers milled excitedly in the courtyard, but nobody quite seemed to know what to expect. At last, they located a higher officer stretched out upon a chaise longue in the orchard, his muddy riding boots splayed listlessly before him as he wrote in a notebook with furious intensity. In fact, his wrist and the tight grip on an old pen seemed the only thing intense about him: his knuckles were white as the pen flew across the creamy pages of the book.

They stood, waiting to be noticed, but for the longest time no such recognition came, and at one point Julian took a breath as if to speak, but the man halted him with a finger raised suddenly like a baton, without bothering to look up.

At last he lifted his eyes and confronted them. His face was one of those ancient, wise creations that only wars or revolutions seem to manufacture: it was a mass of fissures and erosion, all pain,

fatigue, and thought. All the lines in it pulled it downward, as though gravity had a special influence.

"Yes, comrade?"

"Would you be Steinbach?" asked Julian.

"I would."

"I'm Raines."

"English, are you?" The man spoke with a sort of vague European accent. He was balding and thick and looked almost like the abandoned tubers they'd seen rotting in the fields. His belly bulged tautly through his open, sloppy tunic. Under the tunic and against the pressure of the stomach there stretched a thick, dirty wool turtleneck sweater which, at his neck, seemed to catch and contain his jowls like a cup placed under a spigot.

"Yes. Yes, I am, comrade—"

"And your friend?"

"English too, comrade."

"Now, what is it, Comrade Raines?"

"We've come to see the show," said Julian arrogantly, perhaps at his worst. "Nobody out there knows where it's to be held. Could the comrade perhaps inform us? It's good to watch one's enemies perish."

"You're very bloodthirsty. The poet, eh? 'Achilles, Fool,' isn't that it?"

Julian was pleased.

"I am he. The world's fifth greatest living poet."

"I would have put you seventh, I'm afraid, comrade. In any event, the 'show' will be held out front in just a few minutes. You shan't miss it. I hope you enjoy it."

Florry's eyes had beheld Steinbach's and made an extraordinary discovery. One of them was glass: a dead brown orb floating in a sea of flesh. It's what gave him the queer, vexing look, as if he were somehow not quite respectable. And the other eye seemed doubly bright, as if to compensate for what was not there.

"You," Steinbach suddenly said to Florry, having caught

the pressure of Florry's studious glance upon him, "are you a poet, too?"

"No, comrade. A fighter."

"A believer in the revolution?"

"Yes."

"A public-school revolutionary!" Steinbach laughed. "Now I've seen everything."

Steinbach went back to his notebooks and Florry simply stood there for some time before it occurred to him they had been dismissed. At last he turned. But as he turned, he was astonished to notice what the fellow had been laboring so passionately over in his notebooks.

"Did you see that?" asked Julian. "He was drawing pictures of bridges. Damned curious. Perhaps he was an architect or some such."

"Coolish fellow. Not exactly inspirational."

"Something of a legend, however. The intelligence nabob. You'll see. *Seventh!* Now sixth I would have accep—"

At that point a flatbed truck pulled into the yard, and the soldiers were drawn to it as if it were to distribute candy or mail.

But instead, after just a bit, a delegation emerged from the stable. At the center, Florry could see a puffy-faced young lieutenant in Fascist gray. His hands were tied behind him. He was lead roughly along.

"Julian, I think I'm going to head back. I'm not sure I can watch—"

"Oh, you must, chum. Really, it'll be a smashing experience. It'll give you something fabulous to write about. I may even incorporate it into my new poem."

"I've already done an execution piece. I've already seen an execution."

"Why, you are an expert, then."

Yet Florry thought he'd be physically ill. The fat officer was tugged to the truck, and a dozen or so rough pairs of hands pushed him up where he stood, his knees quaking. He was weeping.

"Fascist pig!"

"You bloody bastard!"

"Blow 'is fookin' brains out!"

The cries rose.

"I wonder who the lucky chap is gets to pull the trigger," Julian said.

"Really, this is—"

At that point, somebody climbed aboard the truck. It was the stout, one-eyed Steinbach who'd been drawing bridges in the orchard.

"Death to Fascists," he shouted.

"*¡Viva Cristo Rey!*" shouted the tied man, as Steinbach pushed him to his knees. Steinbach had the revolver out and with a cinematic flourish showed it to the crowd, drawing their cheers. He cocked it and Florry, stupefied and mesmerized, watched the physics of the thing: how the fluted cylinder ticked in the light as the hammer's retraction drew it around so that a charge was placed beneath its fall.

Steinbach pushed the pistol against the quaking officer's spine and fired. The sound of the shot was muffled in the intimacy between muzzle and flesh. The man pitched forward on the truck bed, face a sudden blank. Steinbach stood over him and fired three more times into the man's body. Florry could see black splotches where the spurt of flash scorched the uniform. The cheers were enormous.

Steinbach leaped off the truck with surprising agility. "Take the dog away," he shouted. Meanwhile, the smoking body lay flat and inert on the truck, its total death like an ugly charm that kept the crowd away. Florry watched as Steinbach strode through the men and went back to his chaise longue. He sat down again and began to draw.

"What a piece of work is Steinbach," said Julian.

The sound of a shell awakened Florry, and he bolted conscious in a shower of dust. He was back in his bunker. He blinked in the

flickering candlelight, barely remembering his final collapse into an oceanically vast and dreamless sleep.

"Easy chum," said Julian, close by.

"What time is it?"

"Near dawn."

"Good God, I've missed sentry-go."

"No matter. Schedule's off."

Julian, in the candlelit bunker, semed queerly agitated.

Florry hauled himself up from the warmth of his sleeping blanket and sat back against the earth wall, amid a welter of hanging water bottles, bayonets, bombs, and knives, and asked for a cigarette.

Julian gave him one, lighting it. Florry could see his hands tremble and feel his eyes upon him, hot and bright, almost sad.

Florry inhaled, the glow suffusing the narrow space with weird, ominous illumination for an instant. His head ached, and he was ravenously hungry.

"Stinky," Julian said, "tonight we attack. After five bloody months of waiting, it's the big one. The Anarchists on the other side of the city go at nine, then the German battalion at ten, and we jump off at ten-thirty. It's a terrible plan, one of those fancy, clever things that Royal Marines couldn't pull off with a month of rehearsal, a three-pronged, clockwork masterpiece that'll be a ball's up from the start. This time tomorrow we're dead. But I must say, I feel rather good about it. No more of this awful mudbath living. It's over the top for us, Stink."

Florry felt a curious sense of relief slide through him. Yes, he welcomed it, too, to be done for a time with the damned trench and also with his other confusions.

All right, Florry thought. If you're truly a spy, you won't risk your bloody neck in a battle for a silly Spanish city that nobody ever heard of.

"Well, it's bloody wonderful, if you ask me," said Florry. "I'd like a fair chance at the bastards in a fair fight."

Julian laughed.

"Damn you, Stinky, your Eton fairness will get us both kip-

pered. If you've a chance, shoot 'em in the guts with your rifle and stick 'em in the throat with your spike and maybe you'll come out of it."

"I wonder why *now*," said Florry. "One supposes it was in the cards ever since we got up here, but why *now*, so suddenly?"

"Who knows how their brains work?" wondered Julian. "Generals are all the same, you know. Ours or theirs, it makes no difference. But listen here. I've hired a boy who's about to leave for the rear. I've some messages to send, perhaps you'd like to say something to lovely Sylvia before the balloon goes up, eh? Say it quick. He's leaving shortly."

He slid out, leaving Florry alone. Florry pawed through his kit, found paper and pen, and, squinting in the candlelight, quickly scrawled his message.

APRIL 26, 1937

SYLVIA,

I've no right at all to the feelings I hold for you, but I hold them anyway. We are about to go out to battle and I wanted to tell you. In another life, perhaps.

ROBERT FLORRY

Drivel, he thought, and almost threw it away, but then he thought how much easier it would be to die without regrets, having at least made his idiotic declaration.

Then he felt the need for another note, another bit of unfinished business.

APRIL 26, 1937

SAMPSON,

A chance to push the inquiry forward tomorrow night. We're throwing a party and our chap the poet is invited. I'll know by his behavior, one way or the other. Good hunting!

FLORRY

He folded it and scratched Sampson's address on the Ramblas.

He crawled out and found Julian chatting with a boy in the lee of the trench.

"Can he take another one?" he whispered. "A professional thing to a *Times* chap I'd signed up to do a piece with."

"I suppose. Why not?" said Julian. He spoke quickly to the boy in Spanish and Florry was mildly surprised to learn that he spoke it so well.

The boy folded the messages into a pouch on his belt and at last darted off.

"Where on earth did you find him?"

"Oh, I'm smashing at scrounging up things, Stink, old sport."

"Will he get through?"

"Oh, Carlos will get through. He's very good at that sort of thing. Used him before, he's always made it. Well, Stinky, ready for the big parade?"

"To march at the head of it, in fact," Florry said, happy at last.

15

THE GRAND ORIENTE

THE CAFÉ GRAND ORIENTE WAS PACKED THAT NIGHT WITH the children and the ideals of the Revolution. But there was also murder in the air.

Someone will die tonight, Levitsky thought. He felt the violence in the atmosphere, rich and potent. There would be blood on the pavement and screaming women and furious men with drawn revolvers. But for him at least, the long wait underground was over. It was time after the months of boredom to move.

He took a sip of the green schnapps. It was wonderful. The girl sat with a group of young POUMistas at a table near the bar. They were all gay and lively, full of everything, themselves mostly, but hope and politics, too; or maybe it was only fashion for them, a game. They wore their blue overalls and had militia caps tucked into the epaulets. Yet still the girls were slender and quite lovely, especially the Lilliford girl, the loveliest of them all. But she held the key to the next step on the way to Julian Raines.

Levitsky was well behind them, sitting with his back to the wall. Getting to the Oriente had been easy, once he left his shelter in the Anarchist neighborhood. SIM agents were everywhere with their NKVD advisers, and he'd been stopped twice by Asaltos, as the Revolutionary Assault Troops brought in from Valencia were called, but in each case his papers had gotten him through. Still, it was frightening. How tight was Glasanov's net? Well, it was a net, that was clear, but was it not drawn and gathered? Perhaps it had

been at the start; but Levitsky knew the longer he waited, the looser it would become.

Now, a clever man, a man with his wits and a little presence and a nice selection of identities, could get through. It must be driving poor Glasanov insane. With a battalion of NKVD troops, he could have closed the city down and gone through it like an archivist, examining each alley, each hallway. In days, he'd have him back. However, with only a skeleton of NKVD people, but mostly earnest, unpracticed Spaniards, Glasanov was doomed.

Glasanov, I will be the death of you, Levitsky thought with a wicked little smile.

"Comrade? Another schnapps?" asked the waiter.

"No, I think not."

"We close soon, comrade. The curfew. Not like the old times."

"I see. Thank you."

"You look as though you've had a rough time of it, comrade."

"Some Anarchists. Working men who a year ago never spoke above a whisper. They were feeling mighty about their new world a few days ago and demonstrated their enthusiasm to an old man who wouldn't sing their song or dance to their tune in an alley. They said I looked too bourgeois for my own good."

"Ay. Crazy ones, they're all over the place. These are terrible times, comrade."

"But interesting," said Levitsky.

He took a last look about the room. The smoke in here made his eyes smart. Behind the bar, the mirror stood streaked with grease. The light was amber, almost yellow, shining off the walls and from the flickering candles and the weak bulbs in the glass cups mounted near the ceiling. The place was crowded—all the better—with men and women in uniform, with braids and berets and caps, with automatic pistols and boots, the fighters nut-brown from their days in the sun out at the firing line, the theorists pale from long days of argument and negotiation. They were all getting drunk and the air seethed with boasts and charges and challenges and lyrics and verses. He knew it: of course, easily. It was Petrograd in '17, while

the great Lenin was waging his war of bluff and maneuver against Kerensky and the provisional government.

He looked back to the girl's table. He didn't think any of them at the table were NKVD. He could not, of course, be certain, but after so many years, he believed he knew NKVD on sight: something furtive and sly in the eyes, a certain inability to relax, a certain sense of one's own authority.

No. The waiter, maybe. Surely he informed for someone, but purely out of opportunism, not ideology. Who else? Perhaps that man over there in the black Anarchist's beret who was, Levitsky had noticed, less drunk than he pretended, and whose eyes never ceased to roam.

But Levitsky had to move. Fifteen minutes to curfew. Yes, it was time for the devil to move to the girl.

He got up, edged through the crowd, standing patiently when a couple rose between himself and her and he waited for them to pass by. When they were gone, he proceeded meekly. He slipped next to her and bent to her; she had not yet noticed.

She was a lovely girl, but he could see the gaiety was forced, she was not happy at all, as were the other young POUMistas. They were all excited about an upcoming battle.

"The battle is an imperative process of history," a young man was saying. "Your friend must take his chances like any comrade."

"If we take Huesca tonight, we take Barcelona tomorrow," said an older man, some sort of POUMist leader.

"And the revolution lives," said the boy.

"I just hate the waste," he heard her say.

"Ah. Fraulein Lilliford?" Levitsky said pitifully.

She turned quickly, looking up.

"Good lord, Sylvia, who on earth can *this* be?" someone at the table inquired.

"Herr Gruenwald, no?" he said. "From the ship, the *vasser,* the boat, *ja?*" He began to jabber in excited German.

"Herr Gruenwald, my God. Oh, you look so different. I *do* apologize for staring. It's—"

"*Ja,* Missy Fraulein."

"Look, do sit down—"

"Sylvia—!"

"This man was in the sinking with us. He's been through a lot," Sylvia said tartly. "Sit *down,* Herr Gruenwald. You look terrible. I'd heard that you'd been arrested by—"

"*Ja. Polizoi!* Old business, a mistake, hah! Really hit an old man. My head—it vasn't zo good before, but now is *kaput.* Krazy in der head! Hah!" He laughed abrasively and looked about the table to enjoy the shocked befuddlement of Sylvia's new friends.

"Well, it sounds *dreadful,*" said Sylvia.

"Good heavens, Sylvia, your collection certainly grows by the day. A mad, decrepit German cabin boy!"

"Shut up, Stephen," said the older man at the table. "The old fellow has had a rough enough time. One can tell from looking at him."

"Mr. Gruenwald, you look famished. May I buy you something to eat? What are you going to do?"

"Ach! *Ich*—er, Gruenwald wait for papers, zen ship out. *Nein,* missy, I *haben zie*—haf place to stay. Und food. Ah, my head, it aches so bad zumtimes. Bombs. The Great War. To end all wars, *ja?* Metal plate, *ja?*" He tapped his skull, smiled broadly.

"Missy Fraulein, it's, ach, zomething zo stupid. It's *mein frau.* My wife, *ja?* She is still in Deutschland and, ah, I have no vord from her. And of course, *here,* hah! politics gets in da vay. Dere is no Deutschland embassy—"

"No, of course not. They are for the other side."

"I vish to zumhow send vord dat—dat I am all right. *Ja.* I remember from boat. Mr. Florry a journalist; he vas goink to zee Mr. Raines, another journalist. *Ja?* Perhaps such an intelligent fellow, Herr Raines, the journalist, he know a vay to reach my poor *frau* in Deutschland, *ja.*"

"But Herr Gruenwald, I'm afraid that's impossible."

Levitsky, looking past her in the mirror, saw four men in overcoats enter. The largest of them was Glasanov's Amerikanski.

"Julian Raines and Robert Florry have joined the militia. They are at the front, at Huesca."

"Ach, a fighter," Levitsky said, thinking, _the fool!_ The utter idiot!

Bolodin stood with his men at the front of the room, looking through it.

Levitsky could not look at Bolodin in the mirror. Bolodin would have that extremely fine-tuned sense of being observed; he would feel the eyes upon him and swiftly locate their owner.

"Look here, let me make some inquiries for you," Sylvia said. "There are many Germans in our party. Perhaps I can locate somebody who knows a method of communication."

Bolodin was moving through the crowd. Levitsky kept his face down, his body hunched as if in rapt attention to what she was saying. He tried to concentrate on exits. He could dash for the back; no, they'd have him, strong young Bolodin would have him and smash him down. Bolodin approached; there were suddenly secret policemen all around.

"Comrades," somebody was saying, "you'll excuse if we ask to see your papers."

"And who are you," one of the POUMistas said defiantly. "Perhaps it's _we_ who should ask to see your papers."

"I am Ugarte, of the Servicio de Investigación Militar. We are responsible for the security of the revolution. You excuse this boring formality, of course. One has to take so many precautions these days. There are so many spies about."

"The revolution is in far more danger from Russian secret policemen than from anybody in the POUM," said Sylvia. "You show us _your_ papers."

"There are no Russians here. I don't understand why our brothers and sisters in the Marxist Unification Party are so difficult," said the policeman. "One would think they hadn't the revolution's best interests in mind."

It suddenly occurred to Levitsky: they mean to kill these children. It's part of Glasanov's—

"I don't think we need to resort to extreme methods," said the smooth young secret policeman. "If, perhaps, we could all go outside and get this settled quickly and quietly with a discussion, then—"

Bolodin stood at an oblique angle to Levitsky, his face impassive, his eyes hooded, almost blank. He had not looked at Levitsky at all. He was looking instead at the older man called Carlos.

"I am Comrade Carlos Brea, of the executive committee of the Party of Marxist Unification, and I will not—"

"Comrade Brea, your reputation proceeds you. Surely you can understand the point of a few mild security precautions. We mean nobody any harm; we mean only to establish identities and then walk away."

Bolodin quietly separated himself. Levitsky watched as he pushed his way through the crowd and exited into the street.

"Well," said Brea, "I'll go with you to our headquarters. Let the others stay. They have worked hard enough for their pleasure."

"That's the spirit of cooperation. Indeed, the comrade is to be congratulated. Who says the different workers can't function together?"

"Carlos, don't go," said Sylvia.

"I'll be back in a few minutes. I'm sure the SIM can guarantee my safety in front of witnesses."

"Of course, Comrade Brea."

"Carlos, some of us will go along."

"Nonsense. Stay here. I'll be off; the rules, after all, must apply to everyone."

He rose and, with a smile for the youths at the table, threaded his way out with the policemen.

"I don't like it at all," said one of the men. "They are getting more and more brazen. It's a very disturbing trend."

"We ought to arrest a few of *them* and—"

Sylvia turned to Levitsky. "Perhaps you could meet me someplace tomorrow night, Herr Gruenwald. In the meantime, I'll make some inquiries and—"

Then they heard the shots from the street and a second later a woman came in shrieking, "Oh, God, somebody shot Carlos Brea in the head, oh Christ, he's bleeding on the pavement!"

In the panic, and the grief, and the outrage, Levitsky managed to slip away. He knew he had to get to the front now to get to Julian. And he also knew who had shot Carlos Brea.

16

THE ATTACK

THEY COULD HEAR THE DIVERSIONARY ATTACK OF THE AN-archists on the other side of the city: the heavy clap of bombs, followed by the less authoritative tapping of the machine guns. The plan called for the Anarchists to go in first, from the west. The Fascists would rush reserves over to meet that assault; then the POUMistas and the Germans of the Communist Thaelmann Brigade would jointly rush the city from the east.

Florry shivered in the rain: it had turned the trench floor into mud and made its walls as evilly slick as gruel. It would be a terrible ordeal to scramble up and out. He peeked over the parapet. In the mist and dark, the Fascist lines were invisible.

"Do you think they know we're coming?" somebody asked.

"Of *course* they know we're coming," said Julian cruelly. "D'you think they can keep a secret on the Ramblas? That's the *fun* of the evening."

"Julian, do be quiet," said Billy Mowry strictly. "It's only a few minutes now."

"Yes, commissar, of course, commissar," said Julian. "Do you know," he said to Florry, not dropping his tone a bit, "in the Great War they kicked footballs toward the Hun. Perhaps we ought to kick copies of the bloody great *Das Kapital*."

"Julian, damn you, I said stuff it," yelled Billy Mowry.

"Touchy chap," Julian said. "I was feeling quite gallant, too. Best to go into battle with a quip on one's lips, eh, Stinky?"

"I'm too wet for quips," said Florry.

"Yes, well I'm too frightened *not* to quip. Hush me if I bother you. But I cannot seem to stop chatting. Dear old Julian, never at a loss for words."

It *was* odd; the wait affected each differently. Florry felt sleepy with dread; he could not force himself to think about what lay ahead. Julian, on the other hand, could not think of anything else.

"Gad, I wonder which will be worse. The machine guns or the wire. In France, the men hated the wire. It would snare them and they'd be hung up like department-store mannequins. The more one struggled, the more one was sucked in. My poor father at the Somme ran into a bit of the stuff. Ghastly, eh?"

"I know about your father. Can't you recite some poetry or something?" Florry said.

"Ah, poetry. Yes, poetry before battle. How *English*. And I'm supposed to be rather good at poetry, aren't I? How about, 'In the end, it's all the same/In the end, it's all a game.' Hmmm, no, all wrong. Somehow it doesn't *feel* much like a game about now. What about, 'We are the hollow men/We are the . . .' No, that's not appropriate either. Er, 'If I should die, think only this of me, there's some corner of a foreign field that's forever POUM.' Good heavens, how appalling! Trouble is, they don't write any good war stuff any more. It's out of fashion. They only write antiwar stuff, no help at all to a bloke about to go over the top, eh? I feel like something cheerful and powerfully seductive, something that would make me hungry to die for somebody else's party and someone else's country."

"I don't believe that poem has been written."

"Hasn't, has it? Well, you haven't read the great 'Pons' yet. If I ever can put a tail on the beast, it'll move me from seventh greatest living poet on up to third. And if bloody Auden should drop dead of a dose of clap from some Chineeboy, why then I'm *second*. Gad how exciting!"

"Recite a line, then."

"Hmm. All right.

Among the Druids, in the Druid hall,
the fire flickers, shadows fall.
The past, an icy castle, slowly settles,
while they boil the future in their kettles.
And death was inches, dark was all."

Florry waited. "Go on."

"Out of words, old man. That's where it stops."

"God, it's brilliant, Julian."

"What's it mean, Jules?" said the man on the other side of Julian.

"Now, Sammy, don't you worry. It's just words."

"Ready boys," came Billy Mowry's call through the rain. "It's almost time."

"How's that for inspiration! At least in an aristocratic army, the officers can quote a line of verse at the key moment. 'These in the hour when heaven was falling'—"

"That's about mercenaries, old boy," Florry said through chattering teeth, "who took their wages and are dead. We are not mercenaries. At any rate, if we are, the pay is bloody low."

"*Au contraire,* chum, it's bloody high. A clean soul. Freedom from one's little secrets, eh? From the little men inside one who are always clamoring to get out, eh?"

"All right, lads," Billy sounded calm in the rain, 'it's time."

"Good heavens, it is, isn't it?" Julian said. He reached inside his tunic and pulled out what appeared to be a ring on a chain, brought it swiftly to his lips and kissed it. "There, now I'm all safe," he said. "My old dad was wearing it at the Somme day he cashed in. Wedding ring. It's my lucky piece. Never done me wrong. Care for a smooch, Stink?"

"Thanks, no. I don't think my lips are working."

"Tally-ho, then. Good hunting, and all that rot."

"Luck to you, old man," said Florry, unsure how he meant it. "I'll tell you *my* secrets one day, too." And he became lost in the struggle to get himself up the wall—he'd lost some strength—but

with a sliding, grunting kind of athletic twist, he suddenly achieved it, staggered onto wet but solid ground, and found himself standing up, pretty as you please, in front of the trench in which he'd cowered for weeks. It was both a curiously liberating and curiously vulnerable sensation. All up and down the line, in the ghostly mist, men were rising, shaking themselves off like wet terriers, unslinging their rifles, and facing their death. They were like the children of the Hydra's teeth, Florry thought, his fancy education delivering him a fancy metaphor at just the right time: half-mythical creatures slouching out of some dimly remembered far ago time and place. A hideous joy cut through Florry as he slid the great bayonet-heavy Mosin-Nagent from his shoulder and brought it to the high port. Bombs—grenades—hung on his belt and he wore his Webley at his hip.

"Pip, pip," said Julian, next to him, with a wicked smile that Florry could see through the murk. "I do believe the glorious adventure is about to commence."

Indeed it was. The line, like some kind of creature itself, began to move out across no-man's-land.

Florry no longer felt the cold or the wet and once or twice stepped into a huge cold trough, the water slopping over his boot tops, but it meant nothing. They moved steadily through the mist, toward the Fascist lines. He could feel the incline beginning to rise under him and the heavy, sloshy weight of the clinging mud grow at his feet.

The plan was simple yet dangerous: to approach silently—the rain helped them here—to the wire at the outer limits of the Fascist lines, cut it, get inside it, and hurl a wave of bombs, then leap into the trench before the Fascists had a chance to recover from the blasts. It all, therefore, depended most fragilely on surprise, but the soldiers moved like knights to Florry's ears, clanking and lumbering in the dark. Yet from beyond there was no response.

They seemed to have been walking for hours. Had they lost direction like souped-in aviators and now headed the wrong way?

These thoughts nagged at Florry as he fought through a mass of brush and up a little gulch; for a moment, he was entirely alone. He felt as if he were the last man on earth.

"Jolly fun, eh?" Julian, close at hand, muttered in a stage whisper.

At last they got through the vines and Florry realized with a start that they had covered the ground and had made the wire, which curled cruelly before them in the steady rain. It all had an underwater slowness to it, the steady pelt of the rain, the soaked, heavy clothes, the mud-heavy boots, and now men crouched with the deliberation of scientists to ready themselves for the final few feet. In the slanting sheets of water that descended out of the sky upon them, Florry made out the figure of one fellow scurrying ahead with a kind of lizard's urgency. Billy Mowry, a hero as well as a leader, took it upon himself to scamper up the slope to perform the most dangerous task, the cutting of the wire. He lay on his back under the evil stuff and Florry could see the snippers come out and begin to twist and tug at the strands. Florry knelt, the fingers of one hand nervously playing with his rifle. With his other, he pulled a bomb off his belt. It had two pins. Cradling his rifle against his shoulder, he pulled the easy one out and let it drop. Now he had only to yank the hard one and throw it in four seconds.

With each snap of Billy Mowry's clippers another strand of the wire popped free. Florry could feel his own breath rasping in his chest. His knees felt like warm jelly. How could he be so hot and so cold, so dry and so wet, at once? He could feel each raindrop individually strike against his skin; a million, a trillion of them. And from the Fascists, there was still nothing, though they were less than thirty-five or forty paces away, gathered about their cooking fires.

Hurry, damn you, Billy Mowry, Florry thought.

Sylvia came into his mind suddenly. We had a night, didn't we, darling. Whatever there wasn't, there was that. He could feel the tension in his thighs like steel springs cranking tighter and tighter.

The bomb was growing in weight, deadening his arm. The rifle leaning against him seemed a long ton of coal.

Hurry, damn you, Bill Mowry, _hurry_!

The last snip sounded and Billy Mowry pulled himself up, peeling back the wire. He wore heavy engineer's gloves. His face, even in the dim light, shone with mad excitement and zealotry. He looked insane, like Jack the Ripper.

Julian dashed through the gap first. All right, that's one for him. Would a spy risk the first bullet, the first thrust of bayonet? Florry rose and scrambled after, feeling a singing in his ears. He could feel men clumping through behind him, slipping and straining in the mud. A wonderful strangeness passed over them all: it felt like some huge opera, all stylized and abstract and mighty with song and mass and chorus. It seemed incredible; they were doing it! The excitement poured through Florry's veins and a great hope blossomed like an exotic flower in his imagination and—

The first shot seemed to come from very close by. It was a spurt of flame just at the horizon, accompanied by a loud percussion. Perhaps there was a yell, too, with the noise of the rifle. And then an instant of horrified silence as if each side were unwilling to believe what was about to happen. A second later, a hundred shots spattered out, an attack of fireflies, brief novas of light and sound in the whizzing rain.

Florry was astounded by the cold beauty of the gunfire. He seemed suddenly to be among clouds of insects and could not quite understand what was happening. The bullets struck all about him, kicking up puffs of spray.

Billy Mowry, just ahead, rose and hurled a bomb. It detonated behind the parapet with a flash and perhaps there was another scream lost in the ring of the burst. But the fire on the militia did not lapse in the least.

"Bombs, boys," Mowry screamed, fussing with another. "Throw your fookin' bombs!"

Florry remembered the treasure he clutched, and yanked on the

second pin, certain that at any second a bullet would come along to bash his brains out. The pin would not budge, though he twisted it insanely. He looked down at it: he had been turning it the wrong way! Reversing direction, he got the thing out with a tug and a grunt, and the effort transfigured itself into a toss as he heaved it forward where it immediately disappeared in the dark. He dove back to the earth and it suddenly seemed as if the foundations of the planet had become unbolted. Explosions burst behind the parapet, a chorus of them, three or four or five or six, then far too many to count.

"Again, boys, again!" shouted Mowry.

Florry got the pins out of another bomb and hurled it off, too, feeling all the while the buzz of bullets. He threw himself back and tasted the sandy grit and pebbles of the earth pressing against his lips when suddenly, quite close up, the powerful clap of another bomb shook him. The Fascists were throwing the bloody things, too. The blast was orange and hot and stung him with a harsh spray of pebbles. The echo died reluctantly and he could hear moaning and pleading in the ringing in his ears. Miraculously, he realized he was unhurt. He picked his rifle up, shouldered it, and fired. It bucked against his bones and he threw the bolt quickly, ejecting a spent shell, and fired again.

He was aware that Billy Mowry had risen to fire steadily on the Fascist position with his Luger. Mowry suddenly slipped back, clutching his knee.

Florry felt sick. Without Billy, they were lost.

"Damn!" howled Mowry, coming to rest in his tumble near Florry. "Pranged again. The fookers." He looked at Florry. "Get going, damn you. You're dead for certain if you stay here."

Florry picked up his rifle and began to scramble with the mob toward the ridge. Around him, men were clawing their lugubrious way up the slope through what seemed a sudden, blessed respite in the firing.

Florry reached the sandbag parapet and jumped over, landing heavily in the Fascist trench, ready to get up close and jam his

monstrous bayonet into somebody's guts, preferably an Italian or a Moorish colonel or a Falangist executioner. He was full of murderous exultation and rage; at the same time, he felt terrified. But the trench was deserted; there was nobody to stick. He looked up and down it and could see only his comrades tumbling in like parachutists, as eager for combat as he and as equally disappointed.

Off to the left, there seemed to be a gap in the trench wall of some sort. He moved quickly and discovered it was a communications trench, that is, a sort of gutterlike path scooped out of the dirt to facilitate low-profile movement between the different trenches. He began to work his way through the litter and the mud, heading deeper toward the Fascist position, when a shot flashed in the dark and the bullet whipped with a thud into the trench wall near him. He answered with a shot at the noise and got a bomb off his harness. He pulled the two pins and hurled it down the way, falling back. The explosion was as bright as a flare, fragmenting his night vision and filling his ears with a roar. He sat up, dazed, wondering what on earth to do, when someone grabbed him.

"Eh?"

"No, no. Stay here. They'll be back soon enough." It was Julian. One arm hung limply at his side.

"You're hurt!"

"It's nothing. A piece of shrapnel or something gave me a shaving cut on the arm. Brilliant Julian will never play the viola again. Congratulations on surviving."

"Terrifying, wasn't it?"

"Gloriously full of fear. I'm afraid to check my pants. They may be wet and one doesn't want to humiliate oneself in front of the servants."

"I'm sure they're dry as the Sahara."

"We seem to have won, by the way. That fellow Jones is dead. He caught one in the head and went down as if he'd been . . . well, as if he'd been shot in the head. Several others are variously messed up, including our beloved Billy Mowry, whose leg has been

perforated. But he *always* gets banged up; otherwise, he's indestructible. When he was a babe, his mother dipped him by the knee into a pot of socialist marmalade, thus rendering him invulnerable to capitalist bullets."

"Will they come back, do you think?" Florry asked.

"Oh, shortly. They'll have to get the priests to whip up their frenzy, but they'll come. God, if they had mortars, they could wipe us out in a second. If they had tanks, they'd squash us like insects. Lucky for us these chaps don't know any more about fighting a war than our chaps do. I say, did you get yourself a Fascist?"

"I-I don't know. Maybe."

"I caught one with my bayonet. He's farther down the ditch. Ghastly, but interesting. There was so much blood. I had no idea a man had that much blood in him. You look rather ill."

"It's all so—"

"Elemental. Yes, isn't it, rather."

A bugle sounded off in the distance where the Fascists had retreated. Florry saw shapes scrambling about far off, yet they were too indistinct to waste bullets on.

"They must be massing for their show. I can't imagine they're too happy about all this work on a wet night."

Dust spurts began to kick to life all about the sandbags, just as the noise of high-pitched, rapid typing rose from the dark. Julian and Florry ducked back, hearing the crack-crack-crack of projectiles rushing through the air above them.

"They've a Maxim, damn them," said Julian. "We'll not be going any farther tonight. But we'll have some bloody sport when they attack. Oh, I wish I could get my hands on a Vickers or a Lewis instead of this neolithic *implement*," Julian said, clapping his crude Russian rifle with disgust. "Why is it the bloody nasties have all the fancy toys?"

"Florry!" someone whispered.

"Eh?"

"Bloody Billy wants to see you."

"Where is he?"

"Back down the trench, by the bunker."

"All right. Pass the word, I'm coming."

Florry crawled off, past the shapes of the other section men in the trench. In time, crawling over litter and junk, he reached the Fascist bunker. He ducked into it, finding it as crude as their own quarters. Billy sat on a cot, his bloody leg up and swaddled before him.

"You all right, commissar?"

"Ah, it's nothing I won't survive, the fookers. Listen, old man, I want you to tell the chaps on the left to keep their ears open. Keep track of them, Florry, chum, don't let them wander away. I'm worried. There should have been a lot of shooting on our left, where the German battalion was to have hit the line farther down. Nobody's heard anything. I'd hate to think of us in the middle of this picnic by ourselves, eh? And of course our bloody Colt at last snapped its fookin' bolt, so we've no automatic weapons."

Florry was surprised Billy had chosen him for this tiny smidgen of responsibility; why not the far more experienced Julian?

"And especially watch bloody Julian. You can see the bloody madness in his eyes. He's liable to get himself kippered on something harebrained. He thinks he's Lord Cardigan and Winston Churchill rolled up in one. If he's to die, let him die for *something* beyond his own bloody vanity."

"Right-o, Billy."

"Now get back there, and send word if you hear anything. And get ready. The Fascists are sure to hit us back tonight."

Florry scurried out.

He went on back and spread the word. But someone had vanished.

"Where's Julian?"

" 'E said 'e wanted to do a bit of poking about, and off 'e went."

"Christ, you let him go?"

"Aw, 'n *you* could stop 'is majesty when 'e's got 'is 'eart set on somethin', chum?"

Florry supposed he couldn't. He looked down the communica-

tions trench through which Julian had purportedly disappeared. The seconds ticked by, turning to minutes. They heard bugles again. The Maxim began to pepper the air over their heads.

"Damn him," Florry cursed. "And if he's out there when the bastards hit us, what then?"

" 'E's kippered certain, that's wot. Relax, chum. The bloke figured to catch 'is doin' somethin' bloody ignorant. 'E's too bloody brilliant for this 'ere world."

Well, here it was. Julian off on some mad toot, sure to buy it in the neck.

Leave him, he thought. Leave him and be done. It solves everything. Your life can continue. Your obligations have been met. Everybody's happy.

Yet what Florry discovered himself saying surprised himself as much as the men to whom he spoke.

"Look, I'm going to mosey down there a bit, see if I can't rein him in, all right? Sammy, you keep watch."

"Florry, chum, no point *two* fancy gents gettin' kippered the same night."

"I told bloody Billy I'd look after the fool."

"Florry, mate, it's bloody fool—"

"*Shut up!*" Florry barked, suddenly furious at the man. "I told damned Billy, don't you understand?"

"Christ, chum, no need to get so worked up."

Florry could see nothing down the trench except some broken timbers and eerily reflective puddles. About twenty yards ahead it took a jagged dogleg off to the right and vanished from his vision. He set down his rifle, which would do him no good in close quarters, and pulled out the Webley.

"Don't be gone long, chum. No tellin' when Billy's going to pull us back. I don't think we're here for the season."

"Yes. I'll just be a while."

He began to creep forward edgily, feeling his way with his hand in front of him. He advanced for what felt like hours in this fashion —it was more like fifteen minutes—while the odd shot popped

overhead and the odd bomb exploded in the far distance. He had begun to feel like a Nottingham miner in the deepest, loneliest shaft. He imagined he could hear the groaning of the walls and smell the dust heavy in the air as the cave-in threatened.

Damn you, Julian, where the devil are you? _Why_ do such a foolish thing?

At one point something moved just ahead, and Florry brought his pistol up; it was a rat, big as a cat, with filthy rotten eyes and quivering whiskers. It perched on its hind legs barring the way. Florry hated rats. He felt about on the gummy trench floor for a rock, found one, pried it free, and hurled it at the beast. The throw was off and the thing just stared balefully at him with what seemed to be Oxbridge arrogance. A university rat, eh? A bloody Trinity College rat. Finally, bored, it ambled haughtily off.

Florry was surprised to discover himself breathing hard at the ordeal. Gathering his nerves back in a tight little bundle, he proceeded along, adding rats to his worries. He clambered over a broken timber. A body lay nearby but Florry could make out nothing of it in the dark, so coated with mud as it was; it was like a sack of sodden rags. He went on farther. There was no movement and the only sound was the splashing of the drops into the puddles.

"Julian? Julian?" he whispered.

There was no answer. A fusillade sounded above, and then an angry reply. The Fascists were getting ready to counterattack. At the same time, a mist rose to cling to everything, a kind of ghastly soup lapped everywhere in the trench.

"Julian?" He thought Julian was probably back by this time, full of marvelous stories and having appropriated a flask of Fascist brandy and treated the troops to a sip. Damn you, Julian, so like you! And here I sit out on a bloody limb.

"Julian!" he whispered again. How far out was he? How close to their position? The urge to retire grew heavy and tempting. It was almost an ache. But he knew somehow that he could not. He could not abandon Julian, not here. He was bound to him in peculiar ways.

He squirmed ahead a few more feet, tripping through the mist. He reached another zigzag in the trench. He eased around it.

"Shhh! God, they're right ahead, Stink."

"Jul—"

"Shhh! Do you know I heard you the whole way? It's a good thing they're not paying attention."

Julian was crouched in a niche in the wall.

"Thank God you're all right. Come on, Mowry says they'll attack any moment."

"Of course they will. Now listen here, they won't come through this trench because it zigs and zags so furiously and because they'll assume we have it covered. They'll be above, moving through the mist. When they go by—"

"Julian!"

"Just listen, chum. They'll go by and we can squeeze ahead another few yards or so. It's not far off. I was almost there. And I'll chuck a bomb into that Maxim gun."

"Julian, no. Christ. Listen, Mowry says the attack is all fouled up. We may be out here all by ourselves. The Germans never jumped off. We're out on a limb."

"Well, if that doesn't just prove you can't get good help any more. The cheeky bastards."

"Come on, we've—"

But Florry was stunned into silence by the awkward shambling noise of a large body of men beginning to move up ahead. Julian pulled him back into the niche and they lay in the mud, enwrapped in each other. Florry could barely breathe. He felt his heart throbbing and his chest aching. He pressed himself into Julian's chest and sensed the heart pumping madly. They could hear the low squish-slip of boots moving through the mud close by, but Florry was too scared to focus. Whispered commands in Spanish flew softly through the mist like sparrows. There was the jingle and clink of equipment, the occasional harder clack of a bolt being thrown.

Each second Florry knew they'd be discovered. Wave after wave passed by. They must have gotten reinforcements. A whole army seemed to be creeping by above them through the mist.

"Get ready," Julian commanded, at last disconnecting himself from Florry. He began to slither down the trench with the bomb in his hand. Florry followed, cocking the Webley.

A sudden spatter of shots announced the beginning of the attack. Florry heard the pop and snap of rifle bullets and the bursting of bombs. With the cover of the noise, Julian rose and began to close the distance to the main trench with manful strides. Florry hurried after him.

The Maxim opened fire from quite nearby: its clatter was tremendous. It poured bullets out into the night at an incredible rate and seemed to Florry like some industrial instrument for the manufacture of wickets or camming gears, sparking and laboring mightily in its moorings. He could see Julian pluck the first pin from his bomb and then begin to slide toward the gap that marked the intersection between their trench and the larger enemy one.

What happened next happened fast, particularly after the long, slow miner's descent toward it. A youth appeared as Julian stepped into the trench and pointed his rifle at him. Florry, just behind Julian, shot the young man in the face.

"Good show!" shouted Julian, bounding ahead and pulling the second pin, as he lobbed the bomb underhand toward the sound of the machine gun. In another instant he was back, knocking Florry flat. The burst, so close, lit the sky with burning fragments and hot wind and hurt their ears. The Maxim quit abruptly.

"Come on," yelled Julian, clambering past him. Florry rose. There seemed other dark shapes coming from the Fascist position at them and he fired his remaining five chambers of four-five-five at them, driving them back, and turned to race after Julian.

"Come *on,* Stink," screamed Julian, pulling him along. He was delirious with joy. "Good Christ, man, but that was bloody *marvel-*

ous, that was more bloody fun than old Julian's *ever* had! Blast, you potted him right in the bloody snout!"

But Florry felt only queasy and ashamed. He'd seen the boy's face in the spurt of flame and he knew he was perhaps fifteen, with a vague sprig of mustache. The bullet had smashed into his brain, that huge four-five-five, heavy as the Liverpool Express, shattering the whole upper quadrant of his face. He lay in a slop of mud and blood, utterly defunct. Christ, why couldn't it have been a Moorish sergeant or a German colonel, why a silly, dim little child?

Julian was yanking him along savagely. Explosions and gunfire seemed to be coming from every direction in the dark. Weird illuminations lit the horizon. The trench seemed endless. Bullets pranged into the dirt or thunked against the sandbags, making a peculiar *hop-hop* sound. Julian suddenly leapt back, pinning him to the ground. He heard, besides the thumping of Julian's heart, the heavy sound of a mass of men running through the mud. It must have been the attacking party, unsupported since the destruction of the Maxim gun.

"Listen. We'll never make it back. I think there's a party of them up ahead in the trench."

"Ah! The bastards."

"Yes. Unsporting of them, eh? Why don't we crawl about a hundred meters or so out on the left. If we stay low, we should be all right. When they pass on by, we can return to our own lines. All right?"

"You clever chap."

"Brilliant Julian, always thinking. Come on, then."

Julian pulled himself out of the trench and pivoted to offer Florry a hand. Florry, thus assisted, scrambled out. Julian shimmied away, and Florry began to—

It was as if he were at the center of an explosion. There was no pain, only the stunned sense of a tremendous blow to the throat knocking him down, filling his eyes with light and drama. He fought for strength but could find none; he put his hand to his

wound and was further stunned to discover his fingers were wet and black.

God, he'd been shot. He lay, waiting for death. The blood flowed over his tunic. The numbness and incoherence spread.

Julian appeared, inches from his eyes.

"I'm dying," Florry said.

"Can you move?"

"I'm dying. Go on, get out of here."

"Ah, rot, Robert. I'm the hero here, *I'll* make the dramatic suggestions, the glorious sacrifice, all right? Lord, you're a mess, Stinky. You look worse than when you pissed yourself up in fifth form."

Somehow Julian got him turned over onto his belly and aimed in the proper direction. Florry floundered along ineffectively and Julian shoved him on, half-pushing, half-pulling him. Above them, bullets tore through the night, occasionally popping with a rude sound and a cloud of spray into the wet ground. They seemed to move groggily for the longest time, but at last they reached a less barren area, where gullies and thick brush offered them some protection and Julian got him up and stumbling along.

Behind them, another machine gun opened up.

"Damn them, they've brought another gun up. Come on, Stinky."

But Florry was at last spent.

"I don't think I can make it."

"Of course you can, old boy. Here, let me take another look. I don't even think the thing hit you square. These bloody Spaniards can't do *anything* right. A lot of blood, and you've messed a very nice tunic, but if you'll just—"

"Julian, shut up. I can't make it. I'm going to pass out."

"Now, none of that. Come along."

"Please, go on. Go on, damn you, you always were the brilliant one. Julian, why did you cut me? At school, you cut me dead. You filthy bastard."

"Long story, old sod. No time for it now. Do come on, then, I think I see some of their chaps moving this way. We're going to end up practice for pig sticking if we don't—"

"Go on, damn you. Christ, it hurts."

"Wounds are *supposed* to hurt. Every sod knows that. Now come along."

"I-I-"

"Think of England, old boy. Think of the wonderful piece you can write for Denis Mason. You'll be the toast of Bloomsbury."

"Oh, Christ."

"Think of Sylvia, old man. Think of the beautiful Sylvia."

"I can't think of—"

"Think of her titties, old man. Great soft titties. Think of squashing them about in your fingers while she tells you she wants you to do it harder."

"You filthy bastard!"

"Think of her wonderful cunt, old man, all wet and fishy and warm. Think of grousing it out as a piggy snorts after truffles. That should revive your interest in living."

"You filthy fucker, Julian. I ought to—"

"Yes, that's the spirit, chum. Come along then."

"Julian, you bastard—"

"Stink, she's just quim. Damned good quim, I'd bet, but quim just the same. Come *on,* old boy."

Up ahead, they saw figures on the crestline coming toward them.

17

COMRADE MAJOR BOLODIN

LENNY MINK FELT GOOD. FOR ONE THING, IN THE SOUR AFTER-math of the Levitsky debacle, he had received a promotion from the desperate Glasanov. He was now a major in the SIM and had control of his own unit. But he had other reasons for his joy. For in the matter of Levitsky, he had a considerable edge on everybody else. He knew that the chances of spotting the old Jew randomly were almost nil; Levitsky was simply too smart for that, too shrewd, too much the devil. But Lenny knew why he was here. To see his boy.

To get the gold.

Lenny had figured it out. The old Jew was after the same thing he was. What else could explain the desperation and the cunning and the courage of the old man?

Old devil, Lenny thought, you're not so special. Just another Jew on the track of a big score. You'll see your boy and he'll tell you, huh? He'll point you in the right direction. You've just got to find him.

And his boy was English.

Thus it took no great powers of deduction but only simple cleverness to identify and establish surveillance on the several concentrations of Englishmen around Barcelona. For surely the old devil would be found sniffing in their fringes. These were not many: there was, first off, the press corps, a group of gray-suited cynics that gathered each night in the Café de las Ramblas and sat nursing whiskeys and grousing bitterly about their assignments and their

editors and exchanging sarcastic bets on the outcome of it all. Lenny ordered that Ugarte, his number one, who did all the talking, take up a nightly position there.

"Suppose I get bored, boss?"

"I break every bone in your body. Every single one, no?"

Ugarte had a particularly unpleasant laugh, more a whinny, which he issued at that point, partially to conceal his extreme nervousness. Bolodin frightened him, too.

"Look," said the American, leaning across and pinching him playfully. "You do what I say, when I say it, and you'll come out of this okay. Okay?" He spoke English because among Ugarte's attainments was the language.

"*Sí*, yeah, boss."

Lenny's other trusted aid was Franco, called Frank for obvious reasons, an ex-butcher who had beaten his wife to death in 1934 and was freed from his life sentence in August of 1936 by the libertarian Anarchists, who did not believe in prisons. Lenny stationed him outside the British consulate.

Both men carried with them hand-drawn copies of the original etching from the 1901 *Deutsches Schachzeitung,* as adjusted and improved by Lenny's suggestions after having seen the old man at close range in the cell. It was a reasonable likeness. Lenny knew therefore that if things went as they should, it would only be a matter of time before one of them tumbled across the old man. He had a hunter's confidence and a con artist's patience.

He positioned himself on the Ramblas, across from the third and most likely spot where Levitsky might be counted on to appear: the Hotel Falcon, the enemy headquarters, with its flappng red POUM banner. It was full of Brits. These were the idealistic kids who came to take part in the revolution but didn't quite have the guts to join the fighting. They always came *here,* no place else. As he sat in the 1933 Ford, he conceived the idea that it was like some kind of fancy college club or something, and there seemed to be a lot of screwing and drinking and singing going on. It was a party or something.

Lenny sat outside it day after day, smoking the Luckies he bought on the black market, quietly watchful, utterly imperturbable, in his blue serge suit, his almost handsome, almost ugly, blunt features calm and under control. He merely watched and smoked.

It was on the third day when he noticed her.

She was pretty and slim and lively. Everybody liked her, he could tell. She was the sort of girl you could like a lot.

I never had a girl like that, he thought.

In time, he grew to hate her. She made him think of who he was, and what he was, and he didn't like that one bit. It was her eyes, those sleepy, calm, knowing gray green eyes, and the way she stood, so ladylike and refined, and the way she listened so intently. She seemed to work for their English-language newspaper, _The Spanish Revolution,_ which they sent out, and it meant she knew everybody. One night, Glasanov had them do a crash job on some guy named Carlos. They picked him up at the Grand Oriente and the girl was there. Lenny hung back. He didn't want her looking at him. He was so close to her, yet he kept his face down, not looking at anything because he was somehow ashamed.

The next day, a boy showed up and handed him a note from Ugarte which said he'd seen Levitsky; he'd been calling himself Ver Steeg and claimed to be a Dutch journalist and was heading out to the front. The boss had better get out there fast.

Lenny looked back at the girl. The POUM people were all low today because of poor Carlos.

He thought, You bitch, someday I'll be really fucking big and then you'll know who I am.

Some day I'll have gold. And I'll have you.

18

NEWS FROM THE FRONT

THE INTELLIGENCE AND PROPAGANDA COMMISSAR OF THE Twenty-ninth Division, as the POUM militia was called, issued his communiqué about the glorious victory at Huesca a day and a half later at his headquarters at the big, battered house at La Granja. The recipients of the news were a crew of mangy reporters who had spent the intervening hours in transit to the front by any means possible, in the hope of actually seeing something.

The statement was typed and posted on a bulletin board outside militia headquarters. It read,

Our troops advanced in perfect order in a series of well-coordinated movements until in several places around the city, the Fascist lines were broken. In this new situation, they inflicted grievous casualties upon the enemy, taking from his stores much valuable war matériel. It was another example of working people, in service to the revolution, triumphing against all odds and defeating the German-Italian-Rebel Combine. Many prisoners were taken and much of intelligence value was also removed.

Later in the morning, our troops, sensing they had achieved their tactical goals, repositioned themselves so as to consolidate their gains.

"In other words," said the Reuters man, "it was another bloody muck-up."

"What I'm wondering," said the man from the *Standard*, "is bloody why the whole thing was tossed together at the doubletime. They usually don't like to move so fast, they like to take their bloody time. *Mañana,* eh? Always bloody *mañana.*"

"God, the Spanish. Anytime you've got the Spanish and the Italians in the same war, you've got the potential for a comic opera on a grand scale."

There were several reporters, however, who did not take part in the cynical give and take, perhaps because they were new to the front or new to war reporting or new to Spain. One of these was a tall, elderly Dutchman of intellectual carriage named Ver Steeg— Ver *Staig,* the pronunciation went, he informed them, his only utterance thus far—who worked for a Dutch press syndicate. He appeared to listen intently to all that was said and when at last the bulletin's author, Commissar Steinbach, appeared to answer, however obliquely, questions, this spry old fellow moved to the front of the crowd.

"Comrade Steinbach, we hear rumors that the Thaelmann Column of the PSUC Militia did not enthusiastically support the POUM and the Anarcho-Syndicalists in this attack, even though the worker's militias have been theoretically combined under one leadership," the *Daily Mail* man began.

"Is this an essay or do you have a question, Mr. Janeway?" Comrade Steinbach replied with an icy gleam in his famously bright good eye.

"The question, Comrade Steinbach, is, first, did the Communist militia aid in the attack, and second—"

Steinbach, a witty man whose incisiveness of mind was as famous as his bright eye, enjoyed these sessions, and interrupted swiftly. "Each militia performed its duties outstandingly," he said. "The Anarchists were brilliant, the Communists heroic, and our own Workers Party troops solid as a rock. There is sufficient glory for each." He smiled.

"Is it not a fact, comrade," asked Sampson, the *Times* man, "that your forces are in exactly the same situation—that is, the same trenches—as before the attack?"

"Certain modifications of our positions were necessary late in the attack as a means of consolidating our advances."

"In order, if I may follow up, to consolidate your advances, you had to abandon them?"

"It is well known that the *Times* will write whatever it chooses, regardless of the truth, Comrade Sampson, so why bother to press on this issue?" He smiled blandly.

"We've heard that the German troops of the Thaelmann Brigade, under the command of Communist Party commissars, never left their trenches, thus isolating your people in the Fascist parapets, and that the slaughter was awful."

"Good heavens, how do these terrible rumors get started? Fifth columnists, gentlemen, fifth columnists spreading lies. In fact, political solidarity was observed throughout the operation. Losses were acceptable."

"Why was the attack put together so hastily?"

"The attack was organized at a normal pace."

"Comrade Steinbach, you know as well as we do these things are prepared weeks in advance. It seems clear this one was thrown together in less than forty-eighty hours. What's the reason?"

"The attack proceeded normally."

"Is it true that the Twenty-ninth Division—that is, the POUM militia and the POUM itself—has staked its survival on breaking the siege at Huesca, and as external political pressure against POUM mounts, so will the pressure to take Huesca?" Sampson asked.

"This is a purely military situation; it has no political ramifications. I suggest you check with the Central Committee at Party headquarters in Barcelona for any political questions."

"Will we be able to tour the battlefield?"

"In due time."

"Will you release casualty figures?"

"It would serve no purpose."

"Were British troops involved in the action?"

"The British centura of the POUM militia—excuse me, the Twenty-ninth Division—had a brave and leading role in the drama. The centura is a unit of roughly one hundred men, who have been a proud part of the militia since August of 1936. These were among the most ardent troops in the attack."

At last the Dutch reporter spoke.

"Were there any British casualties?"

Steinbach paused a second.

"It is with deep regret," he said, "that I announce the death of a revolutionary fighter of great heroism, idealism, and discipline. He was also a great poet and scholar. Julian Raines, author of the famous poem 'Achilles, Fool,' was killed in action in the attack against Fascist troops on the outskirts of Huesca."

There was a gasp.

"Also," Steinbach continued, "a British writer named Robert Furry perished."

The press party moved to the trench and Steinbach showed the correspondents the line of attack through a brass telescope.

"As you can see, gentlemen," he said, "it's terrible terrain to cross at night, but our brave fighters were able to get within bomb range before being spotted. You can see the redoubt."

"Keep your 'eads low, boys," called a redheaded Cockney captain with a bloody leg. "Bob the Nailer don't give a bloody damn who you are."

"Is that where the Englishmen died?" asked Sampson.

"Bloody right," said the runty little man. "Up there. Comrade Julian went out alone to bomb an enemy machine gun. His chum went out after him. They sent the gun to hell, but neither man made it back."

"I say, captain" said Sampson, "what's your name? And what part of England are you from."

"Legion, chum. And I'm from all over."

"Hmmm. So there are no bodies?"

"No. But no man could survive up there," said Steinbach.

"Perhaps they were taken prisoner," said a young American correspondent—to some laughter.

"I'm afraid prisoners are seldom taken on this front," said Steinbach, a special, almost magical vividness coming into his good eye. "We all feel his loss keenly. He was one of those special men. You are all familiar with his poem 'Achilles, Fool,' which has been taken to express the confusion of a generation. Well, perhaps by the end, Comrade Raines had solved his confusion."

"What about this other chap?"

"Only Julian Raines is important, as the symbol of a revolutionary generation who, rather than living his life in the comfortable circumstances of his birth, instead chose to come to Spain and risk everything for his beliefs."

"Sounds like you're trying to get one more drop of blood out of the poor wasted sot," said the Reuters man.

"Gentlemen," said Steinbach, coyly pretending to shock, "you are too cynical. Let me read you from Comrade Raines's last, unfinished poem. It's called 'Pons' and was discovered among his effects."

Steinbach took out a sheet of paper, cleared his throat, and read:

"*. . . if I should die, think this of me,*
Wher'ere I rest, men one day will be free."

"Good Christ, *that's* from the man Auden called the most promising voice of his generation? Come on, Steinbach, get your boys to give it a little distinction before you put it out."

Again there was much laughter, and even Steinbach seemed to take part in it. He was able to laugh because he knew it was a good story and they'd use it. Salvage *something* out of this bloody mess, if only one more martyr for the English left.

When it came his turn, Levitsky worked the telescope back and forth across the scaggily vegetated ridge near the city, a good half

mile off. He could see brush, gulches, mud, and the Fascist line of sandbags running across the crest. It was, as this sly one-eyed propagandist Steinbach had said, terrible terrain for an attack at night, in the rain.

Julian, you idiot. To die like a flea among millions of fleas in the mudbath of history.

He stepped back, turned for a second, and looked where the Englishman Sampson stood, a hard, trim young man with narrow, suspicious eyes and precise, perhaps military manners and authority. Sampson smoked a pipe and took notes with impressive efficiency and wrote beautifully, it was said. Levitsky, a little shaken perhaps, tried to adjust to the immensity of his loss and, worse, the hideous resonating irony of it.

I was so close. I came so far, I was so close.

It had been snatched away by Julian's utter stupidity. How could he be so frivolous with his own life? And poor Florry's, too. God knows, Florry had reason to follow him, but it was all such a bitter waste.

He went back to the instrument. Nothing. It was just the same, scruffy no-man's-land. Did he expect to see the dead rise?

"Mr. Ver Steeg?"

It was Comrade Steinbach, calling from the group of reporters farther down the trench. "We are returning to La Granja. You don't want to be left up here if a Fascist bombardment begins."

"Ah," said Levitsky. Yet he did not at once move. For if Julian were gone, there was nothing left to do, except save himself.

If Koba's hounds are to hunt me, let them hunt me hard.

"Best get goin', chum," said the little English captain, then turned away and headed back to his men gathered at the other end of the trench.

But Levitsky suddenly felt naked and vulnerable. Without his mission, he was just a man. His death, which might have had political meaning, suddenly had only a personal one. It was as if his life, in all its fragility, had been handed back to him.

He started up the trench and as he was drawing near the ladder, he ducked into a bunker scooped in the wall. It was filled with gear; two men slept noisily.

Several bombs lay on the table, iron eggs with checkerboard surfaces. He made his decision in a split second, and snatched one up and put it into his hip pocket. He gripped the thing out of sight. It felt heavy and authoritative in his hand. He could remember flinging them by the dozens into White positions during the civil war.

"Comrade!"

Levitsky turned. It was the English captain.

"Forgot this, old man," he said, holding out Levitsky's notebook. "Sure you ain't too old for this sort of thing?"

Levitsky smiled, took the notebook, and headed out after the other reporters moving back through the scrubland to La Granja.

By the time he caught up, they had come through the orchard and into a meadow. Ahead, through the line of trees, Levitsky could see the big house with its red tiles.

In the courtyard the reporters milled around amid the soldiers, all of them waiting to be served a meal. The smell of rice and chicken from nearby cook pots filled the air. There was much laughter and camaraderie. Levitsky could see the Britishers teasing the American about his prisoner question and he could see the French reporters arguing strenuously among themselves over some political point.

And he could see Comrade Bolodin, with one man, walking toward him.

His first impulse was to run.

Don't, he told himself. You old fool, *stay calm*. Let's see him pull his NKVD card here, in the center of a POUM encampment.

Levitsky began to slide through the crowd.

The big American was drawing closer. They'd grab him first, then pull the cards—guns, too, probably—and haul him away. He only had a few seconds. He put his hand in his pocket and removed the bomb. He held it muffled in his coat and with his other hand

managed to get the first pin out. He continued walking through the crowd toward the big house; then, abruptly, he turned aside and headed to one of the three smaller buildings off to the side. A guard saw him coming.

"*¡Alto! Arsenal!*"

"Eh?" said Levitsky, approaching. "*No hablo . . .*"

"*¡Arsenal!*" repeated the guard.

Levitsky nodded, pulled the last pin, and in one swift motion tossed it through the window. The guard dropped his rifle and began to run screaming. Levitsky ran in the other direction.

The first blast was muffled; the second lifted him from his feet and threw him in the air. He landed, stunned. Men ran in terrified panic. Smoke filled the air. The small house blossomed flames.

"Run! Run! There's more to blow!" somebody shouted. A pair of hands picked him up. He looked up into the face of the young British reporter Sampson.

"Go on, old man! Get out of here! Run for your bloody life." Levitsky ran around the side of the big house and through the orchard. Behind him, there was another detonation.

He turned into a gully and began a little jog down the creek bed. The mountains in the distance were cool and white and beautiful.

"*¿Amigo?*"

A man in a trenchcoat stepped from behind the trees. He had an automatic.

"*Comrade Amigo. Manos arriba, ¿eh?*" said the man smilingly, gesturing for Levitsky to raise his hands.

"*No hablo,*" protested Levitsky blandly.

The man smiled and relaxed as he came near and seemed to lower the pistol, and Levitsky knew this meant he was about to hit him. When the man lashed out suddenly with the pistol, meaning to crack Levitsky sharply across the cheekbone, Levitsky broke the blow with one hand and with the other struck upward, driving the crucifix nail into the man's throat.

The man fell back, gasping, his eyes filled with stunned aston-

ishment that such an old fool could hurt him so terribly. The pistol fell into the dust. The man went to his knees, trying to hold the blood into his throat with his hands. He tried to cry out but couldn't. He tried to rise, but couldn't.

Levitsky knelt next to him and carefully placed the point of the nail into the ear canal, and plunged it inward. With a convulsion, the man died. Levitsky quickly plucked his papers from the breast pocket, finding him to be one Franco Ruiz, according to a SIM identity card. He pulled the body into the brush and picked up the pistol, a short-barreled .380 Colt automatic. He hurried down the creek bed, finding himself surprisingly impressed with Comrade Bolodin. The American was smart, yes, he was. He'd found him, and with a better man than Franco Ruiz, he would have taken him.

Night was falling as Levitsky hurried along the creek bed. He almost froze. He had no exact idea where he was headed other than east, away from La Granja. He shivered as the cold rose to penetrate his coat. The creek bed crossed under a country road after a while, and he chose the road, his feet acquiring an urgency that seemed almost involuntary. On either side in the twilight, the empty fields fell away, their crops unharvested, their farmers driven away. Several miles off a shell or a bomb exploded and now and then came the crackle of shots outside Huesca, but otherwise there was no sign of war in the strange, empty stillness of the land. The Pyrenees off on the left had become indistinct, a wall. Beyond them lay France, and freedom.

You cannot walk across the mountains, old devil, he told himself.

When it grew too dark to continue, he found a deserted stone barn and hid in the straw for warmth. He awoke early the next morning and proceeded on, the hunger gnawing away at his stomach. He was stopped once by a squad of forlorn militiamen who cared more whether he had food to share with them than for his papers. Twice more he came across groups of militia, but they paid him no attention. Finally he came to a larger road. Before him, he

could see the plain stretching out for miles, bleak and flat, gnarled here and there with clusters of rock. Who could want such desolation?

He waited by the side of the road until at last a vehicle came along, an empty lorry driven by two men. He hailed them.

"Comrades?" he asked.

"_Sprechen sie Deutsch, Kamrade?_" came the reply from one of them, a youth of about twenty.

"Yes, of course, comrade. I am Ver Steeg, of the press. I was at the front and missed the lorry back to Barcelona. Perhaps you are headed in that direction?"

"Yes, comrade," the boy said. "Hop aboard. We've got some wine and a little cheese."

Levitsky squeezed into the cab, and the lorry rumbled on through the bright afternoon. The driver's companion was another youth; they were two earnest German Jewish refugees who'd come to fight with the Thaelmann Column against the Hitlerites. They were political naïfs, and Levitsky, exhausted, listened with bland interest to their slogans and enthusiasms, their gross misunderstandings and their outright fabrications. They believed Koba and Lenin were great chums, the spirit of the latter filling the heroic skull of the former. The enemies were all "Oppositionists," who must be tirelessly liquidated, so that the Revolution could be guided by the brilliant Koba. They also thought, somehow, the Anarchists, the bourgeois manufacturers of munitions, and the Catholic church were behind Hitler and Franco and Trotsky. It was the routine nonsense the Party had been grinding out more and more lately. They talked of the big explosion at La Granja. And they talked, finally, of the miracle.

"You've heard of the miracle, Comrade Ver Steeg?"

"Alas, no," said Levitsky, politely, uninterested in miracles.

"The luck of the English, I suppose," said one of the boys.

"Yes, yes?"

"Talk about resurrections. It's enough to turn one to priests and nuns!"

"Go on."

"Two dead Englishmen walked back from the dead. A poet and his comrade. They lay in the brush. The Fascists came and set up a machine-gun post. They lay there, the poor devils, for forty-eight hours, one of them hurt and bleeding. Everyone thought they were dead. A single move, a single breath, and they'd have been shot."

"What happened?" Levitsky asked laconically. At moments of great excitement he was capable of extreme calm.

"When the second night fell, they crawled in. Two full days after they'd been lost, they returned. They went to the hospital at Tarragona."

"Tell the comrade what the poet said. He must be an amusing man. It's on everybody's lips, a famous line."

"Yes, he must be witty, even if he fights for the POUMistas. He said, 'The tea was simply rotten over there and the limes had not been freshly cut, and so we returned.'"

19

THE CLUB

THEY KEPT HOLLY-BROWNING WAITING FOR MORE THAN half an hour. He sat with the coats in the anteroom under the cold, unimpressed eye of the doorman, awaiting his summons. He sat ramrod stiff on the hardback bench—no soft waiting-room chairs for him, thanks—and kept his eyes fixed furiously on a blank point in space some six feet ahead.

At last the doorman came for him.

"Sir James?"

"Yes."

"Will you follow me please, sir."

"Thank you."

The doorman led him to a chap in livery—Holly-Browning knew him, actually, he'd been in the army, a sergeant, and won the DFC in Flanders in '15 before catching a lungful of mustard—who in turn escorted him with elaborate dignity through the study, the dark, almost Moorish bar, the dining hall, and up the club's stairs to its private suites.

The railing was mahogany, richly polished; the walls silk damask of floral print, exquisite, the stairs carpeted in a Persian pattern dating from the fourteenth century. Yet it was all threadbare, tatty, a bit musty. Things never changed in clubs until they had to or were shocked brutally into it. But in the normal course of events one day was not remotely different from the next; again, that was as it should have been. Indeed, that was the very *point*.

They reached at long last the top of the stairway and made

stately, muted progress down the hall, coming finally to a certain closed door. The servant knocked briskly, heard a quick, "Come in," and opened the door.

"Major Sir James Holly-Browning," he announced.

Holly-Browning entered to discover C, as the chief of MI-6 was called, and another man in a beautifully cut suit. The two of them looked as old schoolish as possible; and they were. C's guest was, like C himself, a former naval officer. He was, like C himself, short and pink and bald and beautifully if conservatively dressed. And he was, like C himself, the head of an intelligence service. But there the similarities ceased: he was director-general of MI-5, which specialized in matters of domestic security where MI-6 specialized in foreign espionage and counterespionage. They were, in other words, opposite sides of the same coin.

The two of them were enjoying enormously big cigars as the debris of their luncheon was cleared away by two Hindu boys.

"James, how very good of you to join us. He's about to serve the brandy. Would you care for a tot?"

"No thank you, sir," said Holly-Browning primly. He was shocked to find the two of them together.

"Look, do sit down."

"Thank you, sir," said Holly-Browning, taking the open chair.

"James, you know Sir Vernon."

Sir Vernon was said to be the most affable man in the intelligence departments, though his critics said this amounted primarily to great skill at parliamentary bootlicking. An unfair charge: Sir Vernon had been superbly efficient nabbing Hun spies in the '14–'18 thing, a coup he'd brought off primarily by opening their mail.

"By reputation," said Holly-Browning.

"Glad you could join us on such short notice, James," said C.

"Of course, sir."

"I told Sir Vernon you'd be glad to update him on the Julian Raines case. It is, after all, an area of domestic concern."

"Sir, if I may, it is primarily a Section V matter. That is,

counterespionage operation against the Soviet Union. It is not a matter of domestic security."

"Ah. An interesting point," said Sir Vernon. "I quite see Sir James's point. But after all, we are not competing, but we are colleagues, are we not?"

"Please, James," said C. "It's rather important."

"Of course, sir," said Holly-Browning. He turned and as mechanically as possible apprised Sir Vernon of developments in the situation, most crucially the placing of an agent—whom he did not name—in Julian's close company, and summed up the sparse contents of Sampson's reports.

"And your man is reporting regularly?" asked Sir Vernon.

"He has not been the most habitual of correspondents, no," said Holly-Browning.

"Ummmmm," nodded Sir Vernon. "Nicely done. Damned fine job."

"You can see, Vernon," said C, "that the fluidity of Raines's circumstances somewhat prevents us from mounting the kind of thorough surveillance MI-5 would be able to mount at home."

"Can't be helped," said Sir Vernon. "You'll pardon an Americanism, but you can't play cards you don't hold. This fellow up close to Raines. He's a professional?"

"Alas, no," said Holly-Browning. "Of no great gifts or brilliance. Under the circumstances, however, he is what was available. He is a card we *did* hold."

"And right now?"

"At present, according to our man in Barcelona, Raines and our agent and a curious girl who stands somewhere between them are in Tarragona, a seaside resort fifty miles south of Barcelona. Our agent was nicked at the front; so was Raines. They are recuperating."

"Well, it certainly sounds encouraging," said Sir Vernon. "It's not quite how *we* would have handled it, but in the main you seem to be doing rather well, Sir James."

"Thank you, sir," said Holly-Browning.

'You see, James, Sir Vernon and I have just concluded a rather lengthy session of negotiation. That's why you are here."

"Yes?"

C continued. "Sir Vernon thinks the Julian Raines matter should be turned over to Security Service. Of course, we cannot agree. Sir Vernon has suggested that he might approach the Parliamentary Intelligence Committee and—"

"But good lord, sir, if that happened, it would all be out in a second. There'd be a scandal, the left would make a martyr out of Raines, the papers would get a hold of it, the—"

"I quite agree," said C.

"Gentlemen, I merely want to make certain that all data that is pertinent to MI-5 matters arrives at MI-5 headquarters, that's all," said Sir Vernon. "I think we all agree on the ultimate disposition of the case, but it seems equally certain that Julian Raines will have information of great import to us."

"And so you see, James," said C, "we have cut a deal. The deal is that we will continue to run the operation and you will continue to do what is best. But all reports must be sent on to MI-5, for their analysts. Is that understood?"

"Yes sir," said Holly-Browning, furious.

"It's not really so bad," said Sir Vernon. "It's a good deal better than having a bloody MI-5 snoop in the middle of everything, eh, Sir James?" He smiled.

Holly-Browning nodded politely. But something vexing occurred to him, clouding his smile. Who had informed MI-5?

20

TARRAGONA

BELIEVE ME," SAID JULIAN, HOLDING UP A GLASS OF CHAMpagne and blinking in the sun, "I've been dead and I've been alive and alive is better."

"Hear, hear," said Florry, hoisting his own glass.

"To life, then, darlings, the death of us all," Julian toasted.

Even Sylvia drank, though not as lustily as her two companions.

"And how's the neck, Robert?" she asked.

Florry looked at her shyly. She had not said much to him.

"It's on the mend. Another inch or so and he'd have nipped an artery. But he missed, it whizzed through, and here I am."

"To Spanish marksmanship!" said Julian grandly, "which accounts for the presence of a full two-thirds of this lovely grouping."

"We were just awfully lucky," said Florry. "Halfway through the second day, a foraging party was less than fifty paces off. We were cooked."

"And then some wonderfully ingenious fifth columnist touches off the POUM magazine at La Granja, and all the Johnny Fascist types totter off to watch the smoke rise and cheer for their team." Julian greedily drank more champagne. "Here's to luck, Julian's wonderful luck," he toasted again, this time removing his father's wedding ring from under his shirt and holding it, on its chain, out for them to see. "This little beauty didn't do *him* much good, but it's come in handy for us, eh, Stink?"

Florry smiled wanly. "Indeed," he said.

"Well put, old sport."

"Do they treat you decently in that awful hospital?" Sylvia asked politely.

"The Spanish, it seems, can do nothing well except cook," said Florry, somewhat relieved to turn to a neutral subject. "Three times a day, they wheel in huge steaming, wonderful meals. Meanwhile men die because nobody thinks to change their bandages."

"The future is definitely behind schedule in Spain," said Julian. "I don't believe the present has even arrived."

Florry sat back in the wheelchair. Sylvia and Julian had contrived to spring him from his great bay of bleeding boys for this outing, and they wheeled him down the two blocks of Tarragona's own Ramblas here to the Esplanade high above the sea. Before him stretched a mile of white sand, a rumpled mess of a Roman arena, and the sleepy, tepid Mediterranean. A few bathers dabbled in it, a few more lay in the sun. The breeze was fresh and salty; gulls flipped and fluted on it. A statue of Christopher Columbus stood proudly atop its pedestal, as at the foot of Barcelona's Ramblas.

"It's lovely here," said Florry.

"An odd town, Tarragona," Julian said. "It seems the revolution hasn't quite reached it. Or if it has, it got rather bored and left early, like Noël Coward at a dreary party."

Florry looked past Julian, in a splendid white linen suit, to Sylvia. *Damn you,* he thought. Her gray green eyes were sleepy yet lively; she'd done something to her hair, giving it a kind of frilly, lacy delicacy, and she'd put away her blue overalls and found a pretty dress. How had she met Julian? What was she doing with him while Florry lay in his bed? Was she with him?

He looked back to Julian, slugging down the champagne.

Damn you, Julian. You just go on, don't you?

"Barcelona is no longer a party Noël Coward would enjoy," she said. "The city's ugly. There's a vileness to it. Someone shot Carlos Brea right outside the Café Oriente. It was horrible. Someone shot him from a car. The bullet hit him in the head. They don't know who did it, but everybody says it was the Russian secret police. Poor Carlos."

"Carlos Brea?" said Julian. "The POUM intellectual? Poor sot. Spoke to him at length. Wanted to use it in a piece."

"Julian, you're such an awful cynic," she said, and Florry thought he could hear the love in her voice and see a radiance in her eyes.

They seemed such a wonderful English couple, the tall, blond, elegant poet-soldier who just as easily could have been a banker or a diplomat, and his beautiful, fair woman, as cool and poised as an impeccable statue. They looked so good together that Florry envied them their perfection.

"Have some more of the bubbly, old boy," urged Julian. "Do you think it was easy to find this stuff? Good God, I had to pay a fortune."

"Bottoms up," said Florry, finishing the glass, feeling the buzz in his nostrils.

"Look, you two," said Julian, "eat up and enjoy. I've got to be off."

"Where are you going?" Sylvia asked.

"To see about a car. I'll be back. I told the chap I'd see him at two. Besides, you two must have *scads* to talk about."

He rose from the bench with a smile and darted off down the Ramblas. Florry watched him slide along, graceful and fair. Then he turned back to the sea. Now, just the two of them, he felt all ridiculous.

"Is it so hard to be alone with me?" she said. "We were alone together for quite a while, as I recall. You were never so tongue-tied."

"You must think me an awful fool."

"Why ever do you say that?"

"The note I sent you. You received it?"

"Yes. It was lovely. I still have it."

"The soldier lad's last declaration before battle. God, you must think me the idiot."

"I think nothing of the kind. Do you want me to push you along the promenade?"

"No."

"Do you want some more champagne?"

"No."

"What about some of this food?"

"No."

"Well, what do you want, Robert? Tell me straight out."

"You, of course."

She said nothing.

"Or have you forgotten?"

"I haven't forgotten. It was quite lovely, wasn't it?"

"It was the best."

"Should you tax yourself, thinking about these things? Shouldn't you concentrate on—"

"Stop it. Don't say that. It's *all* I think about. You're with him now, is that right?"

"Oh, Robert, you're such an idiot. He's a charming man. He's no more interested in me than in the man in the moon. Julian's quality. I'm just a daughter of the bourgeoisie with a bit of inherited money for a year's adventuring. He likes *you* better than he likes me. He loves you, in fact."

"But you'd be with him instead of me if that's what he wanted?"

"Please, Robert. Don't put yourself through this. There's no point to it."

"Things have become complicated."

"Not if you don't permit them to, Robert."

Florry could no longer look at her. Her beauty was hurting him more than his throbbing neck wound. He could feel her very close and very still. He could smell her. He could not get the night at the Falcon out of his mind: he remembered how good it felt, how it seemed to straighten the world all out for him.

"I suppose you'd best wheel me back now, Sylvia," he said. "I find I'm quite weary."

"Of course, darling. May we visit you tomorrow?"

We!

Florry wished he could say simply no, damn you, and be done

with it. But he heard himself saying yes, yes, of course, it would be great fun, and as she wheeled him around, he saw Sampson across the street, watching.

It took a day or so, but at last Sampson managed it. He applied for permission with the Republican Propaganda Department to do a profile of wounded Englishmen fighting valiantly on the side of Justice, and the office itself suggested a series of possibilities. Florry was the third of them, and he lay in the bay and watched as Sampson came in with his official escort and plopped down beside one of the other boys and proceeded to interview him at grindingly boring length. Even the lad himself, an ex-miner from Wales who'd been hurt fighting with the International Brigade near Brunete, soon grew uninterested in his own answers. By halfway through the second interview, the Republican press officer had given up in disgust, muttering darkly about English pedantry, and thus when, late in the afternoon, Sampson finally approached Florry it was alone and in privacy; most of the other patients in the bay had been wheeled out to watch the sunset, their one pleasure, and those that remained were beyond caring.

"Ah, Florry," said Sampson with a smug yet prim grin, "and how's the wound?"

"It's all right," said Florry bleakly. "They're going to let me out in a bit. No bones broken, no arteries smashed. There's very little they can do now they've drained it except let it heal. A scratch, really."

"I shouldn't imagine it felt like a _scratch_ at the time."

"No, it did not."

"Look, I brought you a present. A copy of _Tristram Shandy_, by your friend Mr. Sterne. God, I despise literature. Full of nonsense, if you ask me, but I thought you'd like it."

He handed the book over and Florry took it gruffly.

"Ah, old sport. They're beginning to _wonder_ in London if perhaps you haven't forgotten why you're out here."

"I haven't forgotten."

"Good. Then do you think it would be possible—"

"Look, I spent five bloody months with Julian Raines, day in and day out. In battle, he was the bravest of us all. Now would a Russian spy risk everything for . . . for nothing? For his enemies? By all odds he should be dead. Tell your bloody major to find another candidate. Now go away."

"Robert, you've been such a wicked boy. No reports, no communications, no anything. I've had to keep awfully busy covering for you. But far worse, you've allowed yourself to become utterly sentimental about all this. I had expected so much. I thought you were the stuff of heroes. You were my idol."

"Sampson, it wears thin. I'm terribly tired."

"Look, Florry, old sport, sorry to be such a bother. Just a few minutes more, all right? Let me put some things to you?"

"Christ!"

"The attack was betrayed. The attack you fought in. Did you know that?"

"I've heard rumors, yes. But there's—"

"Look here, I was up there. It was quite clear that the general headquarters issued attack orders quickly, if for no other reason than to prevent the Communist brigades from getting counterinstructions from Barcelona as to whether to obey the orders or not. Yet the Communists nevertheless *knew* to tell their troops not to go. Somehow they *knew*, eh? They'd gotten the word. Because someone had reached *them*. Ah, see? It all fits together."

Florry looked out. Yes, the damned message. Julian and his "boy" who disappeared with the message.

"Then there's the issue of the magazine. Somebody blew the POUM magazine, eh? Someone knew where to plant a bomb. The explosion of that magazine all but ends POUM's chances for a spring offensive. And where would the saboteur have gotten the information? Why, from a helpful chap potting about at La Granja."

Florry said nothing.

"Now as for one other thing. There was a chap called Carlos Brea, who was coming into prominence in the POUM party. Yes?"

Florry said nothing.

"Anyway, this chap was murdered. Suddenly one night. Damned strange. But not strange when you consider that someone had interviewed him and realized how important he was becoming. And who was that chap?"

It was Julian.

"It means nothing."

"Julian is communicating with Levitsky, somehow. Robert, I can see it in your face. Like a cloud. Robert, in your heart, you _know_ it to be true. You've felt it in him. Down low, down, far, far away. A reserve. A coldness."

"They would risk him to betray a silly attack and to kill one man? It's nonsense," he said, wishing he believed it utterly.

"Perhaps there's a bigger job. A job we can't even begin to imagine, old man. But don't you see, he's given us no choice in the matter. He's here for the Russians. He spies on their enemies for them. And when he goes back to England, he'll spy on _us_ for them. You can see it, can't you, old man?"

"I can't see anything."

"He's fogged your brain, old man. With the woman. That's the point of the woman, to keep you utterly befuddled and from seeing him perfectly for what he is. He understands where you're weakest and he's got you there. You look at him, and all you see is the man who's bedding down with your—"

"Stop it! You go too far."

"Robert, listen to me. He's to be stopped. No longer just stopped in the general sense, but stopped in the most specific sense. You can do it, can't you? At the front? You're going back to the front, you can see that it happens. You can see that it's your duty to—"

"Sampson, old man, I'm going to tell you one more time. Leave. If you don't, so help me, I'll call the guard and tell him who

you really are and they'll put you against a wall and shoot you."

Sampson looked at him for the longest time. Then a small smile played across his face.

"All right, Robert. I'll go. But watch, old man. Keep your eyes open. And you'll see who owns the heart of Julian Raines."

Florry was permitted to leave the hospital in the next days and given a convalescent leave of two weeks. In the lobby, Sylvia was waiting for him. And so was Julian.

"You and Sylvia must come on holiday with me," said Julian. "I've found a beautiful old resort down the coast at Salou. It'll be great fun. Come along, old man. You owe me. You saved my life and therefore you cannot deny me anything."

"Julian, I'm still awfully spent. I wouldn't be much company. I just want to sit in the sun."

"Then sit in the sun you shall. I'll bring you champagne and caviar every day. Sylvia will read to you. Go on, put it on your furlough form, right there at the bottom. Oh, don't be a prig, Stink. It'll be fun. Look, in two weeks, we'll be back in the trenches."

"Robert, you look so pale," she said. "It would be so good for you."

They arrived, by Julian's car, that afternoon. It was a glorious old hotel, isolated against a blue bay on a broad lip of sandy beach, under a stony cliff. The hotel was an old villa, rambling and white under its mandatory crown of red tiles; the staff were old men, mostly, who called the few guests *comrade* awkwardly, as if they wanted no part of the future. They preferred the ordered past, and pretended revolution had never happened.

Florry settled into a huge room with a balcony overlooking the sea. Each day when he awoke he'd find a pot of thick coffee and a pot of hot cream and a red rose in a vase outside his door. It was a civilized way to begin the day, after the trenches. He'd sit out on

the balcony with a book—besides the Sterne, Sylvia had brought him Dickens and Kipling, which he preferred—and read in the sunlight, losing himself in the thickets of literature and the hot and healing sun. At eleven, the howls of delight would rise from the spongy clay tennis courts where Julian and Sylvia, who occupied suites down the hall, would play, their yelps punctuated by the hollow plunk of the ball on the racquet.

At noon, the three would lunch together on the veranda where they were fed fish and rice and a crisp _blanco_. Then they'd change and bathe by the sea, lazily wasting the afternoon stretched upon the white sand. The war seemed far off, and almost by mutual consent they excluded it from the frame of their consciousness. There was only the sun and the sea, the balmy breezes, and one another. The afternoons were long and slow, under flawless weather. The sky curved overhead in azure radiance, cloudless and immense. The water was calm and warm.

It seemed to be so lovely, and yet it was not. A peculiar rhythm soon established itself, almost like a tide, remorseless and implacable. Yet what was so peculiar about it all was that it went, like the larger war, completely unspoken of, as if by compact.

One half of the rhythm was the Florry rhythm: on a Florry day, she'd hang on his every word, her eyes radiant with attention. She'd ask him questions about every aspect of his life, his school, his parents. He found himself divulging intimacies and secrets he had told no one in years. He found himself at night thinking of new stories he could tell her to make her squeal with laughter and delight.

"I just love to hear you talk," she said.

But there were also Julian days, not so many at first and not quite vivid enough, when they did come, to merit comment; yet still they occurred, and Florry would seem not to exist to her. She wouldn't meet his eyes and she'd hang on Julian. He could see her seem to bend toward him, as if to absorb him. They had their little secrets, Sylvia and Julian, their little jokes, and on these days he

could see a light in her eyes he never saw when she was talking to him. She seemed to be achieving a total oneness with Julian, as if, somehow, she were sinking into him.

Damn you, Julian.

He began to think how perfect the world would be if Julian were not around. If only by some stroke Julian could be removed, and not exist at all.

Yet the next day, she was his again and he felt the pleasure and the triumph of her attentions.

One afternoon, he felt unusually strong and asked if anybody cared to come with him on a walk. Julian said no, he'd prefer to try to drink the world dry of bubbly, but Sylvia rose with a smile for him. It was a Florry day.

They walked down the beach. They reached the base of the cliff in a matter of minutes and walked along it. The sand under their feet was white and dry and fine. The cliff towered above them, chalky and wrinkled, its crown bridged in greenery a hundred feet up. Florry felt prickly and unsure of himself.

"How's the neck?"

"Oh, it seems all right. It's stiff, but if I understand the doctor correctly it will *always* be stiff."

"You've got some nice color now. You seemed so pale in the hospital. You looked so awful there. With those other wounded boys about."

"I hated the hospital. I've already put it out of my mind. I keep thinking about the battle."

"Julian says you were very brave."

"Julian cares about that. About being brave. Do you know, I really don't. It has no interest for me."

"Julian says the war is going badly."

"I suppose it is."

"Julian says that unless the POUM cracks the siege of Huesca, then the Soviet Union will take over the revolution. God, it's so confusing. Julian says that—"

"Do you know, Sylvia, I don't really care what Julian says."

"Why, Robert, what a terrible thing to say. He admires you so. He's your closest friend."

"Ummmm," was all Florry could think to say.

They walked on in silence.

"What is bothering you, Robert?"

"I'm just tired, I suppose."

"Well, you shouldn't say unkind things about Julian."

"Which of us, may I ask, do you prefer?"

"Why, I love you both, Robert."

"Do you go to him at night?"

"Robert. What a rude question."

"Rude or not, do you?"

"Of course not."

"But then you're not coming to my room, either."

"You feel terrible. You've told me yourself. You're too weak. You've had a hellish experience."

"I'm getting stronger."

"Well, if that's what you want, then I shall come tonight."

After dinner, Florry read on his balcony until dark. He was in an odd mood, and thought he might write. He had not thought of writing in some time, when once it had been all he lived for. In his kit, he found paper and pen. He filled the pen and faced the blank paper.

"I came to Spain," he began, "in the beginning of January 1937 because I wished at last to take a stand against Fascism and Spain seemed to be the only place avail—"

Rot, he thought.

I came to Spain, he thought, because a bloody British major said he'd throw my precious hide into Scrubs if I didn't. When I got here, much to my ignorant surprise, there was a war on and I'm right in the middle.

He wrote on the page, slowly, and with much deliberation, "I hate Holly-Browning, I hate Holly-Browning."

Then he crossed it out and wrote the truth.

"I hate Julian Raines."

He looked at his watch. There was a knock on the door. Florry quickly tore up the piece of paper, and felt embarrassed and silly.

He wondered why Sylvia was so early.

"Stinky, get you out here, for God's sake," came Julian's cry through the door. "You'll never guess who's here! You've bloody *got* to see this!"

"God, Julian—"

"This *instant,* old son!"

Florry threw open the door and discovered himself face to face with a man of aching familiarity. There, chunky and self-effacing, stood a young man in the uniform of a Republican captain. Then Florry placed the face and the body and made the discovery that it was the officer Comrade Steinbach had executed on the flatbed truck at La Granja.

"Salud, comrade," said the captain, kissing him.

21

THE HOSPITAL

EVEN IN TARRAGONA, IT HAD CHANGED. LEVITSKY PICKED it up immediately; a change, somehow, in the air. Certain fashions had altered: the mono, for example, was no longer the garment of the day. Fashionable people dressed for dinner. Motorcars had been freed from their garages: everybody who was anybody had a shiny black auto. The revolutionary slogans had somewhat faded. A different feeling gripped the city.

The POUM and the radical Anarcho-Syndicalists no longer articulated the spirit of the times; they seemed, somehow, on the run themselves. Instead, the PSUC, the Communist Party of Catalonia, which six months earlier had some five hundred members, was the new gang at the top, swollen with membership and influence and ties to the government. The new slogan seemed to sum it all up: "First the war, then the revolution."

Koba knew: he didn't want radical regimes spouting off like absurd tea kettles. The truth is, Koba isn't revolutionary at all, that's all illusion. He's a realist, a cynic. Koba wants there to be only one revolution, in Russia, his own.

Levitsky sat in a seedy, dark seaside bar just off the Ramblas and could see a group of bitter young POUMistas in their suddenly outré monos sitting in the gloom, trying to figure out over *tinto* what was happening. Why were they denounced on the radio, called traitors in the posters, followed ominously by NKVD and SIM goons, eavesdropped upon, wiretapped, strip-searched, hounded? Murdered?

It was beginning. Koba's emissaries had prepared well. Whatever Glasanov's failures in apprehending Levitsky—that sure death sentence if it leaked out—the man was a professional when it came to organizing terror.

His drink arrived. The schnapps was minty, sweet, almost smoky. If I ever truly become an old man, I'll do nothing except fuss over chess problems and drink peppermint schnapps. I will drink a lot of peppermint schnapps.

He looked at his watch. It was close to one. All right, old man, time to move.

Finishing the schnapps, he remembered a time when he didn't need schnapps for courage: his beliefs had been enough. But that was when he was a young man.

He stepped out into the salt air, blinking at the hot sunlight. It was so temperate here; June was a lovely month. Taking a breath, he headed up the street, turned left, and walked another two blocks. He came after a time to the graveyard. The markers, white, without ornamentation, looked fresh as baby's teeth against the grass. He walked in. It was completely quiet. Levitsky walked the ranks of the dead and came to graves that looked freshest.

"So many," a voice said.

Levitsky turned, to face an old man.

"Are you the caretaker?"

"Yes, señor. The boys who die at night in the hospital are brought here in the morning."

"Yes, I know," said Levitsky.

"You are perhaps looking for a certain person?"

"No. I meant merely to pay my respects to the fallen."

"So many. I hope they die in a good cause."

One has, thought Levitsky.

He walked back, stopping once to rest. Getting old. An Asalto gave him a curious look but let him pass. When he reached the hospital, he went in.

"What business, have you, sir?" asked the nurse. Another young German Jew, she did not call him comrade any more.

"I seek after my son. His name is Braunstein. Joseph. He was fighting with the Thaelmann Column, but I have been told he was wounded."

"Just a moment, please."

The girl went to her list. Levitsky sat down on a chair in the lobby. Soldiers milled about.

"Herr Braunstein?"

"Please. We left Germany in 'thirty-three. It's just Mr. Braunstein now. You have news of my son? He is all right? They told me at Party headquarters in Barcelona that—"

"Mr. Braunstein, I'm sorry to inform you that your son Joseph Braunstein, wounded May twenty-sixth outside Huesca, died last night of his wounds. He never recov—"

"Ahhhhhh. Oh God, no. Oh God, Oh God. Please. I must . . . Oh, God, I—"

He faltered, dropping to one knee.

"Orderly," the girl shouted, "call a doctor. This man is ill. Please, please, Herr Braunstein, I'm so sorry. Please. Here, please, come with me. Come in here."

He stood up.

"They said it was only a minor wound. Oh, God, he was a flutist. He was studying music in Paris. Oh, such a wonderful boy. I told him not to come—Oh, God, he was such a wonderful boy."

She lead him back into the inner office, where there was a couch. A doctor came by.

"I'm terribly sorry about your son," he said. "But you must understand, the war is terrible. It kills in the thousands. But it kills for a purpose."

"Oh, God."

"Here, take these. Rest here, for a time. Your son died fighting Hitler. Can't you take some pride in that, Herr Braunstein?"

Levitsky took the pills into his mouth, pretended to swallow. He lay back.

"Look, just stay here for a time, Herr Braunstein. When you feel

better, you can move. Perhaps we can find out where they put your son. Then you can—"

Levitsky closed his eyes until they left. He waited another five minutes, then rolled off the couch. Spitting out the pills, he went swiftly to the filing cabinet against the wall, opened the drawer marked *F,* flipped through the files.

There was no Florry.

Damn the Spanish! Of course their files are out of date. Hopelessly balled up. Damn them, the fools. You'd think with these Germans to help them . . . !

He sat back down.

Failure. Another failure.

"Are you feeling better now?"

"Yes, miss. I think I had better go."

"Herr Braunstein, we could perhaps take you someplace? Where are you staying?"

"No. Thank you, miss. I'd best be off."

She led him out through the outer office.

"Here," she said, halting at her desk. "I found this for you."

She opened her drawer and removed something. It was a medal.

"It's the Cross of the Republic. I thought perhaps you might care to have it."

"But it is yours."

"My brother's. He won it last year. But he died in the defense of Madrid. Here, I want you to have it. Your son earned it, after all."

Levitsky seemed suddenly to falter again.

"Are you all right?"

"Could I perhaps have a glass of water. My throat feels very dry."

"Yes, of course. I'll get it."

She rushed off. Levitsky could see the file on her desk. It said FLORRY, ROB'T. (BRIT.); 29TH DIV.

He opened it, his eyes scanned the Spanish until at last he came to an entry that read, *"Liberación,* 5.22.37 *Permiso, Cab de Salou."*

When the girl arrived with the water, he drank it swiftly and started to leave.

"The medal. Sir, you forgot the medal."

"Thank you, miss," he said and took it.

He left for Cab de Salou later that afternoon. But he stopped at the graveyard and found the old man.

"Yes?"

"This medal."

"Yes, señor?"

"It belongs to that boy over there, Braunstein. Would you plant it under his marker."

"Yes," said the old man, and Levitsky hurried off.

It had not occurred to him to wonder why Florry's file had been out on the desk rather than in its drawer. The reason was that it had been flagged by express order of SIM. Comrade Major Bolodin himself was on his way to pick it up.

22

THE MISSION

I'S ABOUT TANKS, COMRADE FLORRY. AND IT'S ABOUT bridges. And it's about our future."

The speaker was a portly yet studious figure of a man in a turtleneck sweater of bulky knit, whose girth was in no way disguised by the garment, or by the raffish Sam Brown belt complete with heavy Star automatic he sported. He rose to greet Florry with an insincere smile as Florry entered Julian's room.

"Glad you could join us," said Comrade Steinbach, his dead eye blank and glitterless, his other fiendishly alive. "How's the wound?"

"It's fine," said Florry, sure Steinbach cared little for the answer. "Stiff. A messy scar, that's all."

"You've met my friend Portela. Under slightly different circumstances, if I recall."

"In considerably better shape now than when last seen," said Florry. "I had thought the Church had a monopoly on resurrection."

"Nothing so miraculous," said Steinbach. "It was simple theater, the little charade with the pistol. We had to shoot him, in case there were spies about. No one could know he was my agent, just returned from a long, dangerous passage behind the lines."

"Welcome back to the living, Comrade Portela," said Florry.

The dapper young Spaniard clicked his heels together with the

216 /

precision of a comic general in an operetta, and bowed stiffly at the waist.

"_Buenas noches,_ Comrade Florry," he said. "It is a pleasure to accept your compliments." For a brave spy, he was a bit on the pudgy side.

"Why don't you sit down, Comrade Florry? I believe it will be an interesting evening," said Steinbach.

Florry sat.

"We've figured out how to win the war in Aragon with a bloody big bang," said Julian. Florry had seen Julian like this before: weirdly animated, beside himself with giddy joy. Julian could hardly control himself. He was still in his dinner jacket, but he paced the room like a panther, clasping and reclasping his arms about himself. Somehow he disgusted Florry.

"As you know from most intimate experience," said Steinbach, "our militia has taken the leading role in the siege of Huesca, supported most enthusiastically by those organizations such as the Anarchists, who share our political philosophies and our passion for the revolution and our belief in freedom. But because we cannot crack Huesca, we are called traitors, secret Fascists, counterrevolutionaries. The lies are repeated often and loudly; people are beginning to believe them. I need not specify who is telling these lies, but they are the same people who arrest or assassinate our leaders. There was fighting in Barcelona early last month. The pressures against us are mounting terribly. A saboteur destroyed our magazine. My ears are still ringing from the blast! And so we must crack Huesca. Not merely for our honor but for our survival."

"Huesca," said Portela, "is the key."

"We must break the city before the Fascists can lift the siege. To do so would be to considerably lessen the pressures upon ourselves. To do so would be to save the revolution from the men in the Kremlin. And to keep it for the people. Perhaps worth dying for, eh?"

Florry nodded lamely. It seemed all gibberish to him.

Where do I stand on this? he wondered. *Whose side am I on? What do I care about? What matters to me?*

"Do you know why we attacked Huesca the night you were wounded, comrade?"

"No, comrade."

"Because Portela reached me with information that a German engineering brigade had almost completed reinforcing a bridge in the mountains on the only direct road between Pamplona and Huesca. When they are done, the bridge will be able to support the weight of the PzKpfw II German tank. We attacked because we had to get into the city before the bridge was finished. We failed. It's clear now why: the attack was betrayed."

"And there are tanks?"

"Thick as flies, old man," Julian said. "Jerry has a bunch of the filthy beasts in the mountains, and he wants to spring them on us. And now he's fixing the rickety old bridge with a nice bundle of fine Krupp steel. Old Jerry's using Spain as a bloody lab and he wants to see how his gadgets work."

"When will this bridge be finished?" he asked because he knew he was supposed to.

"It will be finished three days from today. Today is the thirteenth. And on the sixteenth of June, those tanks will come out of the mountains and they will deploy into an assault formation on the flat plains around Huesca and they will be supported by mechanized eighty-eight-millimeter high-velocity guns and they will chew our militia to pieces. Then they'll crash through the gates of the city and free it. It will be a great victory for the Fascists. And it will be a great victory for the Communists. And we shall pass into history, Comrade Florry."

"Unless somebody unfinishes that bloody bridge," said Julian. "Sounds like fun, eh, Stink?"

"Surely this bridge is guarded," said Florry warily.

"My goodness, yes," said Steinbach, his good eye wide with astonishment. "The Germans are very thorough, as many of us learned in 1914. They've got a special unit of crack troops at the

bridge itself as well as a reinforced battalion of very tough Moorish legionnaires bivouacked nearby. But most importantly, they've built a concrete bunker at the bridge and fitted it out with a brace of Maxim guns. Any guerrilla attack would fail. And we could never get the Russian bombers to help us by bombing the target."

"I have a very good idea you're about to ask me a great favor."

"Oh, it's lovely," said Julian. "Oh, Stinky, you'll just *love* it."

Julian, you idiot, Florry thought. You've bought it all, haven't you? Their propaganda, their insane conviction, their love of themselves and their cause.

"There happen to be in Pamplona two Englishmen in possession of an extraordinary credential. They are representatives of Sir Oswald Mosley's British Fascist Union, on a fact-finding tour in Nationalist territory, and Generalissimo Franco has issued them a carte blanche right-of-travel pass. These two gentlemen may travel unimpeded anywhere they wish in the White zone. Franco himself says it."

"Imagine," said Julian, suddenly producing his small .25 automatic, "imagine, Stink, if a sad accident occurred to those two lads and those documents fell into *our* hands, and we used them to examine this miracle of modern German engineering at the bridge and we just happened to be there when a band of guerrillas led by Lieutenant Portela attacked. And suppose, Stinky, we were able to knock out that gun bunker, so that the guerrillas could come down and plant their lovely little dynamite charges. Poof! As if in a dream, the bridge has vanished and Jerry's toys are stuck up in the mountains and cannot come to the rescue of Huesca. And the bloody Russian secret policemen in Barcelona have got to explain to their bosses what went wrong."

"In three bloody days? How? Do we fly?"

"You could make it, Comrade Florry. Just. You leave for the front tomorrow morning. You'll be there by late afternoon. You cross tomorrow night at nightfall, near Zaragossa. Portela has arranged for a truck to get you into Pamplona by the morning. Sometime that afternoon or in the evening you'll intercept the two

British Fascists. Early the next morning, the morning of the sixteenth, you set out for the bridge by an auto we've secured for you.
You should make it in three hours. It's tight, I grant you. But it's
always tight. It was tight in July, when we started this thing. It
will be tight till the end."

"Who are these Englishmen?" asked Florry.

"Chap calling himself Harry Uckley. Ex-British army officer.
Actually an Eton man, a few years before us. A footballer, they tell
me."

"From the old school," said Florry.

"He and a chap called Dyles, sitting pretty as you please in
Pamplona with their fine uniforms, hobnobbing with Jerry, guz-
zling *tinto,* and chasing the señoritas. Stinky, it'll be *such* fun. Do
join me. You see, the two who replace the unfortunate Harry and
his chum have just *got* to be old Eton boys. The other Brits in the
militia haven't got the polish. Can you imagine poor Billy Mowry
trying to pass as Eton? Good heavens, out of the question."

"It's much to ask," said Steinbach, "but these are hard times.
The hardest times, perhaps."

"It *is* the right thing, Stink. It really is."

"A bridge," said Florry, in private bitterness.

"What say, Stink? What heroes we'll be. How Sylvia will be
impressed with her two brave boyos, and all the rest of the señoritas!" He smiled loonily.

Florry looked at them. Julian, whom he did not know, not
really, Portela whom he did not care to know, and finally Steinbach
whom he did not like. Fools, all. But he could not face saying no
to something Julian had already said yes to. He could not face
Sylvia having said no.

Oh, blast, he thought. In for a penny, in for a pound.

"Let's drop the bastard into the river like a smashed birdcage,"
he said.

Later, near eleven, Florry went to her room and knocked.

There was no answer. He knocked again, louder.

After a while, he felt quite idiotic. He went back to his room. But he could not settle down. Where in God's name was she? He was going off in the morning to risk everything. Where was she?

He went to Julian's room and knocked. There was no answer. He knew he ought to settle down, what with tomorrow coming. But this business with the girl was going too far. He went down into the lobby.

"Have you seen Miss Lilliford," he asked the porter, who spoke no English. "Pret-ty la-dy," he said slowly, as if in adding space between the syllables the man would be able to comprehend him. "*Señorita. Mucho bonita señorita.*"

"Robert. There you are!"

He turned. The two of them were just coming in.

"We went for a walk. We came looking for you but you'd disappeared."

"I was in my room."

"Oh, we thought you'd be in the bar. Time for a last drink, eh?"

"I think not, Julian."

"Listen, old man, you'll want to get a good night's sleep tonight. Busy times ahead."

"Of course."

"Well, I must leave you two lovebirds. Goodnight, darling," he said, and gave Sylvia a kiss.

When Julian had gone, Florry said, "I thought you were coming to my room."

"I'm sorry. I was on my way when I ran into Julian. Robert, please calm down. You look terribly agitated."

"Well, where were you? Where did you walk to? What did you—"

"Robert, it was just a stroll. He told me he was leaving tomorrow. And that you were, too. He was very charming but very vague. What on earth is going on?"

"It's nothing. Yes, we've got to go back to the war tomorrow."

"God, it was over so soon. I'll miss you both so much. You know, I've really had a wonderful time here and—"

"Sylvia, I want to marry you."

"What?"

"I want to marry you."

"Robert, don't be ridiculous. Here? Now? In the middle of this?"

"No, I want you to be my bride."

"Why, absolutely not. Not until I think about it."

"We're going off on a job tomorrow. It'll be quite dangerous, or so they say. It's a special thing."

"For whom?"

"Our old outfit. The POUM people. I can't tell you more. But I want you to be my wife. I want to marry you when I get back. So that you'll be mine forever, all right?"

She shook her head in wonder.

"I love you, Sylvia. Do you understand that? Let me tell you, I'm not as charming as he is, but I love you in a way he never will. What he's good at is getting people to care for him. That's his special talent. I don't have it. But in the long run, I'm better for you, Sylvia, don't you see? Really, I'm—"

"Robert. Please."

"Do you love him?"

"Yes. But in a different way than I love you. I *respect* him. It all means so much to him, the revolution, the war. He's so passionate. That's a part of his charm."

"You don't know him, Sylvia. When he gets bored with you, he'll cut you loose. He doesn't really *care* about other people."

"Robert, I—"

"Please. I must know. Tell me now. If you want, I'll go away forever. Just tell me. I can't stand this business in the middle."

She looked at him.

"I won't marry you, Robert, because of Julian. But I shall make love to you. Julian thinks he's going to die. That is what he told me. I think I'm in love with him, not that it matters to him. But I will make love to you if you promise me you will watch him and

protect him on this job coming up tomorrow. I know you want more, but that is the only thing I can give you."

Their sex had an intensity that was almost brutal. It felt to Florry, after his long hunger and his despair and in his pain, like a battle. It was all muscles and sweat; it was work. He wanted to taste her and he did and it drove her wild, like an animal. He wanted her to taste him and she fought him and he forced her down and made her do it.

When they were done they lay there, smoking cigarettes in the dark. They did not quite touch.

Finally he said, "I love you," and waited for her to respond and she didn't.

"I've lost you, haven't I?"

"I'm not sure. I don't know. I'm going to do a lot of thinking. I'll wait in Barcelona. I have to sort this out."

"Maybe I'll get killed and you won't have to be confused."

"Don't talk like such an ass."

"I think I'm going to my room. I've got some plans to make."

"All right."

"I'm going to tell Julian about this. I think he should know."

"All right. Do you want me to come?"

"No. Good-bye, Sylvia. I'll see you in the morning."

Florry paused at the door to Julian's room. Odd, he thought he heard talking.

He waited. No, it was quiet.

He knocked.

"Good God, what fool can be pounding on my door at midnight? Go away, Wee Willie Winkle, the children are fast asleep."

"Julian, it's Robert."

"Stink, there's plenty of time to talk later."

"Julian, it's important."

"Christ." There was some stirring inside.

Finally the door opened a bit and Julian, looking frazzled, leaned

out. A puff of the warm Mediterranean sea breeze inflated the curtain behind him and mussed his hair.

"Love to have you in, old man, but people would talk. Now what on earth *is* this?"

"Julian, look, I wanted to tell you. Before tomorrow, before we leave."

"God, Stink, from the look on your bloody face I believe you *have* finally succeeded in getting yourself listed ahead of me in Mother's will."

"No, Julian, it's serious."

"You've sprained your thumb and thought better of tomorrow. Odd, I've just stubbed a toe and come to the same conclusion. Quite natural, old man, and—"

"Julian, I've just come from Sylvia. We've been together. Do you see what I'm saying? But I think she would really rather be with you. We've actually had a row. I just want you to know."

"All right, Robert. That's actually less interesting news to me than you might suppose. Now, good God, go to bed, you fool."

Florry stood there and started to walk away, thinking about Julian's luck and his own lack of it. Julian had her and it meant nothing; he'd lost her and it meant everything. He hated Julian for that, most of all: his sublime indifference. And then he noticed what it was that had him feeling odd, feeling peculiar, feeling unsettled about the whole scene.

It was something borne on the sea breeze from Julian's room.

It was the scent, however diluted, however mixed with other odors, and however much Florry willed it not to be, of peppermint.

Florry stood rooted to the floor. He looked up and down the corridor.

Julian, you filthy bastard, he thought.

And then Florry realized what he must become.

He must become a spy.

He went swiftly to the door next to Julian's. The hotel was

largely empty: the chances were that the room would be empty, too. He tried his own key, which didn't work. He opened his pocket knife and slipped it into the doorjamb and pushed mightily; the door popped open with a snap. He stepped in, preparing an excuse in case he should have roused someone, but saw instantly the beds were unused and the room immaculate. He pulled the door behind him and walked through the darkness to the balcony. He eased open the french doors and stepped through. Before him, the formal gardens radiated an icy glaze in the patina of the white moon like a dream of a maze. Beyond, the sea, a sheet of dazzled glow, altered its surface microscopically under the pressure of the light. The wind was soft yet sure.

The leap to Julian's balcony was about six feet and it never occurred to him to look down or to believe he couldn't make it. He slipped off his shoes, climbed over the railing, hung for just a second as he gauged the distance and prepared his nerve, and then with a mighty push flung himself across the gap, snaring Julian's railing with his hand and the balcony ledge with his foot. He climbed quietly over, edged along the wall. The door was slightly open.

"You've never wavered?"

The bloody voice. Unfilled with jangled Germanisms, unaddled with madness, but the same—or different. Calm, somehow; the accent vague, the tone sympathetic, assuring, oddly filled with conviction.

"*Of course* I've wavered," said Julian, distraught. "I've hated myself. I revolt myself. Who do you think I am, a bloody saint?"

"No, of course not. You are only another weak man such as myself."

"*Not* such as yourself. You're a bloody inspiration. I'm just sullied flesh."

"You must be strong."

"Ah, God." Julian seemed to arch with agony and disbelief. Florry had never heard him so close to losing control. His voice was full of tremulous emotion.

"You cannot help yourself," said Levitsky.

"No, I can't," said Julian. "I try. But you've got me wholly, totally." He sounded angry now.

"You'll come in the end to accept your other self, your true self. You'll see how your mission is the most important part of you. How all the misrepresentations, the lies, the deceits—how they make you stronger over the longer course. You will understand things you might not otherwise. Your sensitivities are increased, they are keener, more perceptive. It means you are special. You'll come in the end to define it as a strength."

Florry could stand no more.

That was it, then—utterly and irrevocably. Damn them. Damn them both.

He retreated swiftly, slipping back across the gap and quickly put on his shoes. He checked his watch. It was almost one. The car would come at nine tomorrow and by nightfall they'd be off.

It was time at last to read *Tristram Shandy*.

In the morning, Florry went down to the lobby. Julian and Sylvia were already talking.

"Oh, hullo, Stink. Just saying our good-byes."

She was watching him talk, her eyes radiant with love and submission. She hardly looked at Florry.

"Well, look, here comes the car and bloody Steinbach and his chum Portela. I suppose I should let you have a last minute alone. May I, Robert?" He kissed Sylvia lightly on the cheek, then backed off. "Good-bye, Sylvia. It was splendid."

He turned and went out to the car.

"Sylvia, can you do me one favor?" Florry said.

"Yes, Robert."

"Look here, it's so silly, I borrowed a copy of *Tristram Shandy* from this chap Sampson in Barcelona. A newsman of *The Times*. I know it sounds silly, but I'd like to get it back to him. Do you think you could drop it off? You'd find him at the Café de las Ramblas."

"Yes, Robert, of course."

"Thank you. And I shall see you—ah, the week of the twentieth, shall we say? At the Grand Oriente. At eleven in the morning? Tuesday, shall we say?"

"Yes. I'll be there."

He wanted to take her in his arms and kiss her.

"This would be so much bloody easier if I didn't love you so much."

"I wish I loved you the way you require, Robert. I wish you didn't feel you had to own me. Watch after yourself. Watch after Julian."

Florry turned and left for the car. He would not look back. He could feel his Webley against his side in the shoulder holster. He'd oiled and cleaned it. And loaded it.

23

¡VIVA LA ANARQUÍA!

LEVITSKY SAT IN THE SQUARE AT THE CAFÉ. HE WAS VERY tired. He ordered a cup of *café con leche.* He looked about. It could have been any village in Spain. It was called Cabrillo de Mar, about ten miles out of Salou on the road to Lerida. Soon a Twenty-ninth Division staff car that would be taking Florry and Julian Raines on their mission would pass through the village on the way toward the front.

He was so tired of traveling. Yet there was one last thing to do.

The coffee arrived. He poured the milk into it, mixed it until it was thick, and then took a sip: delicious. As you get old, certain comforts matter more.

You should get going, he told himself. Back to Barcelona. Finish it. Why wait?

I wait because I am tired. And because I must see.

Go on, old man. Leave.

No. He had to *see* the car and *know* they were off. It was the old empiricist in him, that unwillingness to trust what he hadn't observed. He wondered when he would feel the triumph. Or would he feel it at all? He had done it, after all; but at such cost.

Sacrifices. Old man, you are the master of sacrifice. Let no man ever say the Devil Himself doesn't understand two things: the theory of history and the theory of sacrifice. However, perhaps in this century they are the same.

He felt eyes on him and looked up. A member of the Guardia Civil was headed toward him. It was a pockmarked boy with a

Labor a machine pistol slung over his shoulder. He wore a khaki mono and a gorillo cap with a red star on it. He looked stupid.

"Salud, comrade," called Levitsky.

The boy regarded him, and Levitsky, bleary eyed, could feel the hate. What was it, the battered way he looked? The smell of peppermint? His clear foreignness?

"Your papers, comrade" said the boy.

Levitsky got out a passport.

"A foreigner?"

"Yes, I'm an international," Levitsky said, and knew instantly he'd blundered.

"Are you English? Russian?" asked the boy.

"No, comrade. Polish."

"I think you're Russian."

"No. No, comrade. Long live the revolution. I'm Polish."

"No, I think you're a Russian." He swung the machine pistol over onto him.

"Hands up," he said. "You're a Russian, here to take over. Get going." The gun muzzle looked big as a church bell.

Levitsky rose. The boy walked him across the square.

The boy seemed to hate Russians for some reason. Or perhaps it was something else: he had just wanted to parade somebody through the square at gunpoint with his shiny new weapon to show off for the girls of the town.

As he walked he could sense something odd about this place: the slogans smeared on the stucco walls in the hot sun had a kind of stridency to them he hadn't noticed in other such villages. He translated.

FREE THE LAND

UP THE CNT

FAI FOREVER

THE REVOLUTION NOW

He soon found himself in the Guardia Civil station—or what had once been a Guardia Civil station and was now littered and

looted and clearly in the possession of some sort of People's Committee for Order. The boy put him in the one cell of the dirty little building overlooking the square.

They were waiting, the boy had explained, for the *sargento,* who would take care of everything. Levitsky told himself he really ought to get some sleep. You're an old man, comrade, he thought. Almost sixty; you've still got something to do. You need your rest.

And thus he was situated when a car did in fact appear in the square. It was not, however, the car he expected; it was another vehicle altogether, and when it drew to a halt and its door popped open, two thuggish Spaniards in overcoats got out, checked around, and nodded into its dark interior. Comrade Bolodin emerged.

Levitsky drew back. Trapped.

As the two thugs came inside, Levitsky quickly dropped to the straw bunk and turned toward the wall, wrapping himself in the blanket. He heard the two newcomers arguing with the boy. The men kept saying SIM, SIM, over and over. No, the boy kept saying, FIJL, which was the Federación Iberia de Juventudes Liberatatión, the radical anarchist youth organization.

The boy, in short, wouldn't listen to them because they were the enemy, here to take over the revolution from the people in this small seacoast village.

"*Sargento,*" he kept saying. "*Sargento.*"

The two men after a time returned to the car, and Levitsky heard one of them speak in heavily accented English to Bolodin.

"Señor Boss, this snot-nose kid, he say is nothing he can do until his sergeant come."

"Christ," said Bolodin. "You show him the picture?"

"Boss, this kid, he is having a machine gun. Is no toy."

"You moron. I ought to turn him loose on you."

"Sorry, Comrade Boss."

"Don't 'Sorry, Comrade Boss' me. I didn't drive here half the night from Tarragona for the old goat to hear you say you were sorry. Just get over there and wait."

Levitsky was impressed. Bolodin had penetrated his own motives

and taken his inquiries to the hospital, on the belief that Levitsky would be hanging around wounded Englishmen. Now he was up here on the road to Cab de Salou showing the picture of Levitsky from *Deutsche Schachzeitung.* If he showed it to the boy . . .

They walked over to the café and commandeered a table near the sidewalk. Levitsky watched as Bolodin put his feet up on the railing and pulled out a brightly colored pack of cigarettes, plucked one out, and quickly lit it. He did not offer smokes to his companions, who sat on either side with the nervous alertness of bodyguards.

Levitsky looked at his watch. It was about nine thirty. The boy said the sergeant came in at ten. He looked around the cell for a way out and could see none. The boy sat in the front room with his machine pistol. He looked straight ahead.

Another locked room. As if the first weren't terror enough, he had to play the same—

"Boy. Hey, boy. Come here," Levitsky called.

The boy grabbed his weapon and came back. He had sullen, stupid eyes and seemed bull-headedly frightened of making a mistake. His khaki uniform was too big; still, he was lucky to be here, and not out in the trenches somewhere, or caught by opposing factionalists and stood against the wall.

"Durutti?" Levitsky suddenly asked, naming the Anarchist hero killed leading a column of Anarchist troops in the Battle of Madrid late last year.

The boy looked at him suspiciously.

"*Sí,* Durutti," he said.

"*¡Viva* Durutti!" said Levitsky with enthusiasm. He gave the Anarchist's double-fisted salute. He'd actually known this Durutti in Moscow in 1935 at the Lux. The man was a hopeless dreamer and lunatic, exactly the sort of uncontrollable rogue who'd become a great hero in a civil war, but utterly worthless at any other time. The Anarchists were all like that: wedded to absurd notions of a stateless society.

"You're an Anarchist, no?" he asked.

"*Sí,* I'm an Anarchist. Long live Anarchism. Death to the state!" proclaimed the boy.

Levitsky saw just the slightest chance.

"I'm an Anarchist also," he said carefully, hoping his Spanish was right.

"No," said the boy. "Russians can't be Anarchists. Russians are all gangsters. Stalin is the head gangster."

"I'm Polish," said Levitsky. "A Polish Anarchist."

The boy looked at him darkly.

"*Revolución sí, la guerra no,*" Levitsky added, hoping again to approximate the idea of the Durutti slogan.

"*Sí,*" said the boy.

"Comrade," said Levitsky. "*Por favor.* Look at this." He smiled slyly.

He rolled up his sleeve, past the elbow. There on his right biceps a black fist clenched in ardent fury, ready to smite the governments and policemen of the world. The tattoo dated from 1911. He and several others of the Party had been trying to organize the Trieste millworkers but at every step of the way they were opposed by an Anarchist organization that loathed Bolsheviks. Levitsky had been directed to stop them, for their irresponsibility could so enflame the policemen of the Continent that revolutionary activity would be impossible for months. He'd penetrated their secret society under an alias and been tattooed with the black fist as part of his rite of passage. When after months of careful maneuver he had finally met the ringleaders in a Trieste café, he'd betrayed them to the police. They were taken off and most of them had died in prison.

The boy looked at the mark on his arm, his eyes widening in wonder.

"*Salud,* comrade," said the boy.

"*Sí.* I salute. I salute Bakunin. I salute the great Durutti. I salute Anarchism!"

The boy went and got a key and opened the door and embraced him.

"*Está libre, hermano,*" the boy said. "*¡Libre!*" Free, he was saying. "One Anarchist may not lock up another Anarchist. *Está libre. ¡Viva la anarquía!*"

Levitsky could see the American Bolodin through the open doorway, sitting at the café, and beyond that he could see an elderly man in Guardia Civil uniform head across the square, and at that same moment, a black Ford, the Twenty-ninth Division staff car, with Julian Raines and Robert Florry in the rear, pulled through the square and disappeared down the road and out of town.

"*¡Viva la anarquía!*" said Levitsky, and he meant it, for dark forces had been loosed in the world.

He embraced the boy and, seconds later, slipped out.

24

TRISTRAM SHANDY

THE MAJOR WAS EXTREMELY NERVOUS. HE COULDN'T CON-centrate, he couldn't sit still, he couldn't take tea. His stomach felt sour and uneasy: dyspepsia, that scourge of the office animal. By the end he had given up all pretense of organized activity and simply stood at the window, looking down the five floors in late afternoon to the street. He stood there for several hours. He felt if he moved he would somehow curse his enterprise and fate it to catastrophe.

Finally, the black car pulled up and he watched as the queer, eager figure of Mr. Vane popped out. Vane moved with appropriate dispatch into the building. The major thought his heart would burst, but at the same time he felt the killing imperative to main-tain a certain formality for the proceedings. Thus he seated himself at his desk, turned on the light, took out and opened his fountain pen, removed from the rubble a sheet of paper, and began to doodle. He drew pictures of flowers. Daffodils. He could draw beautiful daffodils.

He heard the opening of the lift and the slow, almost stately progress of Mr. Vane, who advanced upon him as a glacier must have moved down from the Pole during the Age of Ice. At last the door to the outer office opened; there was a pause while the orderly and precise Mr. Vane took off his coat, hung it on a hanger— buttoning the top button, of course, for the proper fall of the garment—and hung the hanger on the rack; then put his jaunty

little Tyrolean in his desk drawer, the second one on the right-hand side.

"Sir. Major Holly-Browning?" The man stood in the doorway with the practiced diffidence of a eunuch in a harem.

"What! Oh, I say, Vane, I didn't hear you come in. You gave me a start. Back already, then?"

"Yessir."

"Well, that's fine. Any difficulty?"

"No sir. Well, actually, sir, the plane from Barcelona was slow in getting off the ground. Then I must say I had crisp words with an F.O. chap at Heathrow who insisted that he take the pouch all the way to Whitehall before opening it."

"You should have called me."

"I prevailed, sir."

"Then you've got it?"

"Yessir."

"Well, why don't you set it on the table? Then perhaps you'd like to freshen up, perhaps get a bite. I want to finish this damned report before I get to it."

"Yessir. Here it is then, sir. I'll be back shortly. Please feel free to call me if you want anything."

"Yes, Vane. Very good."

Vane set the thing on the table near the window. He turned and left and the major did not look up to watch him. He listened to him leave. He continued to play at working for some minutes. He told himself he would wait fifteen minutes. He did not want to rush, to queer the thing with impatience. He had waited quite a bit, after all.

The last observation had the effect of sending him back. He set the pen down. The daffodils were forgotten. He remembered the dark cellar of the Lubyanka in the year 1923.

He remembered the Russian sitting across from him, the eyes bright with intelligence and sympathy. It had been a brilliant, patient performance, seductive and terrifying. Levitsky had invited

Holly-Browning to resist, to argue; and each argument had been gently and delicately deflected. The man was a genius of conviction; he had that radiant, enveloping charm that reaches out through the brain and to the heart; it enters and commands.

It was very late in the interrogation, and Holly-Browning was reduced to bromides.

"The British Empire is the most benevolent and compassionate in the history of the world," he recalled saying, filled with exhaustion and regret.

The Russian listened, seemed to pause and reflect.

"I would never deny that. Of course it is. Yet are you not being awfully easy on yourself? Are you really willing to *examine* the reality of it for another point of view? I think you may find the results intriguing."

The first betrayal had been a betrayal of the imagination. Yes, with Levitsky as his guide, the major had allowed himself to *imagine:* imagine the Raj from the point of view of a Hong Kong coolie, making do with eleven children on less than a penny a day; or imagine the world of Johnny Sepoy, sent around the globe to die for a king he didn't know, a faith he couldn't understand, an officer he didn't respect, and five rupees a week; or a textile worker, breathing the dust of a Leeds woolen mill, his lungs blacking up, coughing blood at thirty, dead at thirty-five; or . . .

"The realities of empire," said Levitsky, "are considerably different depending upon one's proximity to the apex of the pyramid of power." He smiled. Warmth and love poured from his eyes. He touched the major on the shoulder. The major loved the touch. He loved the strength and the courage of the man, he loved him in the way that soldiers in a trench for months on end can come to love one another, in a sacred, not profanely physical, way. Their ordeal in the cellar had joined them.

"I can feel you *trying* to understand," said Levitsky. "It takes a heroic amount of will. You're probably the bravest man in the world, James; you've faced death in battle a hundred, a thousand times. Yet what you do now, *that* is bravery, bravery of the will."

The major felt the passionate urge to surrender to the man. It was so very late and they had been together for so very long.

"Think about it. You have been offered a chance to join an elite. One does not look twice at an offer to join an elite, and to live a life untainted by corruption and exploitation. It's a powerful elixir."

The truth is, as Major Holly-Browning knew, most men *are* willing to be spies against their own country. In his way, Julian is not so extraordinary after all; treason, in its way, is quite banal. A careful recruiter, a Levitsky, nursing the grudge and resentment that all men quite naturally feel toward their social betters and toward the freaks of circumstance and luck that explain triumph and failure in the world, can take a clerk and manufacture a spy in a weekend.

The shame began to suffuse the major. He could feel it building. He was so ashamed. He had been so weak. He had yielded.

"Yes," Major Holly-Browning had said to Levitsky in the cellar of the Lubyanka at the end of their very long trip together in 1923, "Yes. I will do it. I will spy for you." When he spoke, he believed it. At the center of his being, in his heart, in his brain, in his soul: he believed it.

The escape, coming by freak luck the next day, changed nothing. When eventually, after a series of colorful but now almost completely forgotten adventures, the major reached home, he had taken a convalescent leave and gone to the hills of Scotland and lived like a hermit in a cottage high up for a year. It was a place without mirrors. For a long time, the major could not deal with the image of his own face.

Now at last, with a timeless sigh, the slow and easeful acceptance of the firing squad by its victim, he rose and with exaggerated calmness walked to the table. He seated himself and looked at the object.

It was *Tristram Shandy,* by Laurence Sterne.

The major reached up to the lamp, deftly unscrewed and removed the bolt holding tight the shade, then removed the shade. He

snapped the light on, filling the normally dark old office with unpleasantly harsh light.

He found a piece of paper, took out his fountain pen. He held the book in his hands and looked at it for some time, trying to remain calm.

Am I here?

Levitsky, am I here at last?

He opened the book to the front endpaper, where Florry had written his signature and a date, *January 4, 1931,* thus informing the major he had chosen to start at page 31 and use the key of four.

The major opened up the book to page 31. He bent the covers back against the spine, feeling it break. With a straight razor he sliced the page away from the others and held it up to the blinding light from the bulb. Like a star over Bethlehem, a tiny flash winked at the major. It was a pinhole under the letter *L.*

The major wrote down the letter *L.* He turned four pages further into the volume and repeated the process. This time, the tiny, almost imperceptible perforation denoted the letter *E.*

The next letter located was *V.* And then an *I.*

"Damned queer," said Major Holly-Browning. "I should feel joy. Or some such. Triumph. The lightening of the load, all that. Instead, I'm just damned tired." He had no desire to do anything at all, much less share his triumph with his new partners at MI-5.

"Can I get you some tea, sir?" said Vane.

"No. I think I'll have some brandy. And I'll get it. Do sit down, Vane, I insist."

"Yessir."

Vane primly arranged himself on the sofa, a study in rectitudinous angles. Holly-Browning rose, feeling the creak and snap in his joints of so much recent disuse, and went to his side table, opened the drawer. But suddenly, he didn't feel like brandy. He wanted something stronger. He removed a bottle of Bushmill's and poured two rather large whiskeys.

"There," he said to Vane.

"But sir—"

"No. I insist. Whiskey, Vane. It's a celebration."

"Yessir."

"Vane, I want you to look at this."

"Yessir."

He handed over the sheet to Vane, who read it quickly.

"Well, sir, I should guess that ties it."

"Yes, it's what we've been looking for: the final, the irrefutable piece of evidence. The last chink in the wall. Florry spotted Raines reporting to his Russian case officer, overheard the conversation, and took notes. Damned fine job, Florry. Florry worked out, Vane, you know he did."

"Yet sir, if I may, it seems to me we got awfully good service out of our man in Barcelona. Young Sampson."

"Er, yes, Vane. I suppose I shall have to recommend that he come aboard full time now."

"Who knows, major? He could end up sitting in your chair someday."

"Not too bloody soon, I trust, Vane," said Holly-Browning.

But Vane had lurched on to another topic. "I say, sir, Florry says here, 'Step to be taken.' What can that mean?"

"You know damned well what it means, Vane."

"It's bloody brilliant, sir. You took a vague young fool and made an assassin of him inside a half-year."

"So I did, Vane. So I did."

"I say, sir, could I have another few drops of the bloody whiskey? Crikey, it's like an old friend coming home after the war, the taste of it."

"Er, yes, Vane. Please, help yourself."

Vane went and poured himself a tot, swigged it down aggressively.

He turned. The major had never seen him quite so flushed and mussed before.

"Here's to hell, sir. Where all the bloody-fookin' traitors belong so as to roast on a spit into eternity. We sent him there, by damn,

and by damn I'm proud to be a bloody-fookin' part of it. And here's to Major Jim Holly-Browning, best bloody-fookin' spy-catcher there ever was." He laughed abrasively.

"Do you know, Vane, I believe I'll drink to that," said Major Holly-Browning.

Levitsky, he thought.

It started in the Lubyanka in 1923. Now on Broadway in 1937, I've finished it.

Levitsky: I've won.

25

BEHIND THE LINES

"THERE," SAID PORTELA. "DO YOU SEE IT?"

Florry lay on the pine-needled floor of the forest and studied the Fascist lines across the valley in the fading light. With his German binoculars, he conjured up from the blur a distinct view of the trench running in the low hills, the odd outpost or breastwork. But the terrain was generally bleak and scorched; it had the look of wasted, untilled land, its farmers fled as if from plague.

"It's quiet here," said Portela, "with all the fighting up around Huesca or down near Madrid. This is where I cross. Zaragossa is not far. My people wait in the hills beyond. You'll see, comrades."

"Good show," said Julian, theatrically chipper. He stood in the trees like one of Our Gallant Lads at the Front in a 1915 West End melodrama. He had been in such a mood since they left, hearty, solicitous, irrepressibly British. He was almost hysterical with charm.

"Time to go, comrade?" he called to Portela cheerfully. "*My* bags are all packed."

"Comrade Julian, you are like a hungry dog. I've never seen a man so eager. But we must wait until the night."

"*Blast!*" said Julian. "Stink and I want to get cracking here, eh, Stink? Have at the beggars, over the top, that sort of thing."

Carrying on like a child. Performing antically for anyone who would pay him the faintest attention. Being Brilliant Julian on the center of a stage designed for him and him alone.

/ 241

Florry issued a deeply insincere smile, as if he, too, were richly amused with Brilliant Julian, but he was so poor an actor he could find no words to speak, out of fear of speaking them transparently. Instead, he turned his back, using his pack as a sort of pillow. He could see through the pine needles above a patch of sweet, crisp blue sky. He hunkered against his pack, thinking how odd it was to be wearing a peasant's rough garb and boots and be sleeping on a pack that contained a Burberry, a blue suit, and a pair of black brogues. Soon he had fallen asleep.

"Robert?"

Florry started. Julian loomed over him, staring intensely.

"Yes, old man?"

"Look, I want to say something."

"Yes?"

"Portela's sleeping. That man can sleep anywhere. Look, old boy, I've got an awfully queasy feeling that my luck's run its string. I don't think I'm going to make it back."

You swine, thought Florry. You deserve an award for your performance rather than the four-five-five I'm going to put in your head.

"You'll make it. The bullet hasn't been made that could bring down the brilliant Julian."

"No, no. And my feelings are never wrong about these things. You will. I won't. Somehow this little gimcrack"—he held out his father's wedding ring on its chain—"has lost its charm. I can feel it. I *know* it. 'Pons' shall go forever unfinished."

He smiled. His teeth were white and beautiful, his face grave and handsome. He had such high, fine cheekbones and glittery blue eyes. Julian, we mere mortals peep about your bloody ankles.

"I wanted to tell you about Sylvia. I want it straight between us. Do you understand there's nothing between us? She's yours. I'd never touch her, is that understood? The two of you: it's so *right*."

"Yes, Julian. Yes, I do understand."

And Florry did. For he knew that Julian could not betray him for love. But as for politics, that was something else. For Florry,

over the long day's drive, had finally reached the final implication
of Julian's treachery. The bridge attack would fail. And that meant
Florry would die. Julian would kill him. Even now as he addresses
me, he addresses me as the executioner talking to the victim,
assuring him that the drop of the gallows trap is nothing personal,
but purely in the best interests of the Party.

"Good, chum," said Julian. "And when I'm gone, you remember
that."

"I will, Julian," said Florry, "I will."

You bastard, he thought, surprised himself at the cold loathing
he felt. You betrayed me at school. You betrayed me with Sylvia.
Now you will betray me at the bridge. The difference is that I know
it this time and I will stop you.

"Sylvia deserves somebody dogged and solid with virtue. And
that's you and it's grand. Be good to her."

"I'm sure in twenty years we'll all get together at the Savoy over
cocktails and laugh about this conversation."

"I'm sure we _won't,_" said Julian.

They crouched in the forest. It was time. Florry found himself
breathing heavily.

"Comrades," said Portela, who had blacked his face out under
his black beret. He carried an American Thompson gun. "For you,"
he said. "Salud." He got a flask out from under his cape and handed
it over. "From Comrade Steinbach. For the English dynamiters."

He handed it to Julian, who sniffed at the snout voluptuously.
"God, lovely. Whiskey. Wonderful English whiskey. Bushmill's,
I believe. To the bloody future," he toasted, taking a bolt, "that
ugly whore." He handed the flask to Florry.

Florry threw down a swallow. It was like the brown smoke from
a thousand English hearths.

"Shall we go then, lads?" said Julian, and they were off.

Portela led them down the slope and out into no-man's-land. A
mist had risen, and the three men seemed to wade through it.
Oddly, up above, the stars were clear and sharp, shreds and flecks

of far-off, remote light. Florry was last in the file. He had the Webley in his hand, and a four-five-five in each chamber. He was just behind Julian.

Wait till you get beyond the lines. Wait till Portela leaves you. Wait till you get to the truck. Wait till you've changed into your fine English suit. Wait till you're in the truck and setting off to Pamplona. Then lift and fire. Clean. Into the back of the head. It'll be much easier than that boy in the trench.

Then what? he wondered.

Then you go on. To the bridge.

That's absurd.

They waded through the mist. The silence fell upon them heavily. The mist nipped and bobbed at his knees. Portela halted suddenly, turning, and waved them down.

Florry knelt, sinking into the mist. For a second, all was silent and still. Then there came the low slush of boots pushing their way through the wet, high grass, and Florry made out the shape of a soldier—no, another, three, four!—advancing toward them in the fog. They were Fascists on patrol, somber men in great coats with German helmets and long Mausers with bayonets. Florry tried to sink lower into the earth, but the men continued their advance, gripping their rifles tightly, their eyes peering about. Florry thought of Julian: had he somehow alerted the NKVD who had in turn alerted the Fascists?

If they find us, Julian, I'll kill you here, he thought, his hand tightening on the bulky revolver.

It was ghastly, almost an apparition, like a lost patrol in some Great War legend, the tall soldiers isolated in the rolling white fog. Florry suddenly saw that they were Moorish legionnaires, huge, handsomely formed men, with cheekbones like granite and eyes like obsidian. Savages. They'd just as soon cut your guts up as look at you. They preferred the bayonet. At Badajoz, they'd put thousands to the blade, or so the propaganda insisted.

Florry gripped his Webley so tight he thought he's smash it: what an opportunity for Julian, and so early on! A single noise, a

cough, the smallest twitch, and the bloody thing was over. Florry brought the revolver to bear in the general direction of Julian. If Julian made a noise, he'd—

He heard the footfalls growing louder.

He could hear them talking in Arabic. They laughed among themselves only feet away, and Florry fancied he could smell the cheap red wine on their breath.

They halted fifteen feet off.

More laughter.

More chatter.

Florry could feel his heart beating like a cylinder in an engine block. The sweat ran hotly down his face, though the night was cool. He lay hunched on the mist, and its moisture soaked him; he could see the damned glow of the Webley barrel.

The soldiers laughed again, and then began to move away. In minutes they had vanished altogether.

Florry felt a stream of air whistle out of his mouth in pure animal relief. He thought he might begin to tremble so hard he couldn't move. But before him first Portela with his Thompson and then Julian with his small .25 automatic rose. He came off his knees and creakily climbed to his feet. Julian flashed the old Great War high sign: thumbs up, chum.

Portela began to move up the slope and the two Englishmen followed. In the fog they stayed closer together and Portela motioned for them to hurry. They seemed to be walking in milk and Florry had lost all contact with where they were. Had they reached the Fascist line yet? Shouldn't they be crawling? What was going on?

Suddenly there was a noise. They sank back into the fog again.

There was the chink of something falling and some laughter. Then Florry heard the sound of running water—it was a man nearby pissing in the fog.

Something tapped his shoulder: Portela, gesturing him to rise quietly. Florry stood and the three began to walk swiftly ahead. They were on flat ground, it seemed, and—

They were in the yard of a small house.

"*¿Quién está?*" came a call.

"*Perdón,*" Portela answered. "*Estamos perdidos. Somos de la* Tenth Division."

"Ha!"

A man leaned out the open window, a cigarette in his mouth.

He yelled something Florry couldn't follow.

Portela yelled back. The two argued back and forth for some time.

Suddenly another voice screamed out.

"*¡Hombres! Calláos, carrajo! ¿Qué pensáis, que es una fiesta?*"

The first man said something under his breath. Portela muttered a reply. The two conversed in low tones. "*¿Jode Chingas las muchachas en Zaragoza por mí, ¿eh, amigo? Hay unas guapas allí.*"

"*Tendré los ojos abiertos,*" called back Portela. "*Les diré su mensaje.*"

"*Adiós, amigo.*"

"*Sí. Adiós, amigo,*" called back Portela, and began to walk smartly away. Florry and Julian hastened after.

From inside the hut came the sound of raucous, dirty laughter.

They walked on, climbing a low stone wall, until they found themselves in an orchard. Portela took them down its ghastly ranks, around some deserted buildings, and down at last a road. They halted in the lee of a wall.

"*¡Por Dios!*" said Portela, crossing himself several times feverishly. "My prayers were answered tonight."

"I didn't think you were quite *allowed* to pray, old man," said Julian. "That's for the other side."

"I have been an atheist since 1927," Portela said, "but on this night we needed the help of God, and so we got it."

"How extraordinary," said Julian. "Do you mean there was actually *danger* involved in all that?"

"I thought once we passed the patrol we were behind the lines. But then I took us straight to their company headquarters. 'Hey, where you go?' a fellow asks me. 'To Zargossa,' I tell him. 'Many pretty girls there.' 'You lucky you got leave,' he says. 'Fuck one for

me.' 'You men, shut your mouths,' yelled the major. God in heaven."

"Good heavens," said Julian. "I thought it was all arranged."

"Come, the trucks are this way."

Florry slid the revolver out of its holster. It was just a matter of time now. Surprisingly, what worried him most was explaining it all to Portela. He knew he could do the thing: raise the pistol, fire it into the back of the head. Once you have shot a man in the face, you can do most anything.

They reached a farmyard.

Florry saw two trucks.

What—

"Well, old man, looks like we won't be able to tell school stories on the way into Pamplona. Ta-ta." And with that, Julian scurried off.

"It's safer," said Portela. "This way at least one man gets through, no?"

"Y-yes," Florry heard himself saying, as he watched Julian climbing into the rear of the first truck. "Much safer."

26

THE CLUB CHICAGO

I T TOOK LEVITSKY NEARLY A FULL DAY TO GET BACK TO BAR-
celona, and nearly five hours into the evening—it was the
evening of the fifteenth—until he found the man that he
needed.

He began his search in the Barrio Chino, among the gaudy
prostitutes and the cheap nightclubs that plied their trade regardless of the official revolutionary austerity imposed on the city.
Levitsky was not interested in women, however, or in companionship of any sort. Bolodin would know he had just missed his quarry
at Cabrillo del Mar; he would certainly deduce that the running
man would seek safety in the one city he knew. Levitsky estimated
that he had very little time left.

The wolf is near, he thought.

A girl came and sat at his table in the Club Chicago.

"Salud, comrade," she said.

She asked him a question in Spanish.

"*Inglés, por favor,*" he said.

"Sure. *Inglés.* You wish a girl for the night? Me, maybe? Some
good tricks I know."

"No. But I have some money for you."

"For me?"

"Yes. Listen carefully. Now, in the time of the revolution, you
have been liberated. You work for yourself, correct?"

"I am a free worker."

"But it was not always so. It was not so before July. Once you worked for a man. A certain man controlled you and all the ladies."

"Before July."

"Yes. Before July."

"Suppose it were so?"

"Suppose this man had a name."

"He was called only the Aegean."

"The Aegean is gone?"

"Who knows?"

"This man would leave all he had built up? He would leave it?"

"Leave it or die. His kind was placed before walls in the early days of July and shot."

"You say he is gone. Yet oddly a ship full of illegal cigarettes attempted to reach Barcelona in January. It was sunk by the Italians. Yet clearly the owner of the ship hoped to make a great deal of money from the contraband. It sounds exactly like the sort of thing this Aegean chap might be interested in. So perhaps this fellow isn't as far gone as you maintain."

"I know nothing of such things."

"And the man who owned that ship. It is said in some quarters that he owned this place—and other places in the barrio."

"Who is asking these questions?"

"Perhaps this fifty-peseta note will convince of my friendship."

She took the bill and stuffed it down between her breasts.

"So. A friend."

"I have something to sell him. But it must be tonight. If it's not tonight, it has no value. It could make him a very important man in times to come. And it could make the girl who helps him very important in times to come."

"I'll be back. I must talk to someone."

He took out a five-hundred-peseta note, tore it in half, and gave her one piece.

"Show him this. And you get the other," he said, "when I meet the Aegean comrade."

Levitsky then sat alone for a time. Two other tarts came by; he shooed them away and ordered another peppermint schnapps.

At last the girl returned.

"Upstairs," she said. "And you better not be carrying no gun or knife or they'll cut you open."

"Salud," he said.

"My money, comrade."

He tore the remaining half in half again, and gave it to her. "You get the last piece when I get there."

They went in the back and up the steps into a decrepit hall leading to a small room.

"The man you seek is behind the door. My money."

He gave it to her and she left quickly.

Levitsky opened the door and stepped into darkness. A light hit him in the eyes. He heard an automatic pistol cock.

"Search him and check his wallet," the voice commanded.

A form approached, patted him down, and quickly relieved him of his money.

"You are a very rich man in these revolutionary times," said the voice. "Don't you know that capital is against the spirit of the people?"

"An astute man flourishes in any climate," said Levitsky.

"So he does. It's said some weeks ago a certain bold man came to possess a great many identification documents obtained illegally from particular foreign visitors to this country. Some of these documents were sold on the black market for a considerable sum. But you would know nothing of this?"

"How would a poor man such as I know anything of these criminal matters?"

"Perhaps the purchaser of the documents marked the bills with

which he paid the anonymous seller. And perhaps the first piece of the bill you gave the girl had the mark."

"What an amazing coincidence," said Levitsky.

"It's said the man removed these documents from the headquarters of the head Russian stooge policeman. I would like to meet this man."

"He must be an amazing chap," said Levitsky. "Imagine walking out of the main police station with twenty-eight confiscated passports under the names Krivitsky, Tchiterine, Ver Steeg, Malovna, Schramfelt, Steinberg, Ulasowicz—"

"Very impressive memory."

"Thank you, comrade."

"You perhaps have more documents? A very lucrative market. The hills of Barcelona are loaded with aristocrats in hiding who desperately need new identities."

"Alas, I have no documents today. I have not paid a visit to the police station lately and have no plans to do so in the future. What I have, rather, is a scrap of information."

"For sale?"

"You would not trust anything given as a present."

"Probably I would not."

"I am told that there is in Barcelona a sinister underground antirevolutionary organization called the White Cross. It's said the White Cross may have ways of reaching Generalissimo Franco's intelligence staff via a hidden wireless."

"I, too, have heard of such an organization. They would pay dearly for crucial military information that an astute man had gathered."

"Yes, they would. I have something to sell you for ten thousand pesetas that you may sell an hour hence to the White Cross for one hundred thousand pesetas, assuming, of course, you have ways of reaching the White Cross."

"There are always ways, señor. But how can I trust you?"

"Play my trick on me. Give me half the money. That is, literally,

half. If you fail to make a sale to the White Cross, you can come take it from me and kill me. I'll wait downstairs. If you *can* sell it, come to me with the money."

"And why should I not simply take your information and kill you without paying you?"

"Because you would have to tear it from my heart. And you do not have time to do so this night."

There was a long pause.

"Pedro," the voice behind the light finally directed. "The money. As he says."

There was shuffling in the darkness, and the sound of bills being peeled out and torn. It took a few minutes. Then, with a slithering sound, the packet of bills slid across the floor to his feet. Levitsky bent, picked up the wad, made a quick show of counting it off.

He smiled. "I'm sure your friends in the White Cross will be pleased to inform General Franco's intelligence staff that at quarter to noon tomorrow, sixteen June, two English dynamiters traveling under stolen identity papers in the names of Uckley and Dyles will be present at the new tank bridge at kilometer 132 on the road between Pamplona and Huesca. The point of their presence is to sabotage the gun position for a guerrilla attack on the bridge. And at one that same afternoon, the soldiers of the POUM and the UGT and the FAI militias will make another assault on the city of Huesca."

Julian had told him. And now Julian must die.

Levitsky sat downstairs, having another peppermint schnapps. He felt exhausted. The goal glimpsed that evening in Moscow when his strange companion let slip the information of Lemontov's defection had at last been achieved. What GRU wanted, GRU had gotten. What happened now—to anybody—did not matter. Levitsky, however, strangely took no pleasure in it. He didn't feel anything except hollowness. He felt, if anything, only *old.*

It's getting to you, old man.

Levitsky had not wept in years. Yet he found a last old tear in

his dry bones for the dead: Julian and poor Florry. Igenko. The Anarchists in Trieste. Foolish old Witte. Tchiterine. Maybe worst of all his father, dead and gone these many years, slaughtered by Cossacks in the time before there was time.

Tata. Salud. You were a man.

He had another swallow of the schnapps. He was turning into an old _shikker,_ boring and stupid and sentimental, an old fool. It was as if the discipline, the passion, the absolute fury of a life had at last spent itself, leaving nothing.

Then he realized with a start that tomorrow, June 16, was his birthday. He would be sixty years old.

"Old one."

Levitsky looked up into a set of dark features, smooth and sleek and Mediterranean. "You are right. Our friends were quite impressed. Here is your money."

"Fuck your money," said Levitsky.

"And here's an old friend of yours," said the Aegean, laughing.

"Hello, old putz. I got you at last."

Levitsky looked into the face of Comrade Bolodin and then two men grabbed him and took him.

27

PAMPLONA

JULIAN STOOD IN THE IMMACULATE CIRCULAR PARK WHERE the Avenida de Carlos III and the Avenida de la Baja intersected in the lovely center of the Carlist city of Pamplona. It was midafternoon, June 15, a glorious day. The sky was Spanish blue, subtly different from English blue in that it is paler, flatter, less voluptuous, more highly polished.

"Sieg heil," said Julian, enjoying the theatricality of it, to a fair-haired, blue-eyed young chap who was but one of the dozens of Pamplona Germans, all sleek, smooth-looking professional soldiers with glorious suntans in the crisp blue uniforms of the Condor Legion Panzer companies.

Florry sat on the bench in the park not far from where his partner flirted with the young Jerry, and loathed himself. Another bloody failure. Julian had not come in gun range since they'd separated, until now, except that he was also within gun range of the entire Condor Legion as well. God damn you, Julian Raines, and your absurd lucky ring around your neck: it seemed to sum him up, that foolish talisman against the vicissitudes of reality. Julian believed in it, and in believing in it, seemed to force the world to believe in it.

Florry watched intently. It was not particularly amazing that Julian could speak so passionately with the young German. To begin with, his German was brilliant and he was himself blond and blue-eyed; but perhaps more important was the force of his performance. It was not just that he was now scrubbed and combed, in a

254 /

beautiful double-breasted gray pinstripe suit, but it was something deeper. He was too pitch perfect and nuance pure for fiction or artifice. He was not, really, acting. He had simply _willed_ himself to become a new and different man on the streets of Pamplona.

After a while, Julian began to show off. He offered the young man a cigarette, lit it for him with his Dunhill, and made humorous observations at which the German laughed heartily. He had even found a pipe someplace, and he gestured emphatically with it.

God, thought Florry.

After a time, Julian and the young officer shook hands, threw each other a _gross deutscher_ salute, and walked amiably away from each other. Julian returned and sat down.

"Interesting chap. Says the Jerry armor doesn't stand a chance against the Russian T-26s. That's why they're pulling them out of Madrid for this little show up here."

"Christ, I thought you'd never finish," said Florry.

"He's just been up to the bridge. His unit is near there. Says we must visit; it's a marvel of engineering. The Führer would be proud."

Florry shook his head.

"Come _on_, Stink, you've got to enjoy this. Think what a tale it'll make for your and Sylvia's grandpups. Won't believe a word of it, though, the little ghastly rodents. Hate kids, myself. So bloody _noisy_."

"What on earth did you tell him?"

"We're mining engineers. Out from the fatherland to advise the bloody olive-eaters on their mining techniques. Know a bit about mines, too. My mother owns one somewhere. Any sign of our pals?"

Florry, from his vantage, looked across the fountain and the street, through the leafy trees and to the hotel on the corner. It was an elegant old place, rather Parisian in appearance. It had been his job to keep it watched, while Julian sported about with Jerry.

"Nothing," he said. "A few Condor chaps. It seems to be unofficial Jerry headquarters," he said.

"The Mosely brutes will love it. What utter swine. To give up their own country to rub bums with German Java men tarted up in Sigmund Romberg uniforms. I loathe traitors."

Florry kept his eye on the hotel.

"*Sieg heil,*" Julian suddenly blurted, as two more officers suddenly came by in gleaming black jackboots.

"Handsome chaps," Julian said after they passed. "Pity they're all such pigs."

"There," said Florry suddenly, squinting in the sunlight.

He could see them in front of the picturesque doors of the hotel, a short, squat, and blunt fellow who must have been Harry Uckley and another who must have been his companion Dyles. It was the uniforms that gave them away: they wore their silly Moseley black shirts and jodhpurs and black riding boots.

"What charming uniforms," said Julian. "So refined."

Florry felt a queer roar in his mind. No matter what, he'd have at Julian.

"All right," said Julian. "Time for some real fun now, eh?"

But the fun did not start for quite some time. They followed the two down the wide, tree-lined Avenida de Carlos III at what seemed a prudent distance, perhaps two hundred paces, until at last they reached their appointment: an office off the Calle San Miguel, near the cathedral, which wore the proud banner of the Falange Espagnole, the violent right-wing Spanish brotherhood that, like the POUM, supplied its own militias to the fighting.

Florry and Julian found shelter down the street at a bench under a tree and waited. By 4 P.M. Julian grew bored and went for a walk. For a time he browsed in the shop windows while Florry sat furiously, vulnerable and absurd, awaiting his return. He was gone about half an hour.

"I say," he said when he returned, "look what I've bought. Rather spiffy, eh?"

He opened a small sack and removed a tie.

"I've always loved this pattern," he said. It was a dark green and dark blue arrangement of diagonal stripes. "But it's the Fourteenth Lancastershire Foot, and if Roddy Tyne ever caught me with his regiment's tie, he'd have a bloody _kitten_."

"It's quite nice," said Florry. "I've never paid much attention to ties."

"Nice? Chum, it's magnificent. Don't you think it goes well with this suit." He held it against the gray pinstripe.

"Julian, I'm trying to keep an eye on——"

"It does, doesn't it?"

"Well, yes, I suppose it does."

"Good, thought you'd agree."

He quickly untied the tie he was wearing—a solid burgundy thing—and rethreaded his collar with the regimental tie, quickly put a small, elegant Windsor knot into it, and pulled it tight.

"There. Really feel much better. This awful _pink_ thing"—he held up the burgundy like a rotting fish—"has been bothering me all day. Can't think why I bought it. Is the knot centered, old man? It's a beastly thing to do without a mirror."

"Julian! Look!"

Harry Uckley and his chum Dyles had emerged in a crowd with a group of Falangists and stood chatting and lounging about two hundred paces down across the street.

"About bloody time," said Julian.

It had taken almost forever: Uckley and Dyles went off to eat with the Falangists at a large, unruly restaurant down the way. The dinner lasted for hours, and more than a little wine was consumed. Then it was time to sing, and Florry and Julian heard the ringing words of the Spanish National Anthem, the bloody Horst Wessel song, some Italian Fascist ditty, on and on until quite late. When the party broke up at last, it was close to midnight and a light rain had begun to fall. The two Englishmen separated with a last round of hearty good-byes from the Falangists, and headed off down the

street. Across the way, from the shadows, Florry and Julian watched as they ambled along, talking animatedly, their boots snapping on the pavement.

Uckley and Dyles passed by directly across from them, and for the first time Florry could see them clearly. Harry Uckley had a thick-set, loutish grace, that pugilist's carriage that took him forward to the balls of his feet as he walked. He laughed at something the thinner, more ascetic Dyles had said, and it was an ablative little percussion of a laugh.

"I see it now," said Julian, in a whisper. "The cathedral. They're off for a bit of praying."

Of course. Harry Uckley would be Catholic.

"Come on," said Julian. "While I was off, I spotted a quicker way."

They dashed across a cobbled street, cut down an alley. The rain was really beginning to fall now. As they moved, they threw on their Burberrys, crossed another street, and then saw it.

It was a Gothic thing and first seen in the dimness looked immense and almost prehistoric, an awesome great hunk of gaudy, lacy stone, its spire climbing toward God himself above.

"Here. We'll stop them here," said Julian, slipping inside the gate. Florry watched his hand disappear inside his coat to emerge with the small automatic pistol.

And I'll stop you, Julian, Florry thought.

"Put this bloody toy to work at last," Julian said, throwing the slide of the pistol.

Florry felt the Webley somehow come to fill his hand. His thumb climbed the oily cold of the revolver's spine, curled around the hammer, and drew it back, and he could feel the cylinder align itself in the frame. The hammer locked with a tensile click.

"Here they come now, our lovely Eton boys," said Julian. It was so. The two men, hunched against the rising chill and the fall of the rain, came across the square in the white cold light of the moon, hurrying to make midnight mass.

Florry stepped beyond Julian, his revolver leading the way. "Beg

pardon," he said, with absurd civility, and stepped from the gate into the moonlight. The two men saw him and seemed to halt for just a second. The street behind them was deserted. From inside the cathedral came the sound of chanting.

"Harry Uckley," Florry said.

"Who's that, eh?" called back Harry, still coming on. His voice filled with the sudden cheer of a man who recognizes a companion. "A mate? Christ, Jimmy, that you, blast it all?"

"No it isn't, old sport," said Julian.

Harry understood in an instant, much more quickly than poor Dyles. He seemed to make a sudden lurch for his own pistol, but it was all feint, and as Florry, fifteen feet away, brought the Webley up to fire, Harry instead gripped his companion by the arm, catching the poor man in utter surprise, and with a strong thrust whirled him at Florry and Julian in a crazed spin.

Julian's little automatic fired almost instantly, the sound a tap lost quickly in the vastness of the night, and the man sagged wretchedly as Florry ducked at the collapsing apparition that was between himself and his target and made to re-aim, but saw it was no use. Harry, fleet as the devil, had turned to flee and ran zigzagging like a footballer across the cobblestones in the shadows. Florry took off after him, cursing the man for his cleverness, and got close enough to see Harry hit the stone wall of the graveyard abutting the cathedral and get over it in a single, clawing scramble. He himself careened toward the gate, raincoat flapping like a highwayman's cape behind him, and slid through it, low.

Damn you, Harry Uckley. If you get away, it's all up, damn you.

Florry knew he should have just done the job of murder. Just shot him cold; that's what the job required. But he could no more shoot even scum like Harry Uckley cold than Julian Raines.

Bourgeois decadence again, the soft, yielding custard center of the middle-class man, the slight pause at the moment when pauses were fatal. Florry, you have not learned the lesson of your century: you have not learned to kill.

Florry studied the maze of the graveyard. He could pick out no forms remotely human in the baroque, marble confusion and the weird colors from the stained-glass of the cathedral above it. It was all jumble and shadow. A few candles flickered.

Damn you, Harry!

He began to move through the grass in a duckwalk, feeling absurd and incredibly excited at once, but not particularly frightened. After so much of wondering and doubting and waiting, the elemental simplicity of killing or being killed seemed almost a luxury.

"Chum, I'm going to kill you."

The whisper was from quite near. Florry halted, freezing up against a marble angel's wing. Harry was close by, calling softly, utterly confident.

"Come on, now, chum. Just another step."

The voice was indistinct and blurred but seemed to be coming from a congruence of obelisks off on the left a few feet. Florry peered into the dark, trying to make sense of it. He had an immense urge to stand up and shoot at the voice and be done with the business.

Yet he held back. Patience in these affairs was everything. Harry was the man of action, the pugilist, the footballer; the urge to move would overwhelm his imagination surely. Florry knew he'd come. Come on, Harry, boy, come on.

He lay still, waiting.

"Robert? Robert, are you there?"

It was Julian, standing in the gate in the moonlight like an utter ass, as if he were posing for a sculptor.

"Robert, I say, are you there?"

In the light of the cathedral, Julian made a wonderful target and he knew that Harry Uckley would fire in a second or so. Julian and his insane conviction that the real physics of the universe did not apply to one so charming and brilliant. His bravery, which was also utter stupidity.

Florry heard the snap of a revolver cocking amid the maze of

marble slabs, perhaps made louder by the looming cathedral walls above them, and then he heard a tick as the hard butt was steadied against the stone.

"Robert, I say, old man, are you here?" Julian called again.

Florry leaped to his feet, raised the Webley, and fired three times in the rough direction of Harry Uckley. Yet curiously he did not hear the sound of the shots but only felt the sensations: the buck of the revolver, the spurt of muzzle flash out beyond his hand, the sudden flooding odor of burned powder. He did not hear because he heard something else instead, the huge and powerful clanging of the midnight bells whose thrill of vibration seemed to fill the air with a kind of blanket of sound, dense and muffling. He ducked back to earth, the bells continuing: they were up to five now. Florry rolled sideways, sure a bullet would come winging at him, and astonishingly discovered a rampaging shape passing by him headed like a crazed bull toward the gate.

He fired, taking the man down.

The bells tolled twice more, then ceased, their echo lapsing after several more seconds.

"Robert?"

"Yes."

"Christ, are you all right?"

"Yes, you bloody idiot. God, Julian, you just _stood_ there—"

"The pathetic thing is, they haven't pistols in those bloody great holsters. Only arsewipe. Let's see what you have bagged."

They rose and walked swiftly to the fallen man. Harry Uckley in the grass, a glassy blackness in his eyes, breathed slowly.

"It was a lucky shot that dropped me," he said. "I'd have had you sure if the bloody olives hadn't taken my Luger. They didn't trust us."

"Are you in pain?"

"No, it's rather numbing. Cold. You'll see when your time comes. Are you reds?"

"I suppose," said Florry.

"I'm damned glad an Englishman pulled the trigger, not one of

these olive-eating bastards. They took my Luger, damn their souls to hell."

"Yes, Harry," said Florry, aware that Harry no longer breathed. "Well, that's bloody that," he said, surprised at the bitterness he felt. "Another great triumph for the Republic."

Now for Julian, he thought. He cocked the pistol.

"Sorry, old man," said Julian, just behind him. Florry felt the cold circle of a pistol muzzle against his neck. "There's to be a change in plans."

28

MIDNIGHT

THEY DROVE THROUGH THE CITY FOR A TIME, UNTIL AT last they reached its outskirts. The traffic increased. The road was jammed with armored cars and lorries filled with Asaltos. Twice the vehicle was stopped but Lenny simply pronounced the password—"Picturebook"—and they were passed on. Whistles blew; there was the tramping of feet on the wet pavement in the dark. It was a night of ugly, ominous magic, a night of history. Lenny figured even Levitsky, hands manacled, mouth taped, would see that something was about to happen.

Then they pulled into the courtyard of a large house. More troops milled about. But they took the old man straight through the house, across the courtyard, and to a smaller house. The tape was ripped off. He was stripped naked. The manacles, however, remained.

Lenny looked at the old man and was surprised at the body. It was chalky white and mottled with discolorations. His feet and hands were veiny blue and white and hideous. His muscle tone was flabby. His cock was long and flaccid and his balls two dead weights. Where was the strength? Where was the will? This was just an old white-headed geezer who probably couldn't open a jar of pickles without help. The great Levitsky! Trotsky's right-hand man. Kolchak's nemesis, hero of the underground, Cheka terrorist, Yid spy-master! Lenny laughed. A single blow would send his old bones flying apart.

Levitsky looked cold and numb. His face didn't show much

except that he knew he was going to catch it but good. Lenny wanted to hurt him. Lenny felt powerful and beyond fear next to this old geezer.

"Old Yid," he said in Yiddish, "I've got plenty of trouble for you now. You think you've seen trouble? Put the blindfold on him."

Blackness engulfed Levitsky. He felt the thing being tied tight behind him. He was led outside, pulled along by several pairs of hands. His feet crossed mud and straw.

"Step up here," they told him. He felt himself climbing crude steps. The smell of straw and mud was everywhere. He knew he was in a rough building. It was very cold.

At last Bolodin spoke.

"You know," he said, speaking in Yiddish. "I've seen guys like you. They had 'em in New York. Tough, I give you that. Smart, too. Guts. Lots and lots of guts. Now I could have this kid here smash you until morning. When he gets tired, I could do the smashing myself."

Bolodin laughed again.

"And that's just what you want. You're one of these guys, the more you get smashed, the more stubborn you get. You feel pure. The pain makes you clean. You're a pilgrim, the blood you shed gets you into heaven. Sure, I know. I've seen plenty of it before."

He took a deep breath. The old man's head didn't move.

Lenny studied him carefully. The old man was still.

"You've got a piece of information," Lenny said. "The name of a guy. It's your most precious treasure. It means more than your life. I want it. I got to figure a way to get it out of you, right? So I ask myself, what does this old Jew fear? Everybody fears something, even the Devil Himself. I have to find something so special to you, so much a part of you, so deep in you that getting away from it becomes even more important than your treasure.

"So what would this be? Pain? Nah! Torture? For most, not for you. Death. The fear of death? No. If you die before I get what I want, you win. You'd love that, wouldn't you? It's how your mind works. I've thought a lot about that, how you think. I'm the world's greatest living Levitsky expert. Nights I stay up thinking about how to get this piece of information out of Levitsky.

"And then I figured out where to look."

Lenny paused again, still enjoying his discovery.

"You know where? I'll tell you, this is really interesting.

"I looked inside . . . of me. You and me, Levitsky, we're the same guy. Jewboys born in that cunt Russia. We left her, went somewhere else to make a better life. We learned to be hard. We learned to do what was necessary. We learned to look and see the world for what it was and deal with it as it was. We learned not to be afraid. We learned how to hurt. We became big shots. We forgot everything. Or almost everything. But when I'm a kid and even when I'm a young _shtarker_ in the gangs and even when I'm making my hits and everybody in the city is scared of me and even when I come over here and get in this racket, there's one thing I don't ever forget. Because always it scares me. I don't like it now, even. Being this close to it makes me nervous. And I bet you don't like it so hot either."

He smiled.

"Remember, old man. What, fifty years ago? With me it was only thirty years ago. But you remember it just like I do. They came in on the horses. Always with the horses. The horses so big and so tall they could smash a kid to pieces in the snow. And there was no place to run and maybe you were lucky because they only felt like doing a little killing or maybe you were unlucky because they wanted to do a lot of killing. And they came galloping through. And I remember the horses. Big as a house, all muscle and steam and power. I saw my two brothers go under the hooves, old man. Just sucked under and gobbled up, like a machine, and they come out the other end, all smashed into the snow."

At last the old man spoke.

"That was in the time before there was a revolution. We changed all that. We made a revolution."

"Yah! A revolution! Get him! Tonight, old man, tonight there's no revolution. It's 1897, it's forty years ago. And the horses are coming, old man. They're coming."

He ripped the blindfold off.

Levitsky saw he was in the loft of a stable, over a pen. It was maybe twenty feet to the ground and as he watched, a gate was opened.

In they came.

"The Spanish have lots of cavalry, old man. They like horses, and there are plenty of them left around. These beauties are mean as hell. They haven't been fed in a week. Instead, I got a guy, he comes in and he whips 'em. He whips 'em hard. He plays sirens for 'em and he honks horns at 'em. Oh, these horses are mad. These horses are crazy. You never saw any horses like this, old man."

He brought Levitsky to the edge of the loft.

Beneath him, the old man could see them. They bucked and jostled and rubbed together, a seething, almost singular thing. Their cries came up at him and their dusky smell and their ugly violence.

"You want to go down there, old man? You'll drive 'em crazy. They'll crowd in over you. Their hooves are really sharp. Old man, you want to go pet the horsies tonight?"

He held Levitsky farther out.

What am I, Levitsky thought, an old man. God help me, I'm no devil. He's going to throw me down there. God help me.

He remembered them smashing through the village. It was so long ago.

"Hah, old man. You going to talk? I'm getting tired of holding you."

Levitsky spat in his face and Lenny threw him into the pit.

✦ ✦ ✦

He fell for a long time, screaming, but then the rope caught him and jerked him backward with a terrible explosion of light and pain; it was tied to the manacles. He hung in the pen, his shoulders wrenched the wrong way, the pain radiating out from the pressure. But worse, he was in the center of the horses, only the rope preventing him from descending the last few feet to the muddy floor of the pen.

A horse's breath, steamy and rancid, flushed across his face. The beast nudged him with its big head and as it nudged, the pain was terrible on his shoulders. Another horse smashed its flank against him. He swung on the pendulum of his rope and shoulders, bashing against another beast which screamed, leaped to its hind legs, and kicked savagely at Levitsky, crushing against his sternum. The horses were being driven into a frenzy; they were everywhere around him, nipping and bucking and kicking him. They were so huge; he was so weak.

He remembered the Cossacks. It was a day when they felt like a lot of killing. He remembered the animal bucking over his father and saw the flash of blade, the spurt of blood. He smelled the burning huts, but most of all he remembered the cries and screams of the horses . . .

He awakened.

He lay on the floor of the barn. Bolodin was over him.

"You passed out, old man. You fainted. I must be right. You must be plenty scared." He turned. "Get him up."

They lifted Levitsky and brought him back to the edge of the loft. The horses had quieted.

"The lamp," said Bolodin.

The one called Ugarte picked the kerosene lamp off a table.

"Go ahead," commanded Bolodin.

The boy threw it into the pen; it smashed and the kerosene, flaming, spread across the floor. The horses went insane. They twisted and leaped and yelped in their terror of the fire. The flames rose, showing red in their mad eyes and against their sweaty flanks.

"Okay, old devil. Back you go."

The rope was tied to his manacles. Bolodin held him out over the animal pen, which had become the site of grotesque frenzy.

"They'll rip me apart!" shrieked Levitsky.

"Down you go, old devil. To your own private pogrom."

"No. No. Please. Please."

It seemed as if an incredible light had come into his mind. He struggled to tell the man what he wanted to know, but it was as if he could feel himself being sucked down. It was as if his mind were shattering. He would not go.

"Please. Please, don't do this to me."

They laid him down.

"So talk," said Bolodin.

He looked up at Bolodin as if at a stranger. He had no idea what the man wanted. Nothing made sense. The light in his mind was growing in its blinding intensity.

"He's not saying anything," said Ugarte.

"Water," said Bolodin.

The liquid, icy cold, flooded over him, into his eyes and throat. He felt it going into his nose and entering his body. He was dying. It was all slipping away, in a confusion of water and pain and horse's screams and the freezing wind and the straw beneath him.

"The name, old man. The name of the boy you recruited."

The question was crazy, it made no sense.

Levitsky thought he was drowning. He could feel the fluid in his lungs and the will to surrender choking through him. There was nothing else. He was drowning, the water was sucking him down. He could see only lights flashing. His life was over; he was barely conscious. He was sinking.

Then strong arms had him. They gripped him tightly and pulled him up. He could feel a man's hands on him, bringing him to air. The pain was so bad. There was so much pain, endless and unyielding. The hands had him.

"Florry," he gasped. "God, Florry, it's you."

Lenny checked the list he'd made from Glasanov's files. Yes, Florry, a Brit, in the POUM, a journalist originally. It all fit. He was one of the two guys who'd been at the seaside hotel, too, the one Levitsky had probably been trying to reach. He figured the guy would be at the Falcon.

"Comrade Bolodin?" The call came from down below.

"Yes," Lenny called back in Russian.

"Commissar Glasanov says it's time to go."

Lenny looked at his watch. Yes, it was 0430. It was time to move on the Falcon.

"Comrade, what do we do with the old one?"

Lenny looked back to the old man, naked and shivering, his eyes black and crazed and staring madly into nothingness.

"Give him to the horses," he said.

29

THE OBERLEUTNANT

ULIAN PLUCKED THE REVOLVER FROM FLORRY'S HAND. HE had a queer light in his eyes and seemed wickedly, marvelously excited.

"You fool, the Guardia will be—" Florry began.

"Oh, I hardly think so, what with those bells coming along to mush all our noise. No, this is a fine and private place, Stink, for our little talk."

Florry could see the muzzle of the small Webley .25 automatic upon his chest.

"Where were you going to shoot me, Stink? Head, I'd bet. Well, then, that's where I shall shoot *you*."

"You bastard," Florry said. "You sold us all out to bloody Joe Stalin and his goons. God help you, Julian. No one else will. It doesn't matter. Shoot me and be done. They know in London. I've told them. You're a dead man."

Julian smiled softly in the pale, weird light of the cathedral.

"Were you going to give me a chance, old man? No, I'd bet not. Just pot me, eh? I wouldn't even know what hit me; I would simply cease to exist."

"Damn you, you—"

"God, wonderful," he said. "It's priceless. Stink, you're such a rotten actor. I could see the loathing in your eyes since you arrived here. God, Stink, you'd never make a spy."

Florry just looked at him, thinking *How do I get at him?* He tried to gauge the leap. It was too far.

"Any last words for Sylvia, Stink?"

"You filthy swine," said Florry. "There's nothing you can give me you'll not catch yourself. You're a dead man."

"I'll tell her something quite heroic, old man. She'll be devastated, of course. I'll comfort her. I can feel her hot tears and her trembling shoulders. We'll be all alone. Perhaps my hand shall accidentally brush against her breast. It'll be quite embarrassing, but of course at moments like those one doesn't worry about propriety, does one? And perhaps I should happen to feel her nipple grow hard. Perhaps I shall hold her tight and as I'm squeezing her my penis will get quite lumpy. And yet, rather than drawing _away_ from it, as one would expect, why, the grief-stricken thing actually presses her mound against it. Perhaps then as I kiss the tears away from her sweet cheeks, I shall encounter—good heavens, can this be a _tongue?_"

"You filthy—"

Julian raised the weapon. Florry saw its dark shape rising. Julian was not trembling. You swine, Florry was thinking in the raging urgency of it all, you bloody swine.

"Bang," said Julian. "You're dead."

Julian was pointing at him with his pipe.

Florry looked at him.

Julian opened Florry's revolver, tilted it, and the cartridges emptied into his hand. He flicked it shut and handed it back.

"Thought I'd take it because you were so swollen with triumph you might turn the bloody thing on me." He snorted with contempt. "Robert, I was so disappointed to learn that you were merely human. Among your many good qualities there are some bad ones. Among them, your evil stupidity and your blindness. I suppose it's that underneath it all you hated me so for cutting you at Eton. And then Sylvia came into it."

"Look, you—"

"Hush, Robert. You're so thick. Listen and learn the ways of the world. In the first place, I know all about your smelly little job with the voodoo boys at Whitehall. MI-5 or -6? Don't suppose it

matters. I knew it would happen. All sorts of people have been telling me about the 'questions' that have been asked, the delicate inquiries back in London and at Trinity. Then there's your awful chum Sampson, the world's most revolting prig. He was at university, you know, one of those awful chaps who had a brief flirtation with the Apostles and then veered right. Everybody knew he'd signed on with the voodoo boys. I must say I was crushed you'd agreed to join them."

"They say you're a spy. They have proof. *I* have proof!"

"And you believed it. Still, one supposes that it's remarkable you didn't pot me when you had the chance in the trenches. May I ask, old man, why not?"

"I had to have proof. Then I *heard* you with the Russian—"

"Oh, tiptoeing about in the dark, are we? How seedy, Robert. How sadly seedy, like some two-bob-a-day private inquirer who specializes in divorces for the smart set."

"I *heard* you tell Levitsky that—"

"Is that what he's calling himself these days? When I knew him best, he was Brodsky the poet. He was a wonderful poet, by the way. Met him in 'thirty-one at Trinity. Sent me a note admiring some verses and included one of his own. Well, one thing led to another. When I ran into him at the hotel he said he was a journalist for *Pravda*. We had a jolly good reunion. He's quite a chap—"

"He's a bloody GRU—"

"Listen, chum. Listen and face the ways of the world. He was my lover, old boy. My first, my best. I'm queer, you blind sot. God, Robert, you are so *thick* sometimes."

Florry looked at him. He felt his mouth hang open. He blinked, thinking perhaps it was some dream. Something odd and chilled and huge moved through him, a glacial sense of regret, white and vast and glazed with ice.

"I say, don't look so *stricken*. Why on earth do you think I cut you at school, Robert? I bloody found myself *wanting* you. Your body. I wanted to do things. It was more than I could stand, and I had to get away. Who do you think I was writing to the night of

the attack? My current lover, a sailor in the merchant fleet whom I had not seen in a *devilish* long time."

"But the women," Florry said, still half disbelieving.

"Of which there have been exactly one, old man. A chambermaid who rather insisted when I was thirteen. It was disgusting."

"But all the lies. All the boasts. *Why?*"

"Florry, chum, being a queer, in case you don't know, is illegal. One can end up in the Scrubs. And there's Mother, whom it would kill, and there's the hallowed memory of Father, the martyred hero of the Somme. There's all manner of relatives. And there's the bloody will, old man. Brilliant Julian does not need to lose his little chunk of England by being branded the Oscar Wilde of 1937. Actually, I rather like girls. They're perfect fools, but enjoyable in their silly ways. They usually have wonderful senses of color, which I admire deeply. Men have no sense of color at all."

Florry wasn't sure he believed him.

"All right, old man. You think I'm lying? All right, here, I'll prove it. Put out your hand and close your eyes, and you shall get a big surprise."

"Julian, I—"

"Don't worry, old man. It won't be John Thomas. Now there's a good boy, you needn't bother with the eyes."

He put something in Florry's hand.

It was the small automatic.

"It's all cocked. It's only been fired once, into that Dyles fellow. Now, Robert, if you still believe Brilliant Julian is a terrible Comintern nasty, then you must do your duty. England demands it. Come on, now, make up your mind, old man. This is, after all, the second chance I've given you." He made a show of closing his eyes.

Florry felt the pistol grow heavy in his hand.

Finally, he handed it back. "You fool," he said.

"We're all fools," said Julian.

"I cannot wait to see the look on Sampson's face when—"

"No, I don't quite think that would do, chum," Julian said

darkly. "I don't really care to explain myself to the Sampsons of this world. It's not something I'm terribly keen about. Actually, Robert, there is one other thing that needs to be straightened out. The bridge, eh? Let's not forget the bloody bridge."

"No, Julian. No, I haven't forgotten the bridge."

"You know, Stink, I don't think it makes a pig's whisker's worth of difference as to who really wins out in Barcelona, the bloody POUM or the bloody Russian lads. The truth is, I'm not even sure I could tell you the difference. But do you know I've never really finished anything in my life? My masterpiece 'Pons' is the perfect example. I am a man of brilliant beginnings. And I find that what I would like to do more than anything is finish something. I would like to blow that fucking bridge into the next world. Would you care to join me, old man?"

"Yes. Yes, let's do it. You know you always get what you want, Julian."

"Perhaps it's only that I want what I know I can get. But see here. There is a technical difficulty. Look at this."

He handed over a document.

"Good Christ," said Florry.

"Poor Dyles had it over his heart. It was not as effective in that regard as a Bible."

It was the travel authority, sodden with blood. It was utterly worthless.

"Damn," said Florry. "Oh, balls. Perhaps we could somehow *bluff* our way to—"

"Won't work. Perhaps it might with the silly amateur Falangists, but the truth is we'll be up against German professionals. I've seen them. I spent the summer of 1933 in Germany and watched all the Hitler stuff going on. I must say, those lads won't be easy to fool."

"Then we'll—"

"Robert, listen to Brilliant Julian. Englishmen would *need* papers in order to approach the bridge, and upon that premise was this

mission planned. But Germans? German officers? Why, they could get close enough to piss upon the thing."

"But we are *not* Germans."

"Oh, no? Stinky, I speak it like a native and I look it a bit, too, with my blond locks and these terribly blue eyes. You'd do for a Bavarian, a lower, coarser sort of brute."

"I speak it terribly."

"But you do understand it?"

"Yes. I read it best of all. And *papers*. We'd need papers and uniforms. How on earth could we change the whole thing in mid-course—"

"Robert, listen. It's almost one. In half an hour I'm due to meet a chap in a Turkish bath nearby for a bit of sport. It's that nice young Oberleutnant that I chatted up in the park. We can tell each other, you know. I rather think we could persuade him to lend us something to wear."

Florry looked at Julian.

"What choice have we?" he asked.

"That's the best part. None at all."

Was he a Nazi—or just a big stupid young army officer? Florry tried to convince himself of the former. He'd beaten Jews and tortured the innocent, burned books, worn jackboots, carried torches, the whole ugly theater of the thing. It was difficult, however, to maintain this pretense in the face of his actual flesh, which was on the ample side, the freckles in his great white behind, his almost feminine body, soft and shapeless. Quite a difference once the uniform came off: something about a naked man so defenseless that it almost defies action.

He could hear them talking softly; it was infernally hot in here, the steam and everything, even though he wasn't quite in the steam room proper, but just outside, having come in after the officer. He glanced at his watch. He was dreadfully tired and yet tomorrow rushed upon them swiftly.

"Yes," Julian was saying, in German, "I have been to Dresden often. The china is so magnificent, the old town with its gingerbread architecture so ordered. Of course this was before the Party era. Perhaps it's all changed now, all modern and full of factories."

The two men, swaddled in towels, sat in the steam room.

"No, Karl," said the officer. "No, it remains essentially a storybook city. One can have the most fabulous dreams in a place like that. It's a lovely place. My mother and I were very happy there."

"Yes. It's good to know some things haven't changed."

"It's so lovely to have found one in whom I can confide," said the young officer. "You have such lovely eyes. They are so pale and lovely."

"Thank you," said Julian. "It's odd how one yearns for human contact and touch. For gentleness and sympathy."

"Yes, yes," said the officer. "Something *deeper* than comradeship."

Florry swallowed hard, pulled out Julian's automatic, and prepared to play out the final lunatic act.

He burst into the steam and began waving the gun about wildly, shouting, "Attention! Attention! You are under arrest. Gestapo. Do not move."

He pointed the pistol at the young man's head.

"It's Dachau for you, *liebchen,* you homosexual disgrace!" shouted Julian, leaping up, gathering the towel about his slippery body. "That'll teach you what the German Reich expects of its young men."

The officer began to cry. He offered no resistance, as if he knew the inevitable had at last arrived. He had gone ashen with shame and terror. He began to tremble absurdly. They brought him out of the steam room and into the locker room. Julian, pulling on his suit, began to assail him for moral turpitude.

"You swine. The army sends you out here to train these people in the arts of war, to gain valuable experience for yourself, and to show the world the finest of German manhood. Yet you spend your

time trying to bugger everything that moves. The KZs are too good for you."

"Please," the boy begged. "Sir. You must give me an alternative. I am so weak, but I will not fail. Your pistol and I will end it all if only you tell my parents that I died honorably in battle."

"There is no honor for you, swine."

The boy crawled to the toilet and became sick. Florry thought that Julian was rather overdoing it. The naked boy wiped the vomit from his face with a towel. The rancid odor of sweat and farts hung everywhere in the steam. The fat boy was such a nauseating sight that Florry began to feel ill at his plight. Julian continued to harangue him with terrifying force, as if it were his own hated flaws against which he was lashing.

"You are not *fit*," Julian was screaming, "to wear this uniform." He had gathered it up.

"*Bitte,* Herr Offizier," sobbed the boy. "Please. Please don't do this to me."

"You will be taken *naked,* as you deserve, to the civil guardhouse, and there detained among thieves and pimps and Communists until suitable arrangements can be made. Is this understood?"

"Y-yes, Herr Offizier."

Julian turned to Florry.

"Have you called headquarters for a car?"

"Yes, Herr Sturmbannführer," said Florry. "It's on the way. But Herr Oberleutnant Von Manheim wishes to talk with you."

"That bloody fool," cursed Julian. "I trust, Herr Oberleutnant, that without your clothes you can be trusted to remain here."

The boy only wept into his towel.

"Ah!" snorted Julian in disgust. He stepped out and Florry followed as they raced out through the foyer of the bathhouse, stopping only to gather the boy's uniform and boots, and then headed down the cold street in the moonlight.

30

THE ENGLISH DYNAMITERS

THE CAR WAS WHERE PORTELA HAD SAID IT WOULD BE, IN a garage, on Ohte, near the Plaza de Toros. Helpfully, it was a Mercedes-Benz, black and spotless, all topped up with petrol.

"Ah, bravo," crooned Julian, seeing it there, gleaming in the dark. "Splendid. By the way, old man, do you drive?"

"Good God, don't you?"

"Poorly. Dangerously. I shall smash us up, I'm sure. You *must* drive. You were in the coppers. Surely they taught you such things."

"I suppose I drove once. I haven't driven in years. You're rich, you're supposed to have a car."

"I do have a car. I just never had to drive it. There was a man who drove it. I wish he were here now."

"I wish he were, too," said Florry, slipping in behind the wheel. He fiddled with the choke, turned the key, and nursed it into life.

Julian opened the garage doors behind them and Florry edged out into the wet gray street. Dawn was beginning to break. Florry looked at his watch. It was nearly five by now, and he was going on his second day without sleep and the bridge was nearly one hundred kilometers away, and where now was Julian?

Florry looked back. What the devil was he doing? The seconds ticked by as if they weren't desperately precious until—

"*Achtung!*"

The officer who emerged from the garage was imperially thin

278 /

and blindingly correct in the khaki tunic and trousers of the Condor Legion Tank Corps. He wore a black beret, black boots, and black belt. The Panzer skull-and-crossbones gleamed over the swastika on the front of the beret. He had a riding crop and two utterly pale blue eyes, killer's eyes. Odd that such a terrifying apparition was a queer poet in love with sailor boys.

"Oh, I wish Morty Greenburg could see me now. What a hoot he'd have!" he said.

"Where did you get the crop?"

"Oh, in there. It's one of the braces to an uncomfortable chair. Don't suppose the owners will miss it, do you?"

Julian climbed in back.

"Pip, pip, fellow," he commanded with his crop on the seat top.

Florry drove through early-morning Pamplona, crossed the river, and headed toward the flat Argonese plain that lead to the Pyrenees. The road climbed, but the trim little Mercedes chugged along. Ahead, the mountains were stony and gray, still capped in winter snow.

"Now here's the plan. I am Herr Leutnant Von Paupel, newly appointed to the front, a special engineering officer. Expert on bridges. You are Herr—oh, pick a name, old boy."

"Brown."

"A _German_ name, Stink. _Braun_. Herr Braun, of the embassy staff. You've escorted me out from Pamplona at the general's instructions."

"What general?"

"Just say, 'the general.' It will drive Jerry crackers. He's scared to death of generals. If anybody looks at you hard, merely say '_Sieg heil,_' and flip up your paw. And believe it. That's the trick. You must _believe_ it."

Florry nodded, fascinated. Of course that was the core of Julian: the belief. In himself, primarily, and in the primacy of his needs. Julian, the homosexual. Florry pondered it in silence.

If that is what he is, what am I, he wondered.

For I love him, too.

In the mountains, the German military traffic picked up and it became abundantly clear they were entering a war zone. Moorish sentries—tall, brown, grave men with sour looks and long Mausers slung over their capes—stood watch at crossroads; trucks full of Moors made a slower way along the road, and Florry, pushing ahead smartly, passed them. When the men saw Julian sitting in sober Nazi regalia alone in the back of the Mercedes, they saluted; he responded blankly, touching the riding crop to his hat.

As they climbed into the Pyrenees, it seemed to get colder. The air was thin and pure. Florry opened the vent and sucked in the air as he kept turning to look at his watch at the fleeting seconds. The mountains were white and massive now, chalky, craggy, rugged peaks and beneath them spread the Argonese plain, a patchwork of buff and slate in the bright sun.

They sped along the Embasle de Yesa, a high, green lake that ultimately gave way to the Rio Aragon, along whose stony banks they passed for some time. The jagged mountains were clearer and bolder than they had ever been from the lowland trenches about Huesca.

I lived in a hole in the mud for five months with this man who now tells me he has sex with boys. I never guessed it. Julian was another illusion, it turned out, a self-created one. Or did I, at some odd level, really, truly know, *even if I lie to myself about it now?*

Finally, they came to the bridge over the Aragon at the Puenta la Reina de Jaca. It was a fine old girdered thing, as sturdy as a Victorian building, and just beyond it, where the road curled almost due south down through a final splurge of mountains toward Huesca still some fifty kilometers off, the Germans had established a car park—except that it was a Panzer park, and the things were spluttering into life, ready for the job ahead. These were the PzKpfw IIs, small gray tanks, no taller than a man, with double machine guns mounted in their tiny turrets.

"Of course," said Julian, "the Russian T-26 would prang these

tinpots like the toys they are. But of course at Huesca there are no T-26s. The Russians have seen to it."

Farther down, men were limbering up some wicked artillery pieces to lorries. The guns, lean and long-barreled, rode on pneumatic tires and crouched behind shields an inch thick.

Julian carried on like the best ROTC candidate in the world, pleased to be good at this, too.

"And that, of course, is the famous eighty-eight-millimeter gun. Supposedly the most efficient long weapon in the world. Extraordinary velocity and penetration. They can use it with a fused shell against planes, with an armor-piercing shell to pot tanks, with canister to make fish and chips out of infantry, or just good old high explosive to smash buildings. God, Stink, I admire the Germans. They really do _do_ things, don't they? Bloody pity they do the _wrong_ things. Oh, hullo, what's this. _Sieg heil,_ Herr Major." He carelessly threw a salute at a man by the side of the road.

"Let's go, old man," he commanded.

But Florry, driving slowly by, watching the force assemble itself, wondered in melancholy at the odd link between him and his chum. He thought of Sylvia, perfectly innocent of it all. He wished she were there. What a laugh they would have once had over something quite this silly! He gunned the car past the vehicles, fled by a sign that said HUESCA 44 KM, and pushed ahead. The road was relatively clear for a time, but after a bit they came to a small garrison town called Baiolo, and pulled into it, under the watchful eyes of several Moorish sentries.

"God, it looks like Berlin," said Julian.

Indeed it did; the square was jammed with gray Jerry vehicles, not only the tanks but armored trucks with machine guns and tank tracks on them. German specialists stood about barking orders stoutly to their assistants who translated into Arabic. For of the vast population of the village, nearly three-quarters were Moorish infantry, now loading aboard the trucks with the grave look of men headed into battle.

"These would be the shock troops headed for Huesca," Julian said.

"We'd best get going," said Florry. "It's drawing near. The bridge must be just ahead."

"You. You there!" a voice screamed at them with great authority and Florry could see an ominous figure in black leather raincoat and helmet approach with a forceful stride.

The man, some sort of senior officer, leaned into their car and said to Florry, "Who the devil are you?"

"Herr Colonel, I'm sorry to be a nuisance," said Julian from the back. "Von Paupel, Panzer Engineers. Poor Braun here of the embassy staff to help me was rather hurriedly pressed into service."

"*Jawohl,*" barked Florry earnestly.

"I've got to get to that damned bridge," said Julian nonchalantly. "They're worried that the thing might last only a few hours under beating from the tanks. I must say, I had no idea Panzer Operations had such a show planned up here."

Florry could feel the colonel's breath warm upon him.

"You damned engineers, if you can't build a bridge that'll hold up my tanks, I'll see you in the guardhouse."

"Of course, Herr Colonel. But we want to get it down pat. When we move across the Russian plains, we won't have time for mistakes. You bring your Panzers and I'll build a bridge to hold them."

"In future, Herr Leutnant, the Panzers will get bigger," said the colonel.

"And so will the bridges, Herr Colonel," said Julian tartly.

"Go on then. Fix that bridge. I'm planning to liberate Huesca by suppertime."

"Yessir."

"And keep your damned eyes open, Von Paupel. We've received word saboteurs are about, English dynamiters. It seems the reds have fifth columnists also."

"*Jawohl,* Herr Colonel. *Sieg h—*"

"Please, leave that paperhanger's name out of it. This is a war, not some Bohemian's political fruitcake. Now, get going."

He waved them on brusquely, and Florry pressed the gas, the car shooting with a squeal through the square, narrowly missing a queue of Moors filing into a huge iron boat of a vehicle. He slipped into another lane and began to zip along. He took the Mercedes-Benz south. The country was scruffy and severe. Off on the left an immense mountain, looking like an ice-cream cup, bulked up, gleaming with impossible whiteness in the sun.

"Hurry," said Julian, looking at his watch. "It's after eleven."

"Somebody betrayed us," said Florry.

"Oh, Robert, rubbish. Keep driving."

"They knew. 'English dynamiters.' If we'd have come on with Harry Uckley's credentials, we'd be dead. Your Russian chum. Did you tell him?"

"He'd never do such a thing."

"You'd be surprised what he's capable of."

"Robert, he'd never do such a thing. I won't talk of it. Some lout at Party headquarters talked too loud in a Barcelona café—"

"It was your bloody Russian chum who—"

"HE WOULDN'T!" Julian screamed. Florry was stunned at the passion. "He's above that, don't you see? He's a _real_ artist, not a poseur like me. I don't want to hear another bloody word."

They drove on in silence. Florry could hear Julian breathing heavily in the back seat.

"He's _different,_ don't you see?" said Julian. "All this is squalid and base. Politics, compromise, bootlicking: it's all dung. Brodsky wouldn't—"

"When I knew him he was a bloody German cabin boy. With a plate in his head. Good Christ, Julian, the man can—"

"Stop it. I won't hear another WORD! Not another word, unless you want to turn back now, chum."

Florry said nothing.

In time the land changed, yielding its arid, high stoniness to pine forest, which spread across rolling ridges and gulches and crests like some kind of carpet.

"What time is it?" Julian asked at last.

"It's half past eleven," he said.

"Oh, bloody hell, we shan't make it."

But they came suddenly to a slope, and a half mile down the tarmac, flanked by stately green pines and high, shrouded peaks on either side, they saw it: the bridge.

31

THE SUPPRESSION

AT 0600 ON THE MORNING OF JUNE 16, TWO ARMORED CARS equipped with water-cooled Maxim guns in their turrets pulled up the Ramblas and halted outside the Hotel Falcon. The range between the gun muzzles and the hotel's ornate façade was less than thirty meters. Two more armored cars went to the hotel's rear. Down the street lorries unloaded their troops of Asaltos, and German and Russian NCO's formed them into action teams.

At 0605 hours, the machine guns opened fire. Three of the four guns fired approximately three thousand rounds into the first two floors of the old hotel; the fourth gun jammed halfway through its second belt, perhaps the only Russian setback of the day. Still, the firepower was adequate. Lead and shrapnel tore through the hotel, shattering most of the glassware in the Café Moka, ripping up tiles and woodwork and plaster in the hotel meeting rooms and offices, cutting through the chandeliers and the windows. In seconds the three guns transformed the lower floors of the building into a shambles of wreckage and smoky confusion.

"Bolodin," said Glasanov, watching as the armored vehicles at last ceased fire, "take them in."

Lenny Mink nodded, pulled his Tokarev automatic from his belt, and gave the signal to the troops. He himself began to rush through the smoke toward the shattered hotel; he could feel the men behind him, feel their energy and tension and building will to violence. They were screaming. Lenny reached the bullet-splintered main

door first, kicked it open. There were two bodies immediately inside, a man and a woman. He stepped over them. A wounded man behind the desk tried to lift his rifle toward Lenny; Lenny shot him in the chest. Another man, already on the floor, moaned, tried to climb to his feet. Lenny smashed him in the skull with his gun barrel.

"Go, go," he screamed in Russian as the assault troops began to pour through the building. He could hear them on the stairs already and hear the screams beginning to spread through the hotel as they pounded through, beating indiscriminately, threatening, screaming curses, smashing furniture, and in all other respects attempted to shatter the will of their victims.

He went up the stairs himself to the second-floor offices of the Party. The Asaltos had already been there. Torn papers and shattered furniture were everywhere. The smell of burned powder hung heavily in the air. The walls has been ripped with gunfire. Two men were dead and two others wounded. Lenny went to one of the wounded, a redheaded runty fellow bleeding from the leg and from the scalp.

"Nationality?" he demanded in English.

"Fuck you, chum," said the man, in a heavy Cockney.

"A Brit, huh? Listen," he spoke in English, too, the English of Brooklyn, "listen, you know a guy named Florry? A Brit, I'm looking for him."

"Fuck off, you bloody sot."

Lenny laughed.

"Look, you better help me. You're in a shitload of trouble."

The man spat at him.

Lenny laughed.

"You a soldier boy, huh? Nice suntan. Spend a lot of time in the trenches. Look, tell me what I want, okay?"

"Bugger off, you bloody scum," the angry Brit said.

"Okay, pal," said Lenny. He shot him in the face and began to roam through the building in search of somebody who had a line on this Florry.

Meanwhile, Asalto units neutralized other targets around the revolutionary city. The Lenin barracks was held the most important, because its arsenal was the largest and its troops held to be the most dangerous in Glasanov's mind. This turned out to be an illusion; most of the arms had been moved to the front and the soldiers were largely illiterate peasant youths who'd joined for the promise of steady meals. They surrendered in the first minutes.

Among the other targets were the main telephone exchange on the Plaza de Catalunya, guarded originally by Anarchists but since the fighting in May by POUM fighters; the Anarcho-Syndicalist headquarters; the offices of *La Bata*lle,* the banned POUM newspaper whose physical plant was still a gathering place for dissidents; the offices of *The Spanish Revolution,* the POUM English-language newsletter; the radical Woodworkers Guild; and the Public Transportation Collective, a number of former estates seized by the youthful radicals for a variety of political purposes. In every location it was the same: the swift shocking blast of gunfire, the brutal rush by the well-trained Asaltos, and the mopping up.

The prisoners, who accumulated rapidly and were the principal booty of the operation, were swiftly separated into three categories. Leadership, including Andres Nin, POUM's charismatic chief, and thirty-nine other intellectuals and theoreticians, were taken to special, secret prisons called, in the colloquial, *checas,* for careful and extensive interrogation, in preparation for what was expected to be a series of show trials very like the ones that had so shocked the world when they had been performed in Moscow. The second category, the militant, bitter rank-and-file—that is, mostly the fiery young anti-Stalinist European leftists of all stripe and coloration that had flocked to the POUM banner—was taken to the Convent of St. Ursula, which would rapidly earn, in the next few days, its nickname in history: the Dachau of Spain. These men were interrogated, though rather perfunctorily and without much nuance or subtlety, and then shot. The executions, as many as five hundred in the first several hours (though estimates vary), were carried out in the graveyard near the convent, hard by a grove of olive trees

under a little bluff. The shootings were done in batches of as many as fifteen or twenty by special NKVD death squads, using Maxim guns mounted on the backs of old Ford lorries. The bodies were buried in mass graves gouged into the meadow.

The last category of prisoners—those not on Glasanov's leadership list and those lacking the fiery believer's spark in their eyes—were dispersed to a number of hastily improvised disciplinary centers for further interrogation and incarceration until their destinies could be determined. Included in this category were the "Milicianas," or female members of the POUM. In many cases, these prisoners had no idea what was going on and were completely certain it was some idiotic misunderstanding that would in some way be straightened out. In this group was Sylvia. She was removed with several dozen other Milicianas of POUM and the other groups of women, many of them internationals, and taken to a wire stockade in the courtyard of a small convent near Bardolona, just north of the city. It was a jaunty, uppity mob in whose company she found herself, who bandied with great sarcasm at their Asalto guards.

"Hah. Fascist sister, how about a nice fuck?" the tough young men would call.

"Fuck your face. Or fuck your cow saint, La Passionaria," the women would call back through the wire.

"Fascist cunts," the soldiers chimed merrily, "can't wait to screw Moors and Nazis."

"I'd sleep with ten Moors and ten Nazis before I'd sleep with scum like you, with a shooter so small it would fall out."

There was much laughter.

Sylvia did not share it. It wasn't that the banter upset her, but she had a profound mistrust of men with guns. Although it did not occur to the others that there was danger, Sylvia was quite uneasy. She didn't like the way the soldiers joked with them, unafraid to say anything; she did not like the loose, confident way they carried their rifles; she did not like the coarseness of the experience or the absurdity of the situation.

In the stockade, there was surprisingly little political rhetoric, as if everybody was by this time quite exhausted with politics. At the lunch hour they were brought a little wine and some bread—no less, really, than their guards, who seemed as confused as they were —and everybody waited patiently until somebody showed up to set it all straight.

An hour after lunch, five of the women were called out by name —two Germans, a fiery Frenchwoman named Celeste, who seemed to be the spirit of the group, and an Italian anarchist who had actually fought at the front as a man—and taken over to the wall and shot.

Their heads flew apart when the officer leaned over each and fired a pistol bullet into the ear as a _coup de grace_. Sylvia didn't scream, although most of the others did; she simply cursed her luck and tried to figure a way out.

An hour later, another six women were led out and executed. The survivors had become by this time exceedingly morose. A few wept and were comforted by the stronger. Sylvia sat by herself, with her arms wrapped about her, and though it was warm, she felt her teeth chattering.

Then her name was called.

She stood.

"Be brave, comrade," said one of the Belgian women. "Don't let the bastards see your tears."

Hands all around touched her. She was smothered in a kind of love that had been transformed radically from the generally political into the specifically personal. A woman hugged her and held her tight and told her to be brave.

"Spit in their faces," she was told.

"Don't give them the pleasure of seeing you beg. Long live the revolution."

"Yes," said Sylvia, though it had a kind of irony to her, "yes, long live the revolution." She turned to face her suitors, two stony Asaltos with submachine guns.

They led her from the courtyard into the church, over to one of

its axial chapels, where a young man with gray eyes sat writing at a small table.

"Comrade, ah, Lilliford," he asked, not really looking up. As soon as she saw that he wouldn't look up, she knew she was in trouble. When a man didn't look at her, it meant he'd already seen her and been somehow hurt by her beauty, and would therefore go to great lengths to show her how unimpressed he was, or how indifferent he could be.

At last he looked up. He had pale, pimply skin and blondish hair and large circles under his eyes. Though he wore the khaki Asalto mono and a brace of pouches and holsters and belts about him, he was clearly not Spanish but some kind of Russian or European and rather pleased with his own authority.

"Yes?" she said, hating herself for the way her voice quavered.

"Please. Sit down." He gestured to a wooden chair adjacent to his table.

"I think I'd rather stand, actually," she said.

"As you wish." He smiled charmlessly, showing bad teeth. "You travel on a British passport?"

"Yes. I am a British citizen. Would you please tell me on what authority you hold me and what charges have been pressed, if any."

"No. What specifically is your connection with the Party of Marxist Unification?"

"I'm a volunteer on their newspaper. I help with the page layout and I do some proofreading for them."

"You are not specifically a member?"

"I am not a joiner."

He considered this for a time. "Do you sleep with the boys?"

"You can't expect me to answer that."

"Why would an Englishwoman become involved with Fascists and Trotskyites and—"

"These people aren't any more fascist than I am. I don't know where you got your ideas, but—"

The young commissar smiled deeply, his eyes merry with con-

descension. It was his huge sense of moral certitude that she loathed.

"My dear lady," he said through his grin, "could we not argue this all day? Perhaps if I refrain from attacking the POUM, you could refrain from defending it. Cigarette?"

"Thank you. No."

"You're a very attractive woman."

"What on earth does that have to do with anything?"

"It has to do only with my romantic nature. A weakness for which I consistently apologize. So then. Let me ask you this. Could you explain your true relationship to this illegal organization."

"It wasn't illegal until this morning."

"Times change, Miss Lilliford. Answer, please."

"I said all I care to on the subject."

"You know, it would help if you would look upon me as a friend or at least an interested person. I'm not without a certain amount of sympathy in these matters. Could I have from you please a list of all the names of your—look, why don't you sit? I feel quite silly sitting in your presence."

"Then why don't you stand?"

He smiled again. His eyes took on the aspect of a person about to deliver a treasured and much-rehearsed witticism. "Why are pretty women so headstrong? All my life I have wondered this. I think that your daddies did not spank you enough."

"Will you please get to the point?"

"Forgive my little jokes. I am not as serious as I should be. So: will you be prepared to provide a list of the names of your coworkers over the past six months. If you would list the names of all the people you have—"

"You must be joking."

"In my private life, Miss Lilliford, I joke all the time. I am indeed proud of my sense of humor, which is said to be rather keen. In this matter, pretty lady, alas, no, I do not joke. Serious charges have been raised. It's not our policy to make jokes."

"I've noticed."

"You'll cooperate?"

"Absolutely not."

"You could end up against the wall. Such a shame, a pretty woman like you."

"You are an exceedingly slimy young man."

"You are brave now, but when the Asaltos are getting ready to shoot you, you may find your courage somewhat reduced."

"I'm sure you are right. You are probably an expert; you have probably sent many women to their death. But I'm not frightened now. Not of an ugly little man like you."

"Well, no matter," he said.

"I demand to see the British consul."

"Miss Lilliford."

"This is an illegal detention. I demand to see my consul or representative of my government."

"I am sorry to report that such a demand cannot at this time be accommodated."

Another volley of shots crashed out; Sylvia jumped.

"You had better get used to the sound of gunfire, Miss Lilliford, if you expect to be a revolutionary."

The three *coups de grace* came immediately.

"Why?" she said. "For God's sake, *why?*"

"It's a matter of discipline, one supposes. These things are ugly. I've seen them before."

"It's so pointless and awful."

"It is indeed awful, Miss Lilliford, but it is never pointless. Now let me ask you one more question. Now wait, don't interrupt me. You may even be surprised. The question is: If I let you go, will you do me the favor of leaving Spain as quickly as possible?"

"I—"

"You have friends, it seems, in high places. I will have a driver return you to the city. Please, please, leave Spain as fast as you can make the arrangements. As charming and lovely as you are, I have no desire to repeat our conversation. I might not be able to enjoy

myself as much if I had to shoot you. And one word of advice: get out of that mono. Wear some womanly things. Be pretty. Return to the bourgeoisie. You will be safer."

Sylvia thought it some crude Russian prank. But in fact, at the young commissar's nod, two guards took her outside to an unmarked car, and a driver took her swiftly and without incident into the city. He told her there was a nice hotel across from the cathedral; would she like to go there? Yes, she said. She went and had no trouble getting a room. Then she went into the Gothic quarter and found a small dress shop and she bought a dress. They let her change in the rear.

She went back to her room and locked the door and sat breathing heavily. Occasionally through the night there was the sound of shooting, but in all other respects the city seemed much calmer. The sense of oppressiveness had vanished. There was no longer any feeling of waiting for something ominous to happen. It had.

Sylvia thought she'd been lucky. Some bureaucratic slip-up had somehow spared her. She looked at her calendar; June 16 had been a long day.

She might not have slept nearly so soundly as she did that night had she known that her escape from the firing squad occurred not by virtue of a slip-up. In fact, somebody in high places *did* know her, or had that day learned of her. It was Colonel Bolodin, commander of the SIM.

32

THE BRIDGE

Now Lili," Julian said, "Lili was a rare beauty. Her father's estate, near Breslau, had this wonderful hunting schloss, where the old brute went to shoot boar in the winter—and Lili and I had some exquisite weekends there. In the spring. Oh, it was wonderful."

Florry nodded enthusiastically. His breath was ragged and dry.

They had passed unnoticed beyond the first construction sheds, where the Spanish workers had been quartered during the rebuilding. Up ahead there was some kind of guard post and beyond that Florry could see the bridge, an ancient rough stone arch, now buttressed smartly with a gaudy framework of Krupp steel. Beneath it, a surprisingly mundane little river cut its muddy way through a deep gorge, but neither Florry nor Julian cared for a glimpse. Rather, they had by this time seen the low concrete blockhouse that had brought them all this way.

It seemed so utterly nondescript, a prosaic little cube of concrete ranged with gun slits. They were too far to see, but Florry guessed the Germans had at least four Maxims—one for each slot—in the little fort. Against and upon it now, a batch of Condor Legion troopers lounged in their undershirts, smoking and telling jokes. Indeed, all about the bridge, Condor Legion officers could be seen.

"They certainly don't look as if they're expecting raiders," said Florry. He glanced at his watch. It was five to twelve.

"Now Suzette," Julian was saying in German, "Suzette had wonderful, wonderful breasts."

"You! You there!" The voice had a commanding ring to it.

"Why, yes," replied Julian, turning mildly.

"Just who are you?" The officer, whose hair was cut short as peach fuzz, had a set of ball-bearing eyes and a scar running down his face as if his head had been once disassembled, then reassembled, though hastily and somewhat inexactly. On the one side of the line, the skin had a dead, plastic look, an abnormal sheen.

"Herr Leutnant Richard Von Paupel, Combat Engineers Section, Condor Legion, at your disposal, Your Excellency," said Julian crisply, snapping off a salute—the army's salute, not the Party thing.

The half-faced officer returned the snap perfunctorily.

"I'm here as an observer, Herr Colonel," Julian said coolly.

"Ah! And for whom, may I ask?" the officer demanded.

"Certain elements, sir."

"And what is that supposed to mean? Or do you mean to have me play a little guessing game?"

"Perhaps I'd best just say not only is the general staff interested in the outcome of this afternoon's exercise, Herr Colonel, but equally so are certain elements in Berlin. They have requested an independent report on the outcome."

"You're from Security?"

"I'm not Gestapo, Herr Colonel."

"If you were, I'd get you a seat on the lead tank into Huesca. And your skinny friend in the raincoat. You're out of uniform, Herr Leutnant," said the officer. "Your boots are not shined."

"You'll find, Herr Colonel," Julian took up and threw back the challenge, "that the new German hasn't time to shine his boots, he is so busy climbing the stairway of history, as our leader directs."

"Papers, Leutnant. Or I'll have to call my guards to escort you off the bridge. You may watch from the guardhouse. Perhaps you're the English dynamiters the Spaniards fear so adamantly."

He nodded to two noncoms, who reacted instantly and hurried toward them with machine carbines in hand.

"Herr Colonel," Julian began—but at that instant a roar arose

in a sudden surge, and everybody looked for a cause and could see, just at the top of the slope, a column of dust.

"The panzers are coming," somebody yelled.

They must have left just after *we* did, Florry thought. They were fast. He glanced at his watch. It was a minute till noon. The blockhouse was still almost fifty yards away. They hadn't even reached the bridge. If Portela attacked now—

"My papers," said Julian, "are my blond hair, my blue eyes, my embodiment of the racial ideal. My credentials are my blood, sir."

"Your blood is of very little interest to the German army, Herr Leutnant."

"And this—"

Julian reached into his tunic and removed a document and opened it up.

"There," he said, handing it over. "I think that should do the trick."

The German colonel looked at it intently for some seconds.

"All right, Herr Leutnant," he finally said. "You may of course position yourself where you want. But don't get in the way. I'd hate to wire Berlin its representatives had been squashed into strudel."

"Thank you, Herr Colonel. Your cooperation will be noted."

Julian smartly walked past the man, and Florry trailed along behind. In seconds they had moved beyond the last guard post and were on it, on the bridge itself.

"What in God's name did you show him?"

"My party card. When I was in Germany in 'thirty-two I actually joined up one night as a drunken lark, under the name of a chap I was quite close to at the time, to see if I could get away with it. It was felt to be clever in the set I was running with at the time. I used to show it off at parties in London for laughs to prove how bloody stupid it all was. It's a very low number, I'm told; impressive to chaps who understand how such things work."

They turned to look at the brown water forty feet below, which trickled under the bridge.

"Robert, old chum, I've got that funny buzz again. About the next several minutes."

"Stop it," said Florry.

"I think my magic ring is fresh out of tricks. Tell my foolish old mother I loved her dearly."

"Don't be an idiot, Julian."

"Say tally-ho to all my friends."

"Julian—"

The first shot sounded, from high in the pines.

"Shall we go, old man?" whispered Julian, removing his pistol.

A klaxon sounded from somewhere, and the call "Partisans! Partisans!" in German arose. Yet panic did not break out among the professional German soldiers, who instead responded with crisp, economic movements. Or maybe it was that for Florry the entire universe seemed to slip into another gear: a monstrous, strange _slowness_ somehow overcame and then overwhelmed reality. More shooting began, rising in tempo from the occasional bang of a bullet to, several seconds later, what seemed like a crescendo of fire.

Julian ran toward the blockhouse just a few feet ahead, his automatic out. A bullet kicked up a puff of dust nearby and then another and then another. A few of the Germans were already down. From the blockhouse there came a noise that sounded like strong men ripping plywood apart, and Florry realized one of the German machine guns had begun to fire. Yet still he could make no sense of events: he could not see the guerrillas, and in fact could see nothing except some stirred dust down the road.

"In, in," yelled Julian, and they ducked into the dark little entrance of the blockhouse, immediately finding themselves in subterranean blackness.

"Hold your fire, god damn it," somebody was shouting in the closeness of the fortification. An electric light snapped on; Florry heard the snap and click of gunbolts being set and heard the oily rattle of belts of ammunition being unlimbered. The officer with the half-dead face was shouting crisp orders, telling his gunner to

prepare to engage targets at a range of about four hundred meters. Florry watched the gunners lift the weapons to their shoulders and move to adjust their positions against the firing slots. He recognized immediately that these weren't heavy Maxim guns at all, but some frighteningly streamlined new weapon, supported at the muzzle by a bipod, yet with a pistol grip rather like a Luger's and a rifle's buttstock.

"Well, Herr Leutnant," said the colonel, "you're in luck and so are we. I was afraid our guests might not take the bait. But they're right on schedule. You'll get to see the new Model 34 in action against some Spanish guerrillas who think their horses are a match for hot steel. It should make an amusing few minutes."

Julian shot him in the throat.

Florry got out his four-five-five.

Julian shot the gunner, then he shot one of the guards. Florry shot the other guard.

The pistol shots in the close space were painfully loud. There were six Germans left and Julian said very calmly, "Gentlemen, please drop your weapons or we shall kill all of you."

Florry saw something in the eyes of one of the other gunners and he shot him in the arm. He went quickly to the machine carbine one of the guards had dropped and picked it up, swinging it about on the remaining men.

"If anybody so much as breathes heavily," said Julian, "my nervous companion will shoot you all down. You stay absolutely still, do you hear? Absolutely still."

They waited, almost frozen in the dicey intensity of the moment. Outside the firing seemed to rise, and then there was a banging at the iron door to the blockhouse.

"What's going on, damn you? Fire, you bastards, get those machine guns spitting."

"Easy lads," said Julian. "Just hold it still as little mice and maybe you'll see tomorrow."

"English fucker," said one of the Germans.

Julian shot him.

"Who's next?" he said. "I'll shoot each and every man here if I must."

The firing outside had ceased. The pause seemed to last forever, and then there was a hoot or yelp of sheer giddy joy, and Florry heard the thunder of hooves as the air seemed to fill with dust. A few more shots sounded, until at last someone else pounded at the door.

"*¡Inglés! Dios te ame, ven acá!*"

Julian went swiftly to the iron door and unlocked it. Portela, looking like some kind of buccaneer in a cape with crossed bandoliers on his chest and a long-barreled Mauser automatic, ducked in.

"Get these bastards out," yelled Julian.

Florry backed off and let the Germans file past him. When the last man had vanished, he himself climbed out.

"Go on, run, you bastards," yelled Julian in English, firing a shot in the air. The Germans began to flee across the bridge.

"God, Stink, look at them run!" yelled Julian joyfully. "Christ, old sport, we bloody pulled it off."

"They'll be back," said Florry darkly, for he knew the Germans would reorganize in minutes and take the offensive. Yet even as he spoke he was astounded by the strangeness of what was happening. The bridge seemed to swarm with an astounding crew of gypsy brigands, all in leather and dappled with an assortment of bullets, bombs, daggers, strange obsolete weapons, incredibly colorful costumes, all of them stinking evilly of sweat and garlic and horses. Their leader, a hideously ugly old man swaddled in the most absurd of all the outfits, a voluminous dress under his leather coat, immediately threw his arms about Florry and hugged him violently, and only when Florry felt breasts big as any wet nurse's under the leather did he realize she was a woman. Her face seemed carved from ancient walnut, though her eyes were bright and cunning; she had nearly half her teeth.

"*Ingléses, me permiter a verles. Que bravos. Que cahones estos hombres tienen. Mira los héroes, cobardes,*" she crooned into his ears, her breath flatulent with garlic.

Florry had no idea what she was saying.

"Pleased indeed," he said.

"Gad, what a spectacle," said Julian. "What an extraordinary woman. Is she not a woman, Stink? She reminds me rather too much of Mother."

"Let's not chat," said Florry. "Let's blow this bloody thing and get quit of this place."

"Yes, let's go," called Portela, already shed of jacket and preparing to monkey climb down the bridge's new scaffolding to plant his charges.

"Where's the bloody dynamite?" said Florry.

"*¡La dinamita está aquí!*" screamed the old lady, and one of her men came ambling over with a scabby horse laden with crates.

"It's very old," said Portela, "from the mines. But when she goes, she'll go with a bang that'll be heard in Madrid!"

"Yes," said Florry, unnerved by the old stuff, when he'd been expecting gear somehow more professional and more military, "well, let's get bloody cracking."

"Stink, old man, I've found a wonderful toy," said Julian. Florry looked to him to see that he'd just climbed from the blockhouse with one of the German light machine guns. He'd chucked his Condor Legion tunic and wrapped himself with belts. "Light as a feather. Bloody German genius for engineering. I'd say the perforations along the barrel housing keep it cool from the air."

"Perhaps you'd best take some chaps down the bridge and watch for Jerry," said Florry. "I think I'll help with the poppers."

"Good show, old man," said Julian, who dashed down the bridge, the oily belts clinking and jingling as he ran.

"*¡La dinamita!*" yelled the old lady.

"Yes, splendid," said Florry, and he grabbed the reins of the horse and tugged him to the bridge. "Here, Portela?"

"It will do," said the officer.

Florry shot the horse in the head; it bucked once, then sank on its knees, its great skull forward. Florry pried a case from its harness with some difficulty, then beat it open with the butt of his Webley

grip. The dynamite lay nestled inside, waxen and pale pink, looking like a batch of fat, oily candles. It smelled peculiar.

"God, it looks *ancient,*" he said to no one in particular.

"This is a detonator," said Portela, producing something similar to a cartridge from the pouch at his belt. "You press it into the end of one of those sticks. Then you wire up the leads and run it back to the box. Then you prime the box and push the lever and send the spark over the wire. Then you get your big bang."

"And who's to lash the stuff to the bridge? This fat old lady?"

"I'll rig the one side," said Portela. "Perhaps Comrade Florry could help on the other. We must have *two* charges for the great destruction."

Somehow this was a detail that Steinbach had neglected to mention. "And I suppose those guerrilla boys wouldn't be able to wire it up?"

"Alas, no."

"Bloody hell. Well, then, let's get going, eh?"

At that moment, the first sniper's bullet struck near the bridge, followed by two more.

"Christ," said Florry, as the old lady rose, selected a weapon from her bewildering assortment—a broom-handle Mauser—and fired off across the bridge into rocks near the treeline. Shots opened up from all around. Florry heard Julian's machine gun begin with that absurd, fast, ripping yelp.

He lugged the box to the railing and slung himself over it. For just a second, he thought he'd gone too far; he almost lost his grip and could see himself hurtling down, screaming for Sylvia as he fell, until he was smashed to pulp on the stones below. But then he had himself and hung for just a minute, gathering his breath. The old lady, her eyes dark with love, touched him on the hand.

"*Bien hecho, inglés,*" she said, and laughed, showing her black stumps.

Christ, you beauty, was all Florry could think, would you be my last vision? But he lowered himself onto the abutting structure of steel, reaching foot by foot, finding a grip and then lowering him-

self again and again by the same laborious, experimental process, trying all the while not to look down or believe those actually *were* bullets whanging against the metal or kicking into the old stone of the bridge with a bang and a puff of dust, until at last he found himself perched like some grubby ape in a monkey house on a gym apparatus, surrounded only by bars and space. He clung tightly to the girders with his legs, hoping the sweat—he had begun to perspire wretchedly—would not run into his eyes. He was now in a forest of German iron and the word KRUPP darted before his eyes. A shot banged off the metal. Up top he could hear heavy firing. He tried not to look down.

"Dynamite!" he screamed.

"*¿Eh, inglés?*"

"Dynamite, damn you!" he screamed, and in his urgency forgot his vow not to look down. Far below the stream seemed like a green, scummy ribbon of tin foil breaking over pebbles strewn by a child. He felt the vertigo buzz through him. He clung more tightly than ever. A bullet ricocheted nearby with a metallic clang.

"*Aquí están los cachivaches.*"

Something swung blurrily before his eyes: it was a peasant's basket on a cord. Weakly, with one hand, he plucked at it, pulled it close, and pinned it to his body with an awkward elbow. He reached in to find two bundles of six waxy sticks of the explosive. He pulled one out and wedged it into the nearest joint in the girders he could find. He jammed the other bunch in atop it and wrapped it tight into a ligature with some long strands of electrician's tape somebody had thoughtfully included in the basket. It looked dreadfully sloppy, the tape wrapped in a messy sprawl about the uneven nest of sticks.

"Hurry!" someone else under the bridge called. He looked over to see the fat Portela similarly astride a girder on the other side, working just as desperately as he was.

What the devil does he think I'm doing? he wondered, bewildered and flooded with bitterness.

Florry was halfway through the next load when the bullets sent

his way seemed to increase dramatically. One pinged off the girder inches from his face and he felt the sharp spray of fragments, winced, and almost fell. Evidently a Moorish party had worked its way down the gorge, descended it, and had begun to move along the creek bed toward him. Another bullet exploded dangerously close to his head.

He twisted to see them two hundred meters away, shooting quite calmly, three gray-uniformed, lanky figures who seemed to be potting pigeons.

"THE LEFT!" he shouted. "THEY'RE ON THE BLOODY LEFT!" Another bullet whizzed by. "Damn you, *there,* there on the left!" he screamed again, feeling the panic squeak through his limbs. Oh Christ, Christ, Christchristchristchrist!

Above him the machine gun spoke rapidly, raining spent shells over the railing, and the three Moors collapsed in a lazy string of bullet spurts that kicked up clouds of dust and slate at their feet.

"Do hurry, old man," yelled Julian. "Jerry's getting ready for a push."

Florry now had only the detonator to insert. He plucked it from his pocket and awkwardly plunged it into the exposed end of one of the sticks, felt it crumble into the chalky stuff.

There! Ah! Now for the bloody wire. If only . . . ah! He unspooled the blasting wire and with his fingers tried to locate the posts on the detonator. It was tricky business. Florry kept thinking there should be an easier way. Twice he . . . almost had it . . . blast, the loop coiled off. The damned raincoat felt heavy and constricting; he wished he'd chucked the bloody thing. He could hear the chatter of Julian's weapon and some others and suddenly an awesome WHOMP as an artillery shell detonated hard by. Florry shivered, shrank, and almost lost his grip on the metal. Shrapnel sang in the air and the odor of smoke hung heavily. He had trouble breathing.

"Stink, damn it, hurry," Julian called. Florry looked and saw that Portela had vanished, either killed or done. Damn him. He didn't think he could find the strength. Finally, with a great lurch,

he managed to get the wire twisted about one of the posts and proceeded to desperately knead it tight. He found the other one and duplicated the process, all the while experiencing the terrible sensation of doing sloppy work, but at that second the whole river gorge seemed to break out afresh with fire, as new troops apparently reached it. He hoped he'd done it right, but there simply was no time to check.

He scrambled up the framework, the bullets popping nearby, and he knew that at any moment he'd catch one in the spine or skull, but the Moors shot no better than the Spaniards and he managed his destination and with a last push swung himself over.

"Thank God," said Julian, crouched near him, the hot gun in his grip.

"Your hand, Christ," said Florry. Julian's hand was pink and scalded where he'd been holding the barrel.

"Nothing, old man," said Julian, and Florry looked down the bridge to see at least fifty Moorish bodies on the road.

"Get going, sport," said Julian. He pushed at Florry and Florry was off, sprawling toward a ditch beyond the bridge. As he ran, he payed out the wire from the spool. He reached the ditch and skidded into it, the coat flapping around him as he went. He looked back.

Julian was alone now, the fool, the machine gun tucked against his hip. He fired a long burst at the hidden troops across the way and they returned his fire, their bullets cracking at the dry soil and the gravel around him. His hair blew free and his face and shirt were smeared with grime.

"*¡Venga, inglés, corra como el diablo!*" someone yelled. A man took the spool of wire from Florry and was twisting it to the contacts on the exploder box, an ominously crude-appearing wooden machine with a plunger thrusting out of it.

"Come on, Julian!" Florry screamed over the edge of the gully.

Julian at last seemed to hear him, and turned and ran, just as the first Panzer swung into view atop the far crest.

The bullets struck around him and for whatever reason his luck

held yet again, and except for a bit of a scrape above his eye, he arrived with a mighty vault and leaped into the gully just as the first PzKpfw II began to advance.

"Blow the bloody thing," Julian shouted merrily. His hand looked like some hideous lobster paw, puffy red and pussy and twisted, still melted to the ventilated barrel of the weapon. He winked at Florry, as if it were some monstrous joke.

The fellow wiring up the box at last seemed finished and gave way to the massive old lady who, her black teeth gleaming, gave the plunger a shove, as they all melted into the earth for protection against the blast.

But there was no blast.

"Damn!" said Julian.

"Again," Florry shrieked. "AGAIN!"

Obligingly, the old woman lifted the plunger and again fell forward against it.

Florry could just see the connection he'd so desperately jerry-rigged together having come unwrapped or having been improperly done to begin with. A black, gloomy sense of shame came over him.

"I've got to fix the bloody thing," he yelled, and began to claw his way out of the gully.

Julian smashed him to the ground.

"Don't be a fool."

"Don't you see, I've botched it!"

"You'll botch it good if you go down there and get killed over nothing, chum."

"If only I'd—"

"Shut up, old man. It's time to get the bloody hell out of here, bridge or no bridge."

And indeed it was. Across the bridge, the tanks had arrived. They scuttled down the road with their odd, insectlike approach, somehow tentative. Their machine guns began to rake the guerrillas' side of the gorge. Bullets peppered the earth about the trench. The guerrillas began to edge back until the ditch petered out

against the slope; it was almost one hundred meters up the bare ground to the crest behind which, presumably, there were horses.

A shell—one of the terrifying 88s—whistled in and exploded against the ridge. The air was filled with noise and dust and whining metal and heat. Another went off farther down.

A Moorish suicide squad had reached the far end of the bridge. An officer urged them across, and they began to move forward. The old lady pulled one of the rifles to her shoulder, fired, and one of the men slid to the earth. The others crouched behind the railing, though one hearty fellow made a mad dash to the cover of the far side of the blockhouse. Farther down the gorge's edge, figures appeared and broke for the cover of the rocks on the hillside a few hundred meters away. The guerrillas opened fire, dropping a few, but the majority found safety and began to fire on the trench.

"*Váyanse, hombres,*" the old lady screamed. "*¡Corran! ¡Hace demasiado calor aquí!*"

"Go on, Stinky," said Julian, fiddling awkwardly to get his last belt into the open latch of his gun.

"Hurry," said Florry, scrambling out of the trench, beginning to backpedal with the others up the slope.

It was a feeling of extraordinary vulnerability. His shoes kept sliding in the dust and the bullets whipped and popped all around. Only the terrible Moorish marksmanship and Julian's counterfire from beneath kept any of them alive that mad, backward scramble up. Insanely, Florry fired the six charges in his Webley at the chaos of running Moors, screaming Germans, and backed-up vehicles on the other side of the gorge, to absolutely no discernible effect.

He finally reached the top, one of the last. With a sigh of relief and disbelief, he sank to the earth, found a rifle, and began to pot away. He could hear the snorts and shuffles of the horses below him in a little draw, anxious to be gone from the commotion, but it didn't matter; what mattered now was Julian coming up the slope, raking the opposite side of the gorge with a long burst of fire. He didn't seem to be enjoying it much though; he looked chalky white with terror as the bullets struck around him, but Brilliant Julian

continued to climb through the lazy puffs of sprayed dirt. He had almost made it when the bullet took him down.

"God, Julian, JULIAN!" Florry screamed. Florry rose to run, and hands grabbed to hold him back, but he lashed out with his Webley and felt it strike bone and broke free. He raced down the slope.

"Go on, you fool," Julian said. He was coughing blood. The machine gun had fallen away uselessly.

"No," Florry said. He tried to pull him up. The old lady was suddenly at his side.

"Inglés, su amigo está terminado. Muerto. Nadie puede ayudarle ahora."

"NO! NO!" Florry screamed.

He had Julian's limp body under his arms and tugged it upward. The old woman helped and in seconds other men were helping, too, and they had Julian beyond the crest and out of the line of fire.

"You'll be fine, I swear it," Florry was saying, but his hands were wet with blood. The blood seemed everywhere on Julian. He could not yet believe it.

"Well, Stink," said Julian, "Brilliant Julian's brilliant luck finally went belly up."

"No. NO. You'll be fine, you've only just been nicked."

"Your imagination again, old boy."

"No. Horses. Damn you, old lady, get the filthy HORSES!"

"Easy on her, old man."

Up on the ridge line, the firing increased suddenly, and two shells detonated. Florry was trying to wipe the sweat off Julian's grimy forehead when the old lady leaned in with a water bottle.

"Thank you, dear," said Julian.

"Inglés, los fascistas cruzan la puente, tonto. Ven, ovídalo. Tenemos que salir. Están por todas partes."

"A horse," Florry said. "Bring this man a horse."

"Stinky, I hate the brutes. Smelly, filthy beasts, moody and sullen and—"

"Shut up, I'll lash you to me. I'll get you out of here, you'll see.

You've taken care of me, now I'll take care of you. Get me a HORSE!"

"Stinky, listen. Tell all my friends to be happy. Tell them Julian's dying from—"

"You're not dying!"

"Stinky, the bastards got me in the spine and the lungs. I'm half dead already, don't you see?"

"¡Inglés! ¡Ven! ¡No hay tiempo, llegarán en segundos!"

"She's telling you they're almost here. Go on. Get out of here, old sport."

"I—"

"One thing, please, Stink. The ring. Take it, eh? Take it to my bloody old mother, eh?" He smiled brightly.

Florry grabbed the ring, popped the chain, and stuffed it into the pocket of the Burberry.

"Now the pistol. Take it. I can't quite—my bloody arms don't seem to work. Take that bloody pistol."

Florry, with shaking hands, removed the tiny automatic from Julian's holster. It was such a stupid thing; it seemed more like a toy than a weapon, small, almost womanish, difficult to hold in a man's hand.

"Cock it. I put in a fresh clip."

Florry snapped the slide back, chambering a cartridge.

"There now. Shoot me!"

He leveled the pistol to Julian's temple.

"Thanks, Stink," Julian said. "The bastards won't use me for bayonet drill. Stinky, God, hold my hand, I'm so bloody scared."

"¡Inglés!"

"Julian! I love you!"

"Kill me then, Stink. KILL ME!"

"I—I can't, oh, Christ, Jul—"

The explosion was huge in his ears; it knocked him to his side. The old lady put down her Mauser rifle. Florry looked to Julian and then away; the bullet had pierced his forehead above his right eye and blown a mess out of the rear of his skull.

"Jul—"

At that moment, and for whatever reason, the bridge exploded in a flash that was an exclamation point of sheer light, absolute, blinding, incredibly violent; the concussion seemed to push the air from the surface of the earth and blow Florry back to the ground. The noise was the voice of God, sharp and total. The bridge literally disappeared in the explosion. Stones and timbers and chunks of girder kicked up dust and splashes in a circle for six hundred meters around. A cloud unfurled from the blast, black and rolling and climbing.

"*¡Bravo inglés!*" came the cry from the men around him in the stunned second as the echo faded. The Germans had ceased firing. "*¡Inglés bravo lo hizo! Derribó la puente. ¡Viva el demoledor inglés!*" The old lady was kissing him; others pounded him on the back.

Well, Julian, he thought, looking at the rising cloud of smoke, you finally finished your masterpiece.

He dropped the pistol into his coat and climbed aboard a horse. But he could not stop crying.

Part III

SYLVIA

33

ARRESTED

SYLVIA SAT IN THE GRAND ORIENTE FROM NOON TO TWO every day waiting. It was a clean, pretty place and the afternoons were lovely with sun. She sat outside and watched the people on the Ramblas. There were no more parades, because the Russians didn't permit them. But she didn't care about parades. She sat and tried to make sense of the rumors.

The rumors were about death, mainly. The Russians could control everything except the rumors. The rumors said that Nin had been killed in some phony "rescue," led by the ominous Comrade Bolodin of the SIM. The rumors said that hundreds of POUMistas and Anarchists and libertarians had been buried in the olive grove of the Convent of St. Ursula, but nobody could get close enough to the place to find out. The rumors said that the Russians had secret *checas* all over Barcelona, and that if you criticized Stalin, you'd be taken out at night to one and never come back.

Sylvia sat and had a sip of *blanco.* Then she lit a cigarette. Before her, across the Ramblas, she could see a wonderful old palm tree, its bent scaly trunk arching skyward toward a crown of leaves. She had, in the last seven days, grown very fond of the palm. She loved it and knew it like a friend.

The other rumors were the more troubling. They insisted that a big attack had been canceled even though English dynamiters had blown a bridge deep in enemy territory. But as to the fate of the dynamiters, the rumors disagreed. Some said they'd been killed, everybody had been killed. Others said they had been captured,

then executed. In other accounts, they simply vanished. There was also talk that it was a setup from the beginning, a betrayal, some more dirty business by the Russian secret police. But what had *really* happened? She had to know.

It was all so different now, the new city of Barcelona. Every third man was said to be a Russian secret policeman and nobody would talk. Most people just looked straight ahead with lightless eyes. There were no more red nights, with singing and parades and banners and fireworks. The posters had all been ripped down. Asaltos with machine pistols stood about in groups of three and four.

She shivered, feeling cold though it was a warm day. She looked at her palm tree and out, at the dull glow of the sea which she could just pick out beyond the statue of Columbus at the end of the Ramblas.

"Señora?"

"Yes?"

"Something more, señora?"

"No, I think not. Thank you."

The old man bowed obsequiously as any English butler and with the oily, seasoned, professional humility of the servant class, backed off.

She lit another cigarette.

She felt as if she were in a kind of bubble. The events of the city no longer concerned her. She was magically protected; she was watched over. She was also—she could feel it—watched.

They knew. Somebody knew and had marked her out. She felt as if she were under observation all the time. She was very careful in her movements and had thought all about getting out. When it came time to get out, she knew exactly what to do.

She was weeping. She had never cried before, and now, under the pressure, she had become a weeper.

God damn them. God damn them all for making her cry. A tear ran down her cheek and landed on the marble tabletop, where it stood bright and solitary in the sunlight.

I'd better get out of here, she thought.

"I hate it when you cry," said Robert Florry, sitting down next to her. "God, you look lovely."

"Oh, Robert!" she cried, and reached to engulf him with her arms.

They walked through the narrow, cobbled streets of the Gothic quarter toward the cathedral.

"I wasn't able to save Julian."

"It's definite?"

"As definite as a Mauser bullet in the brain."

"Did he die hard?"

"No. Julian died as he lived: dramatically, flamboyantly, beautifully."

"I didn't think anything could kill Julian."

"Just a bullet," said Florry. "Nothing special about it, a silly bullet. I'm just glad we blew the bridge. He would have liked that."

He held up the ring.

"This is all that's left of Julian Raines. Pity."

"You look terrible, Robert."

"I'm so sorry about Julian, Sylvia. I know he meant a great deal to you. He meant a great deal to me. He was—" He paused.

"He was what, Robert?"

"He was in a certain way not what he seemed."

"Nobody ever is. Here, let me take that awful coat."

Florry put the ring in the pocket and peeled off the filthy Burberry, handed it to Sylvia. She was right: it was dusty and wrinkled and looked as if it had been in battle. Though the blue suit under it was also wrinkled, it had held its shape better; and Florry was light-bearded enough so that from the distance his whiskers didn't show. Without the coat, he looked surprisingly bourgeois.

"After the bridge, we rode for three days through the mountains and forest. They chased us on horseback, a column of Moorish cavalry. We were bombed and strafed twice. The group split up.

Finally, it was only myself and this crazy old lady. We got across the lines two nights ago and were stopped by military policemen, but they let us go. We hitched a ride into Barcelona late last night. We were stopped again. They let me go, because I was British. But they arrested her. Because she was in the wrong category."

"Yes. Yes, if one is in the wrong category, one is in queer street. The Party is against the law. You are a criminal for having your name on the wrong list."

"We've got to get out of here."

"Yes. There's nothing here for us any more."

As they spoke, Lenny Mink watched from a black Ford, which shadowed the two from a distance of about two hundred meters.

They had reached Sylvia's room in the hotel.

"I'm all packed," she said. She took his coat and put it in her suitcase. She knew exactly what had to be done; she'd thought about it.

"You've got to bathe and clean up," she said. "The chances are, they won't stop you if you look middle class. Their enemies are the working-class radical people. If you look like a prosperous English tourist, then you're all right."

"God, it's certainly turned around, hasn't it?"

"You've got to get some sleep, too, Robert. Then tomorrow, we can—"

"Sylvia, it's my papers. They've got bloody POUM stamped all over them. One look at them and—"

"Robert, I can help. I've got some—"

"There's a chap who should be able to help named Sampson, a newspaper chap who—"

"Yes, Robert, listen, I've got it all planned."

"Aren't you the wonder, Christ, Sylvia. You've got it all figured out." He felt dizzy. He glanced past her, toward a mirror, and saw a stranger staring back, haggard and grayed. Christ, look at me.

It suddenly seemed important to tell her something.

"Sylvia, first I have to tell you something. I've meant to for

weeks. I want to tell you why I came to Spain and why Julian was so important to me, and what I've done to him. Sylvia, listen, I have to explain—"

There was a knock at the door, sharp and hard.

He felt her tense. He pushed her back, reached under his jacket, and slipped out the Webley. And what would he do now? Shoot an NKVD man? Yes, and with pleasure.

"Comrade," came the muffled voice.

"Who's there?" he called in English. "I say, who's there?"

"Comrade?"

"Sorry, old man, you must have the wrong party. We're English."

He could sense some confusion outside. But what if they demanded papers? He looked at Sylvia on the bed, her face numb, knowing they'd finally caught up to her. He could see it now. He was death to her.

He bent to her.

"I pulled the gun on you, do you hear? I made you come here. I said I'd kill you. You never saw me before, do you understand?"

"No, Robert, God!"

"No. No, I'm an escaped criminal and I was using you to hide behind. Do you understand? Now scream."

"No. Robert."

"Yes, scream, damn it, don't you see, it's your only chance."

"Comrade!"

"Robert, we can—"

"Shut up, Sylvia." He moved to get away from her. He cocked the revolver and aimed at the door. He'd get the first one sure and maybe a second. No firing squad for him.

"Comrade Florry," the voice called. "We are from Steinbach."

Their saviors took them down the freight elevator to the basement of the hotel and into the boiler room. There, behind the ancient furnaces, was a narrow door. It led through an ancient tunnel under the plaza into the deserted cathedral itself. Florry and

Sylvia spent the day there, not a hundred paces from their rooms and not fifty paces from the furious SIM stooges outside. But the illusion of safety soon evaporated in the sullenness of their angels, who treated them with contempt. Florry was edgy; the men would not give him back his revolver, which he had yielded in a weak moment, nor were they particularly sympathetic to their plight.

"Cold chaps," Florry muttered to Sylvia as they huddled in an obscure transept chapel beneath shrouded religious statues, waiting for the time to pass.

"Better than the Russians," the girl replied.

Florry slept through the afternoon, surrendering at last to his desperate fatigue, but still the day passed with excruciating slowness in the dim space beneath the hugely vaulted roof of the cathedral. It smelled of piss and destruction.

Finally, at twilight, it was time to go. They crept out a back entrance to a truck. Florry and the girl were ordered into the back.

"I suppose you'll be taking us to our legation now," Florry said.

The man, a heavyset worker in a butcher's smock, didn't answer. He had a German Luger in his belt, evidently a prized possession, and he was given to fondling it, and he now took it out to do so, meanwhile ignoring Florry's question.

The ride lasted for hours. Twice they were stopped and once there was yelling. But each time the van continued. Finally, it began to climb and Florry could feel the strain against gravity as it rose. He had a wild moment of hope that they were heading through the Pyrenees, but then realized they'd never left the sound of the city.

The truck stopped after what seemed an endless voyage up a narrow, twisting road. The doors were opened. Cool air hit Florry's lungs; he blinked in the dark and stepped out. He had the illusion of space, oceans of it, and beyond the unlit but somehow nevertheless vibrant tapestry of the city spreading out to the horizon. As his eyes adjusted, he became aware of unreal structures immediately about, as if he were in the center of some dream city, a utopia of crazy, cantilevered streamlines, odd futuristic bulges and girders.

"Good heavens," he said. "We've come to a bloody amusement park."

"You are atop the mountain of the devil," said one of the men close by. "From here Christ was offered the world. He did not take it. Unfortunately, the same cannot be said of others."

"Tibidabo Mountain," said Sylvia. "We've come to the park atop Tibidabo Mountain."

"Yes," said the man. "Just the place for the trial and execution of the traitor Florry."

34

BAD NEWS

I T FELL TO UGARTE TO TELL COMRADE COMMISSAR BOLODIN that the Englishman Florry and the girl Sylvia Lilliford had evidently vanished from the hotel, despite his team's scrupulous scrutiny. But surprisingly, Comrade Bolodin took the news stoically.

Lenny, sitting in his office at the SIM headquarters in the main police station cleaning his Tokarev, thought this meant they were getting ready to move the gold. Florry was back from his secret job behind the lines, something for the hidden GRU *apparat* the Englishman, like his crazed master Levitsky, clearly worked for, something so secret it would be all but unknown to the NKVD. He knew it would be harder than it seemed. There was too much at stake.

"Just poof," said Lenny, "and they were gone?"

"Yes, comrade."

"You talk to the hotel people?" Lenny wondered, wiping down his slide.

"Yes, comrade. Nobody saw a thing."

Lenny considered this curiously, ramming a short, stiff brush through the barrel of the disassembled automatic. Then he said, "People go in and out?"

"Comrade, it *is* a public place. My team was on all sides of the building."

Lenny nodded, wiping down the recoil spring.

He felt rage blossom like a precious, poisoned flower deep in his

head, more precious for its containment. It was delicious. He looked at the Spaniard and had a terrible impulse to squash his head. But he didn't lose control. He didn't lose control any more, he was so close to what he wanted.

"Should we put out some kind of alert so the Asaltos or the police can—"

"No, we should not put out an alert. Then we have all sorts of other people all asking the SIM how it does its business. And I don't like to answer questions. Do you understand, my friend?"

"Yes, comrade."

"Don't I take good care of you, Ugarte? Aren't I a good boss, Ugarte? I'm no *mintzer,* am I?"

Although the Spaniard couldn't know the Yiddish word, he answered, "No, boss."

Lenny rose, embraced the Spaniard, drawing him close with one hand, and with the other gathered between thumb and forefinger a fold of flesh from the cheek. He held it delicately as one would a rose, and felt the man's terror.

"Scared, Comrade Ugarte?"

"No, comrade," said the man, trembling.

Lenny smiled, then crushed his fingers together. Ugarte fell weeping to the floor. It was not the first scream heard in those quarters.

Lenny picked the little one up.

"We can't let this bird fly," Lenny explained calmly. "You tell your gang, Comrade Bolodin is a very busy man these days, and he expects his special friends in Ugarte's section to do their very best."

Lenny could see the terror in Ugarte's eyes. "Okay? Do you understand?"

"Yes." Where Lenny's fingers had come together, a purple hemorrhage now blossomed.

The little man scurried off.

Lenny sat back with his pistol. He knew where Florry would be. He'd have to be with Steinbach, the new number-one gangster of Barcelona, who'd slipped through the big net of June 16 and whose

capture was Lenny's most pressing official business. Clearly Steinbach was being run by GRU; how else could he be so effective? It was a battle between two Russian gangs, he now saw, and he was right in the middle.

When they got Steinbach, they'd get Florry. And Lenny knew they'd get Steinbach. In the spirit of capitalism, the SIM had offered a great deal of money.

And money, Lenny knew, money talks.

35

THE TRIAL

I T SEEMED RATHER STRANGE, FLORRY HAD TO ADMIT, THAT IN the heat of its death convulsions, the POUM had chosen to liquidate *him*. One would have thought they were rather busy for such trifles. But no: this last act was crucial to them. He was surprised to discover how much passion had been invested in such a seemingly ludicrous act.

Sylvia was led off, and the trial began almost immediately in a large maintenance shed at the rear of the deserted amusement park, in which at one time the park's mechanisms and gizmos had been tended. As a courtroom it was barely adequate, certainly nothing like the elaborate courtroom in which another innocent man, Benny Lal, had met his fate. It was a cavernous old garage, with stone floor and a single bare bulb, almost a cliché of illumination borrowed from the cinema, and it was exceedingly drafty. One could see one's breath. However, it did seem adequate, Florry had to admit, to the sort of justice being dispensed.

The evidence was indisputable, especially as marshaled in the dry tones of the well-informed prosecutor, none other than the one-eyed Comrade Steinbach whose eloquence held the panel of judges —three meatpackers, a pimply teenager, and a wild-haired German youth—spellbound. Steinbach, without so much as a hello to his old chum Florry, pushed ahead with his case, as if he were eager to be done with the business.

"Is it not true, Comrade Florry," Steinbach said with the trace of an amused, ironic smile on his lips, and his good eye radiating

intelligence and conviction, "that on the night before the attack against Huesca on April 27 of this year, you sent a message out from the trenches via a secret post to certain parties in Barcelona announcing the time and direction of our efforts?"

Florry, cold and exhausted and suddenly terrified, knew the answer would doom him. But he supposed he was already doomed.

"Yes, yes, I did. But I was trying to reach—"

And he halted. He was trying to reach Sylvia. To mention Sylvia would be to involve her.

But Steinbach was not interested in explanations anyway.

With a flourish, he reached into his pocket and removed a sheet of paper. Florry recognized it instantly.

Steinbach read it in a dry tone and its romantic conceits sounded absurd in the huge, cool shed.

"Note," said Steinbach, "how the clever Comrade Florry camouflages the crucial military information among terms of bourgeois endearment. To read it uncynically is to encounter a lover writing to another on the eve of battle. To read it in awareness of its true purpose is to see the nature of the betrayal."

"The girl has nothing to do with this!" shrieked Florry. "Where did you get that?"

"It was in her purse," he said.

Damn, Sylvia. You should have thrown it out!

"And is it not true, comrades of the tribunal," he argued in his public voice, "that the attack was betrayed, our men pushed back, our party humiliated and weakened?"

They nodded.

"You don't understand," said Florry weakly. "It was innocent. I love the woman. I wanted to tell her that before the fight."

"Yet the attack failed, did it not? Because the Communist Brigades of the Thaelmann Column would not move out in support of our men and the Anarchists. Because they had been ordered by Barcelona to stay put. I give it to you, comrade, from one professional to another: a brilliant stroke."

Steinbach paused, as if to catch his breath.

"Then," said Steinbach, "there is the curious business of the explosion. Florry goes on the attack and does not come back from it; in the intervening day, an unknown fifth columnist detonates our magazine at La Granja. Then, miraculously, Florry returns with a minor flesh wound. Can this be coincidence? Or can Florry have inflicted his own wound as an excuse to go into hiding because he knew a Stalinist agent, acting on information he had supplied— and perhaps had been sent to enlist in our militia to obtain—was planning the potentially dangerous destruction of our munitions?"

Florry saw his chance. Give them Julian, he thought. It was Julian. Give them Julian Raines, spy and traitor, neatly tied and bundled. You believed it yourself. Yet he said nothing.

"Now we come to Comrade Florry's masterpiece. The masterpiece of the bridge."

"I almost died on that bloody bridge!" shouted Florry. "Damn you, a hundred good men died that day!"

"Yet the Fascists knew well in advance of the attack that it was planned, did they not?"

"Yes, they did. We were betrayed. But not by—"

"And is it not true that only you—you alone—of the attacking party survived?"

"Yes. Yes, but we blew the bloody thing. We dropped it into the gorge—"

"Yet is it not true, Comrade Florry, that the attack on Huesca had already been betrayed? By you? So that the bridge itself was irrelevant? And is it not curious, Comrade Florry, that on that same day the English poet and socialist patriot Julian Raines was murdered? Your own friend. Your own countryman?"

"He was killed by Fascist bullets. He was a bloody hero," Florry said. "He certainly would never have given up his life for you bastards if he'd have known—"

"We have reports that place you over his body with a pistol in your hand. Did you shoot him?"

"No."

"Who shot him?"

"An old lady. To put him out of his misery. He'd caught one in the spine and another in the lungs. He was paralyzed and coughing blood."

"You ordered the woman to shoot."

"You bastard," said Florry. "You even turn *this* against me."

It's not too late, Florry thought. Give them Julian. The argument is perfect. Julian is the spy.

"It may interest the tribunal to know that even the poet Raines had his doubts about Comrade Florry. I produce for you now a stanza discovered in his effects from his last poem, alas unfinished, 'Pons.' " He smiled at Florry before reading.

> *"Under the outer man, with his gloss, his charm,*
> *under the skin, the hair, the teeth,*
> *among the bones, the blood, the grief,*
> *there's another man, a secret man, who would do harm."*

"Now isn't that interesting, Comrade Florry? It seems he's describing *you,* does it not?"

No it did not. It was Julian describing himself and his own secret self.

"Who else, Comrade Florry, could Julian have been describing?"

Florry looked to the rafters. Give them Julian, he thought, but it occurred to him that he was doomed anyway. They didn't have Julian. They had him.

"I have these many hours pored over the records," Steinbach continued, "until at last I could see the pattern. I hold myself personally responsible for not seeing it sooner. I am an idiot. Perhaps my trial should begin after the conclusion of this one. But the truth is, wherever Comrade Florry or his lady friend have been and whomever he talks to, they have an odd habit of disappearing. Each mission he is assigned to has an odd habit of failing. And each disappearance and each failure is another nail in the coffin of our party."

"Sylvia had nothing to do with it," said Florry. "She's utterly innocent."

"And yet, Comrade Florry, is it mere coincidence that when our Comrade Carlos Brea sat at a table in the Grand Oriente, who should show up next to him but the girl? And within minutes, the Russian secret policemen arrive. And minutes later, Comrade Brea is shot dead in the street by parties unknown, in the care of the NKVD?"

Then Florry had an inspiration. "The dates," he argued. "Look at the dates. I didn't arrive in Barcelona until the first part of January. Yet the arrests of your people had begun before that. There, does that not prove my innocence?"

But Steinbach was ready for this.

"Actually not. Before January there was no pattern to the arrests. The NKVD was clearly scooping up people blindly. In fact, as one example of their gropings, the category which suffered the most arrests was clearly nonpolitical: it was dockworkers and minor maritime or port officials. Literally dozens of these chaps disappeared. Then Mr. Florry and Miss Lilliford arrive, and as if by magic, the arrests and liquidations of POUMistas begins in earnest."

Florry stared at him in fury.

"I fought for you people. I killed for you. I nearly died—I would have died—for your bloody party. A man I loved more than any other died for your bloody party. The girl worked for months on your silly stinking little newspaper. Why are you doing this to us?"

"You betrayed the comrades at Party headquarters. You betrayed the working classes of the world. You betrayed your countrymen Julian Raines and Billy Mowry. You betrayed the future. You and your master in the Kremlin. Only we have you and not him. So you will have to pay his debt, too."

When it came time for Florry to address the court, he had it all planned out.

"Comrade?"

"I ask," he said, feeling very much the fool, "that since you are

going to kill me, you at least spare the girl. She had nothing to do with any of this."

"If you confess, it will help," said Steinbach. "Help her, that is. You are clearly beyond mercy."

"I cannot confess to what I have not done," said Florry. "You ask a great deal of me."

Steinbach came over to where he was sitting and leaned over to talk more intimately.

"You know," he said, "you'll make everybody much happier if you confess. It would put a pretty ribbon on it."

"I cannot confess to something I haven't done," said Florry. "If you're going to shoot me, shoot me. But let's be done with the game."

"It doesn't really matter in the end. I just thought you might care to help the party out a bit."

Florry looked at him in dumfoundment. After several seconds his mouth closed.

"I *say*," he said, "you do expect a lot! I'm innocent and you know it and you're evidently going to shoot me. And you have the nerve to ask if I care to pitch in?"

"I suppose it does seem somewhat much. But look at it this way: whether you're innocent or not isn't really the point."

"It is very much to me."

"But in the larger view. You must learn to see the larger view, though admittedly it's a bit late in the game for you. The point is, there *was* a spy. Indisputedly. I know where he was, how he worked. I've spent hours on the pattern. Yes, he was there, all right. You, perhaps six or seven others, including the late Julian. The girl even—"

"Stop it."

"Comrade, please. We have no time for sentiment. It doesn't matter in the long run, for just as surely as *you* are doomed, so are *we*. I am the most wanted man in Barcelona and these others will go down with me. But what is at stake here goes beyond us and

beyond Barcelona. You see, there are others in our struggle against Stalin for the soul of the left. Trotsky is one, but again, the man doesn't matter so much as the idea of the world revolution. It's worth dying for. The point, however, is this. If we were defeated in Barcelona because our ideas were bad, because we could not compete ideologically, because the people would not believe in us, then our theory is wrong, and we are doomed. On the other hand, if we were defeated because we were betrayed—because of a Judas planted by Stalin—then our ideas remain sound and will continue to inspire. They in fact are so frightening to Moscow that Stalin himself leads the fight against us. That is impressive. Thus it is necessary that there be a spy. It doesn't even really matter if he's the right spy. Just so that we find him, try him, sentence him, and execute him. Thus, surely you can see how nice it would be for you to leave that confession. That little ribbon for history. Where's your sense of duty? Surely they taught you that at Eton?"

"Bugger Eton," said Florry. "I only care about Sylvia."

"She *is* a lovely thing. Florry, I was once young myself, and in love. She was killed by Friekorps officers in Munich in 'nineteen. Raped, beaten, shot. It cured me of my illusions. And my eye."

He smiled.

"Let her live, Steinbach, and I'll sign something."

"All right," said Steinbach. "You've made your bargain."

It took them a while to work something out that Florry could put his name to, but in the end, the document, though more vague than Steinbach would have preferred and more explicit than Florry wanted, was complete.

"This is utterly idiotic," he said, scratching his name at the bottom.

"Perhaps. Perhaps not. In any event, it shall eventually be run in a leftist newspaper someplace or other as part of our testament. You have managed one thing, Comrade Florry. You have managed to enter history."

"History is revolting," said Florry.

✦ ✦ ✦

The execution was set for dawn; about an hour before, they served him his last meal, some scrawny chicken cooked in too much oil, and a large skin of red wine.

"The chicken isn't terribly good, I'm afraid," said Steinbach. "But the wine should prove helpful."

"I'm already numb, you bastard."

"Try not to be bitter, comrade. Surely all the men here will join you under the ground in the weeks ahead."

"It can't happen too soon for my taste. What about the girl?"

"She's fine. Tough, that one. I'm impressed. Would you like me to bring her by? A sort of last-minute farewell. It might appeal to your romanticism."

"No, spare her that. This is hard enough without that. You'll see that she gets out?"

"We'll do what we must. Would you like a priest?"

"I'm not a Catholic. Besides, I haven't sinned. And aren't you an atheist?"

"In my dotage, I seem to have acquired the habit of hypocrisy. Then, should I tell her anything? The obvious?"

"How would you know what was obvious?"

"I'm not so stupid, Florry. I'll tell her that you loved her till the end. She'll have good memories of you, then."

"She's lost everybody that she cared about in Spain," said Florry.

Steinbach laughed evilly. "So has everybody, Florry."

Florry found he had no taste for the wine, which was young and bitter anyway, but that the chicken was rather good. Steinbach had lied about that as well as everything else. He tried to take a little nap after he was through eating because he was still exhausted, but, of course, he could get no sleep. It was absurd. They were going to shoot him because they needed a demon and he was available. He was in the right category.

Yet as the time of his death neared, he found what he regretted most was not being able to give Julian's mother her son and husband's ring. That was the one thing Julian had wanted and the one

thing he'd thought of at the moment of his own death. It seemed like one more failure to Florry. It was in the Burberry smashed into the suitcase in the closet of the hotel. He brooded about this obsessively until he could stand it no longer. He banged on the door, and after a while Steinbach came by.

"Yes?"

"Have you seen the girl yet?"

"No. She's resting. She doesn't know what's happening."

"Look, tell her this for me. Tell her the ring in the coat is for Julian's mother. She's to get that to the woman, all right?"

Steinbach said he would, though his look informed Florry he thought it a queer last request. Then he left again. In a bit, a gray light began to filter through the cracks of the closet in which they'd locked him. He heard laughter and the approach of footsteps.

The lock clicked as the key turned in it; the door opened. A boy stood there with a rifle.

"*Es la hora*, comrade," he said.

Florry rose and was roughly grabbed by three other boys. His hands were tied behind his back. They fell into formation behind him and led him through the deserted garage.

In the half-light, the deserted mountaintop had turned ghostly. Mist had risen and clung everywhere and the amusement apparatus, scabby ancient machines, loomed through it. The Ferris wheel was a circle of comical perfection standing above it all. The boys led him to the scaffolding that was the base of a roller-coaster.

"Cigarette, Florry?" asked Steinbach, waiting with several others.

"Yes," said Florry. "God, you're not going to do it here? In a bloody park?"

"No. The boys will take you down the hill into the forest. The grave has been dug. Actually, it was dug yesterday morning." He lit a cigarette in his own mouth, then placed it in Florry's in a gesture of surprising intimacy. Then he added, "Or rather *two* graves."

He could see her now, in the group of men. They had gotten a cape for her, to keep her warm, but her hands had been tied.

"You told me—" Florry started.

"I argued, old man, but the judges were insistent. You wrote that note to her. She sat with Brea. Clearly she was involved."

"Oh, God, Steinbach, she's *innocent,* don't you see? Tell them, for God's sake."

"Take them," said Steinbach, turning away. "And be done with the filthy business."

The rough teenage boys pushed Florry along.

"God, Sylvia, I'm so sorry," he said. "It's all so unfair."

Sylvia looked at him with dead eyes. "I knew what I was getting into," she said.

"I love you," he said.

"As if that helps," she replied, with a little shake of her head.

They walked down the steeply sloping road away from the park surrounded by five boys, the eldest perhaps twenty, who was the *sargento* and chief executioner. On either side of the road, the dark, dense forest rose. It was perfectly still, though the sky had begun to fill with light, and the air was moist. The road descended Tibidabo by virtue of switchbacks, and after they had gone around several sharp turns and had traveled perhaps half a mile, the young sergeant halted them.

"This way," he said in polite English. He had a big automatic pistol; the others had gigantic, ancient rifles.

He took them off the road and through the damp bracken and groundcover of the woods. They followed a path a few hundred feet in, though the going was awkward, given the extreme slope of the land, until they reached a small clearing in the trees, where two shallow graves had been scooped out.

"It's a pity, isn't it?" Florry said. "All of it. They're just bloody fools, doing their worst. Animals, idiots."

"I say, do you mind awfully shutting up?" she said. "I don't feel much like chatter."

The boys got them to the edge of the holes, then stood back to form what appeared to be an extremely amateur firing squad. Each seemed to have a different firearm, and the youngest looked abso-

lutely sick at what was about to happen, not that Florry could spare the wretched boy any pity. The _sargento_ was the only one among them who had any sort of self-possession. He busied himself importantly examining weapons and setting caps just right and making sure belts were properly adjusted. He'd make a fine little Bolshevik commissar, Florry thought; too bad he'd picked the wrong party.

Damn these boys: could they not get it bloody over? Florry's knees had begun to knock and his breath came in little pinched sobs and his eyes were wide open like upstairs windows into which flew birds and clouds and everything on earth. Sylvia leaned or almost huddled against him; he could feel her trembling and wished he could at least hold her or offer her some comfort in this terrible moment.

"_¡Preparen para disparar!_" barked the _sargento_.

The boys attempted to come to a formal position and lifted their rifles to aim. The muzzles wobbled terribly, because the weapons were so heavy. One of the idiot children had even fixed a bayonet to his rifle.

Sylvia had begun to weep. She had collapsed against him, yet he could not hold her because his hands were tied. He looked about. His eyes seemed magically open—the forest, filled with low beams of light and towering columns of mist and soft, wet, heavy air, seemed to whirl about him.

Let it be clean, he prayed. Let it be clean.

"_Apunten,_" the _sargento_ barked.

"The bastards," Florry heard himself saying.

Then they heard the noise.

"_Esperan. ¿Que es eso ruido?_"

At first it was a far-off putter, almost something to be ignored. Yet it rose, persistent, the labored sound of an engine—no, two, perhaps three—climbing the steep road of Tibidabo.

"_Es una camion, sargento,_" one of the boys said.

"_¡Carrajo! Bueno, no disparen,_" the sergeant said, looking about in confusion. The soldiers let their rifles droop.

Through the trees, they saw the vehicles, big and cumbersome, loaded with troops as they lumbered by.

"Asaltos," somebody whispered.

Just beyond them, the trucks halted. An officer got out and the men climbed down in their clanking battle gear. Their bayonets were fixed. They formed into a loose attack formation, rifles at the half-port, and began a jog-trot up the hill toward the amusement park. Two men at the rear of the column carried a Hotchkiss machine gun and tripod.

"The Stalinists have caught up with Steinbach," Florry murmured.

Sylvia collapsed to the ground, but only Florry noticed. At the top of the hill, there was no suspense. The firing started almost immediately. They could hear the dry, rolling crack of the rifles and the stutter of the Hotchkiss gun.

"They're really giving it to them," Florry said.

He turned back to the firing squad. The sergeant was clearly bewildered, not sure where his duty lay. But the boys of the little unit weren't: they were at the point of panic with the gunfire so close.

Florry watched as the sergeant struggled with his indecision. And then he said, as if having at last conquered himself, "¡No! ¡La hora de su muerte está aquí!" He pointed at Florry melodramatically.

"¡Muerte!" he said, raising the pistol. Then he slumped forward with a spastic's drool coming from his inert face and thudded heavily to the earth. Behind him, the boy who'd crushed his skull stood in shocked horror for just a second before pitching the rifle into the brush and heading out at a dead run. His compatriots studied the situation for perhaps half a second, then abandoned their weapons just as resolutely and fled just as swiftly.

Florry rushed to the rifle with the bayonet, bent to it, and in a few seconds of steady sawing had himself free. He slipped the bayonet from the gun muzzle and ran to Sylvia to cut her free.

"Come on," he said, picking up the sergeant's automatic, "we've got to get out of here."

Up top, the shooting had at last died down. Florry and Sylvia pushed their way deeper into the forest, away from the trucks, and found the going nearly impossible for the bracken and the undergrowth. In time, they were swallowed up by the trees and seemed far away from everything. And soon after, they came to the rusty tracks of the disused funicular, by which in calmer days Barceloneans had traveled to the amusement park and the church up there. Descending its gravel bed was easier than trying to fight their way down through the undergrowth, and by noon, they had reached the base of the mountain. The houses were sparse at first, but within a bit they found themselves in what must have at one time been a fashionable district, on a serpentine street flanked by great houses that now seemed deserted.

They forced the gate on one of these and went out back. The house was secure against the return of the owners in some distant, better future, but in the servant's quarters, a door gave way to Florry's shoulder and they were in and safe.

36

TIBIDABO

B Y THE TIME COMRADE COMMISSAR BOLODIN AND HIS MEN arrived at the top of Tibidabo Mountain, the fighting was over. As Ugarte pulled the big Ford to a halt by the assault guard trucks a few hundred feet below the gate of the amusement park, Lenny could feel his rage beginning to peak; it seemed to be replacing itself with some other feeling, odd and sickening. Lenny felt as though he might vomit. Suppose, he wondered, the ache in his stomach watery and loose, suppose they were dead? Suppose his deal was all fucked, shot dead by gun-happy assault guards from Valencia "protecting" the revolution from traitors.

"Ah! Comrade Bolodin," someone said with great smug cheer. Lenny turned to discover a gallant young Asalto officer, his arm in a sling, a cigarette in his mouth, cap pushed back cockily on his head. The youngster looked sunny as a valentine: he couldn't wait for the compliments to come raining down on his handsome head.

"Captain Degas, of the Eleventh Valencia Guardia de Asalto," the young officer introduced himself, snapping his heels together with a flourish and coming to a kind of mocking attention. "You'll see, comrade commissar, that the problem of the Fascist traitors, chief among them the notorious Steinbach, has been solved."

"Any prisoners?" Lenny demanded in his rude Spanish.

"I regret to inform the commissar of the Servicio de Investigación Militar that resistance by the traitors and spies was formidable, and that the taking of prisoners proved imposs—"

336 /

Lenny smashed his stupid, smart young face with the back of his hand, watching the man spin backward and drop, a look of stunned surprise and sudden shame running quickly across his brilliant features.

"*Stupido,*" Lenny barked. "Idiot. I ought to have you shot."

He was aware of the Asaltos going silent all around him. He felt their curious and shocked eyes.

"Explanations," Lenny barked.

"We're stationed down the mountain in Sarria. An informant told us a band of POUM traitors was hiding up here and agreed to lead us to them. We were acting under the strictest revolutionary orders issued by the government and signed by the commander of the Servicio de Investigación Militar, that is, Comrade Commissar Bolodin himself."

"Bring this informer."

"Ramirez," the captain shouted.

A second or so later, a seedy-looking Spaniard in a black jacket was brought over. He held his cap nervously in his hands. Lenny listened as he explained: he was the caretaker of a nearby estate. With the people gone, he got by as best he could and was out late the night before when a truck pulled into the park and he realized that it was being used by traitors. He'd seen a tall man in a suit and a girl get out of the truck.

"*¿Inglés?*"

"Yes, perhaps *inglés.*"

"With a mustache?"

He was not sure. But the man had a dark suit and blondish hair.

"Pay the man," Lenny said. "He did *his* duty. You should have contacted us. It's you who didn't do *yours.*"

"My apol—"

"Fuck your apologies. Now get rid of this man, and take us to the bodies."

"This way, please, comrade. We brought them out for burial."

Degas led him across the yard to the shed. Lenny saw that it was

splintered and ruptured by gunfire, one window blackened with flames where a bomb had gone off. The smell of smoke still hung in the air.

The dead, about fifteen, lay in a row in the sun outside the garage. Most were chewed up rather badly by the machine gun and the bomb and they had the scruffy, ragged indolence of corpses. Flies buzzed about. There were puddles of blood, thick and black, all over the ground.

"That one was the leader," said Degas. "The old man in the turtleneck. He yelled that we were Stalin's killers. He's the one with this."

The boy held up a glass eye.

The little marble sparkled in his gloved fingers, the pupil open wide and black and blue.

"Throw the fucking thing away, sonny," Lenny said.

He went to look at Steinbach. The old man had been shot in the throat and the chest and the hand. His gray sweater was the color of raspberry ice.

"We found this, too, comrade," said Degas. "It is in English. No one here can read it."

He handed Lenny a sheet of paper covered with a blue scrawl:

> *I, the undersigned, take full responsibility for that which I am about to receive and wish to establish that I was acting under orders from the highest authority. I acknowledge that I have taken from the revolution its most precious treasure and that I, and I alone, am responsible.*

It was signed, *Robert Florry (British citizen).*

Lenny looked at it for a long moment, breathing heavily.

"Is it important, comrade?" asked Degas.

"It's nothing," said Lenny, putting it in his pocket. "And this was all?"

"Yes, comrade commissar."

"And nobody escaped?"

"No, comrade."

"And so what has happened to the tall man and the girl that that fellow told you about?"

"I-I couldn't say, comrade commissar."

"Did you investigate?"

"I didn't see the point."

"Could they have escaped?"

"Not unless it was before my men got here."

"Have you searched the park?"

"Yes, comrade."

"Everywhere? The woods down the mountain?"

"I sent a patrol about to check. Perhaps in the melee some POUMistas scampered away. But I do not think so. We caught them entirely by surprise. They were eating. Chicken with rice. They were in the middle of—"

He halted.

"Look, comrade commissar," he said, his face suddenly brightening. He pointed.

Three Asaltos were entering the gates. They prodded before them with their bayonet points a *sargento* in the black mono of the POUM. Blood ran down his face from a wound in his scalp, but it had dried. He had a vacant, stupid look in his eyes.

"Comrade captain," yelled one of the soldiers, "come see what we found snoozing in the woods!"

"Lucky man, Degas," said Bolodin. "If that guy tells me what I want to know, you'll get your medal. And you were about to be shot."

37

PAPERS

"DO YOU KNOW?" SHE SAID, AWAKENING, "I HAD A MARVEL-ous dream. I was back in London, in a nice flat. I had a dog. I was listening to the BBC. I was reading *Mayfair*. It was very, very boring. I hated to leave it."

"Who could blame you?" he said, aware as he took a quick glance about that he had not been included in the dream. What he saw was what he'd been looking at for hours now: the dust was thick as a carpet, the furniture ruined, the walls bare and peeling. An odor of neglect clung to the room. Outside, or rather of what he could see outside in the dark, there was no movement whatsoever, though occasionally a truckload of Asaltos would heave by. He had been at the window for hours, while she slept. He had the automatic in his hand.

"Do you see anything?"

"No. But we can't stay here much longer."

"What time is it?" she asked. "I feel like I've slept for several days."

"It's nearly nine. The sun has been down about an hour."

"God, I could use a bath."

"I admire your sense of self, though I must say it's a queer time to think of bathing."

"I hate to feel dirty," she said. "I absolutely loathe it."

Florry continued to look out the dark window. His eyes burned and the fatigue threatened to overtake him. He was gripping the pistol far too tightly. A few minutes back something had snapped

in the house and he's almost fired crazily. He knew he was getting close to his edge.

"It's the papers," he said, "that will kill us. Or rather, our lack of them. We can get spiffy, I suppose, or at least spiffy by Spanish standards. We can clean up and look the right proper travelers. But if we get to the station and the Asaltos stop us or some NKVD chaps, then we've bought it."

He could feel his teeth grinding in the bitterness of it all.

Papers. Authentication. Perhaps the consulate . . . no, of course not, the NKVD would be watching the consulate. Perhaps they could buy the bloody things somewhere in the quarter. But how to make contact? How to raise the money? How to make sure one wasn't being observed or that one wouldn't be betrayed? Florry had always run with the hunters when he was a copper. Now he was running with the hunted. He shook his head. There were no rules, as there were in the daylight world: you simply did what you had to, that was the only rule.

"I suppose we could try to walk to the frontier, traveling by night. It's only about a hundred miles north. We might make it undetected. Then we could make it across the Pyrenees—Good God, half the International Brigades marched over the Pyrenees, there's no reason we shouldn't be able to make it. Or we—" But he stopped.

It was absurd. One hundred miles without papers, neither of them speaking the language with any authority, the NKVD in full command of the police and hungry for foreign spies to put against the wall.

"Robert—"

"The port, Sylvia. I think that would be our best bet. I've been thinking about it. If we can get down to Barrio Chino, perhaps I can make some sort of contact with a foreign seaman and arrange a passage . . ."

"Robert, please listen to me."

"Eh?"

"I can get us out of here."

"What are you talking about?"

"Do you remember that chap of yours you borrowed the book from. The newspaper fellow. Sampson?"

"Yes." Sampson! Bloody Sampson, of course!

"Yes, well he's gone."

"Gone?"

"Yes. Yes, briefly to Madrid, then back to England. His assignment was over, he said."

Florry said nothing. Yes, it would be over, would it not? Sampson, back safe and sound, leaving them in the lurch.

"But when I gave him the book, he said something quite peculiar. It was the address. He kept repeating it over and over again, in such a way that I'd be certain to remember it. He kept saying, 'You know you're always welcome at my place, 126 Calle de Oriente.' He said it over and over again. Remember, he said, you're always welcome. Any of your chums, too, always welcome. Robert especially. Bring Robert by any time. Then he told me he was leaving for England, but the invitation was still open. Drop in with Robert, if you've a mind, he kept saying, 126 Calle de Oriente."

Florry thought about it. He thought he remembered something about a pro forma invitation dinner at Sampson's, but wasn't that at a villa of some sort? Perhaps he'd moved. But it was queer, was it not? That the priggish, awful Sampson should suddenly come on like an old school chum, so completely out of character. What on earth—?

"Robert, what sort of man was he? It was almost as if he were giving me a message for you. A message that I would—"

"He was telling us where to go," Florry said suddenly, realizing it. "Yes, yes, he was. He was . . . he was *saving* us."

There was no answer at the apartment at 126 Calle de Oriente, in a quiet residential block in the shadow of Montjuich to which he and Sylvia had traveled the next morning with surprisingly little

difficulty. He knocked again, then ran his fingers up top along the doorjamb.

"Christ," he said, almost stunned when he found the key.

They stepped into eerie silence. The place looked surprisingly neat, as if it hadn't been occupied in months. The furniture was coated with dust.

"Sampson didn't have much of a personal life," said Florry. "But at least it's a place to hide out while we decide what to do next. And perhaps we can get that bath."

"There must be something here," said Sylvia, with a note of desperation in her voice. "If there isn't we're—"

Across the room, in the bookshelf, Florry saw a copy of _Tristram Shandy,_ by Laurence Sterne.

He walked swiftly to it, pulled it from the shelf, and pried it open.

"Robert?"

"Sylvia, why don't you take a rest?"

"No, Robert. I must know. That damned book, it's followed us through Spain."

He opened it. In the inside cover, someone had written, _November 2, 1931._

He turned to page 31, held the book against the light, and detected the puncture. He turned two pages and found another.

In minutes he was done.

BEDROOM FLOORBRD 3D ROW 3D SLAT, it said.

He went swiftly into the next room, peeled back the rug, found the board, and tugged at it. With some effort he got it out. There was a paper package. He pulled it out, pried it open. In it were two crisp British passports, a wad of thousand-peseta notes, a wad of pound notes. Florry examined his passport: it was a clever forgery, using the official picture from his copper days. It identified him as a Mr. George Trent, of Bramstead, Hampstead on Heath. Sylvia's, equally ingenious, identified her as Mrs. Trent.

"God," she said. "That's my school photo."

"Well," he said. "It's our way out."

"And you," she said sounding stunned. "Robert, you're a spy."

"Yes," he said. "MI-6, actually."

They enjoyed a curious sense of security in the apartment, a sensation—on Florry's part, at any rate—of having been looked after. It was as if in this one chamber in one building in the revolutionary and political chaos that was Barcelona a kind of separate peace had been obtained. It was something they both needed desperately: a holiday.

The plumbing worked; they bathed. Layers of scum and grime came off Florry and for the first time in weeks he became unaware of his own odor or the terrible sense of crawly things at play in his thick hair. He found a razor—wasn't Sampson the thoughtful one? —and scraped his face clean. He looked with surprise and a sense of shock at the man who greeted him from the steamy mirror. A tall fellow with a thatch of thick hair, its natural lightness beginning to go to gray. Meanwhile, two parentheses had been inscribed into the flesh of the cheeks, seeming to seal off the prim mouth from the rest of it. A network of wrinkles enshrouded the dulled eyes and the cheekbones stood out like doorknobs. A starburst of pink, clustered tissue showed just under his collar line where the bullet had gone through him.

Christ, I'm old, he thought. Old and battered. What happened to that silly youth who wrote bad Georgian poetry amid the moths and pink gins of Burma? Where did that fool go? To dust, with his chums in Red Spain.

He went to preparing his kit: he brushed off his suit and hung it out to smooth itself over the night; it had been through so much and looked shiny and baggy, but the English wool was tough. It would survive. It was Julian's final legacy: aristocratic tailoring, which in fact might get them through.

Julian. You think of everything, don't you?

Kill me, Julian had said.

Florry turned away from a melancholy recital of his own failures;

there'd be a lifetime for that if they got beyond the frontier. He washed out his shirt and watched the grime from it cling to the basin. He hung it on a hanger and hoped it would dry for the morning.

Wrapped in a blanket, he went out into the living room to find Sylvia in the middle of her preparations. She'd brushed and cleaned her dress and hung it out over a pot of steaming water.

"It'll look smashing," he said.

"Yes," she said, "I can hardly believe that tomorrow we'll be out of here. We've got money, we've got papers, we've got the proper look. We can buy some luggage. Robert, we're almost—"

He sat down.

"We haven't had much time together, although we've been in each other's company for about three solid days. I mean, time for us. That is, if there is an us. Now that Julian's gone."

"Robert, let's just concentrate on getting out of here now, shall we? Let's make certain there's a you and a me before we worry about an us."

He looked at her, her neck, her gray green eyes, her mass of feathery hair. A beauty, but someone else's beauty. He'd lost her, but had she ever been his to begin with—or was that merely another Spanish illusion?

"All right," he said. "I won't mention it again until we're out of here. I—I just wish I could stop thinking about us."

"If the NKVD catches you, you'll cease it soon enough, Robert," she said tiredly.

"There is one other thing," he said. "I had just thought how nice it would be if we had our _own_ luggage, Sylvia. After all, you must have had some—"

"It's at the hotel, Robert. The clothes I bought, in a suitcase. But they will be watching the hotel."

"But can they watch it all the time? I mean, let's look at the odds. They're looking for escaping POUMistas, not prosperous British travelers. They're not looking for _us_. They're looking for a certain category. We are no longer in that category, don't you see?

Thus, it occurs to me how easy it would be to simply pop in and get your bag on the way to the station. Don't you see?"

She looked at him, and then explained as if to a child.

"It's too risky. It's a straight run to the station by tram or cab and we can make it. If we putt around after silly bags, then we're fools and we deserve our fates."

"Sylvia—"

"Robert, for God's sake, we can make it. Don't you see? There's nothing—"

"I told Julian I would give his ring to his mother. His ring is in my coat. My coat is in your bag. Your bag is in the hotel. If I could, I would go myself, alone. But don't you see, the room is in your name. They wouldn't let me—"

She shook her head.

"Two weeks ago you hated him. Now you love him. Now you'll risk yourself to perform some foolish romantic gesture in his memory. You really are a fool, Robert. But you certainly won't risk me."

"He was my friend. I must help him. Very well, I'll go by myself. Perhaps I can talk the chaps into letting me in. I'll see you at the station. We can travel by—"

"Robert—"

"*I must get that ring!*" he shouted. He had never shouted at her before and she was stunned. He felt himself shaking.

"I'm sorry. I shouldn't have raised my voice. It's just that—"

"God, Robert, the virtue in you is appalling. It's actually quite repugnant."

"You have no idea how many times I let him down, Sylvia. How I let him down, how I betrayed him. How at the moment when he asked me for one thing, I could not do it. Perhaps we had better leave separately tomorrow. You go your way, and I'll go mine. I'm going to get that ring one way or another."

"Robert, you are such a bloody fool. I shall get your bloody ring for you then, if it means so much." She was quite angry.

✦ ✦ ✦

They left early the next morning, a doddering, nittering couple, fascinated into open-mouthed dumfoundment by all they saw about them. They pointed gawkishly at soldiers. They asked foolish questions loudly, in English. They tried to find a good cup of tea.

It was only a matter of hours. The train for the frontier left at one. They took a tram across town.

"Salud, señor," said the conductor, accepting Florry's peseta piece.

At the hotel, it went with surprising ease. Sylvia's bag had been stashed and they went to look for it. Florry stood in the lobby stupidly, waiting until it came. It was a mahogany room, full of flowers, quite civilized in feeling. He looked about. There seemed to be no one of interest in the lobby. There were no secret policemen or Asaltos. At last the bag was produced.

"Splendid," said Florry heartily, and he gave the boy an enormous tip.

They went outside and found a cab.

"There," he said, "you see, it was easy."

"It was stupid," she said.

"It took us a bloody five minutes. It cost us nothing. We've done it. We've made it. We'll be at the station in minutes. Nobody saw us."

He was almost right. One man had seen them standing outside the hotel, and only one. Unfortunately, it was Ugarte.

38

UGARTE

UGARTE'S CHANCE TO REDEEM HIMSELF IN THE EYES OF his boss came at around twenty minutes to one. He was sitting slouched like the pimp he'd once been on the steps of the cathedral watching the hotel; all sensibly gave him wide berth, for he was a dangerous-looking man, chewing a toothpick with the arrogant sullenness of one who is willing to commit violence. As he brought his eyes up in a lazy scan of the crowd—it was that close, another second and he'd have missed them entirely—he saw a tall gentleman of obviously foreign extraction and his missus blinking confusedly as they attempted to negotiate, bag in hand, their way toward the street and eventually a cab.

Ugarte's eyes beheld them, almost dismissed them, then almost lost them in the crowd, and then at last brought them into focus for study as they bobbed awkwardly through the crowd: yes, perhaps. They looked older and graver, somehow; he'd been expecting glossy, beautiful children, and these two dodderers were gray and halting. Yet as he watched them he became aware of how much of the illusion of age was merely the result of profound fatigue, amplified by the gauntness of hunger. And that, furthermore, there was a queer theatrical dimension to them: he sensed their strain. They were not, not quite, who they seemed to be.

Ugarte's dilemma became vivid. Comrade Bolodin's instructions had been precise: observe, but do not intercept unless absolutely necessary. At first chance, contact headquarters. Retain observation. Do not apprehend.

Ugarte was most anxious not to offend the great Bolodin, whom he loved and feared as no man he'd ever met in his life. Yet he watched with a sort of hypnotized dolor as they entered the vehicle, closed the door, and it pulled away. His eyes felt hooded and sleepy, his brain damaged. What was involved here was something quite beyond his experience: a decision. *Carrajo,* what to do? His misery increased.

Then, without willing it, his feet begin to move. He found himself racing back through the crowd, pushing his way into the street. He waved down a car and pulled his SIM card. Terrified eyes met his.

"The station!" he shrieked, "or it's your death!"

When he got there, he could not find them. He had a moment's terror. It occurred to him he could lie about the whole thing. He could deny it had ever happened. Bolodin would never know. That's what he would—

Then he saw them. As they pushed their way through the crowds, they moved with uneasy tentativeness that was almost their best disguise. He watched as they made their way. They reached Via 7 where a huge train was loading. They showed their tickets at the gate and were admitted. Ugarte looked up to the black sign under the numeral seven that displayed destinations and saw a long list, the last entry in which was PORT BOU (LA FRONTERA).

Ugarte leaped ahead through the crowd. He pushed his way along, under the few revolutionary banners that nobody had gotten around to removing yet, and made his way toward the set of iron stairs against the far wall of the station which led up to a balcony, a door, a window, clearly some sort of station headquarters. At the top, there stood a young Asalto with a machine pistol.

"*¡Halto!*" screamed the boy, quaking at the apparition of the crazed man flying toward him.

"Fool," yelled Ugarte, shaking with excitement. He pulled out his SIM card again, feeling very much like a real policeman. "Do

you know what this means? I could have you shot! I could have your family shot! Out of the way!"

The boy, a Valencia bumpkin, seemed to melt, and Ugarte pushed his way into the room where several bored and seedy but vaguely official-looking men sat at desks.

"I command you in the name of the people," said Ugarte, who had heretofore only commanded low women in the name of his wallet, "to delay train number seven. Now, where's a telephone?"

Lenny did not panic when the call came, nor did he stop to quiver at the closeness, the tentativeness, of the connection to his quarry. He simply knew what had to be done next and set about to do it. He knew that if Florry were leaving, the gold was leaving, presumably among his effects, or perhaps by way of a shipment, melted down in some innocuous way. He knew that the gold was most vulnerable when it was being moved, because guile, not armed guards, were the essence of the GRU operation. Whatever, he knew that the answers rested with the man Florry, who had to be persuaded, somehow, to share his knowledge. Lenny did not doubt that he could convince Florry to cooperate but what terrified him was the danger of discovery. He wanted to separate Florry from his secrets at his leisure, far from inquiring eyes. He had decided, therefore, to allow the man to leave the country and to take him in France.

Lenny left instantly for the station. In fact, he was packed and ready in more ways than any of the men who worked for him or any of the men he now worked for could possibly know. He had planned toward this day for some time, and the planning was exquisitely complete. It was not merely a question of a bag, a change of clothes, and a tin of toothpowder; he had such a bag, but sewed into its lid were, first, a British passport in the name of Edward Fenney, an expensive forgery, and, second, fifteen crisp thousand-dollar bills U.S., his savings from various unofficial activities in Barcelona.

The plan was simple: Comrade Bolodin of the NKVD/SIM would board the train and Mr. Fenney would emerge to cross the frontier.

However, once in France, Lenny had still another identity into which to slip—he would become one Albert Nelson, citizen also of Great Britain—and it would be as Nelson, four full identities removed from the scrawny, furious, half-mute East Side Jewboy whose bones and furies he had carried for so many thankless years, that he would close upon and take his quarry and begin his prosperous new life.

He raced for the courtyard car park with extraordinary eagerness for what lay just ahead. He could feel his heart beat and his blood begin to sing. The moment he had glimpsed months back in Tchiterine's dying confession had finally arrived.

But he did not even get to his car and driver before a shout came from behind to halt. He was more surprised than angered: who dared address the mighty Bolodin in such a haughty and commanding tone? He turned to discover his mentor Glasanov closing on him with a look of terrible desperation, at the same time gesturing to two of the other Russian thugs from the new mob who had arrived in the aftermath of the coup.

Glasanov appeared almost mad with fury. Lenny had never seen him so distraught.

"Bolodin!"

Mink fixed him with the dead eyes, waiting.

"Bolodin," said Glasanov, "damn you. We found the old man, Levitsky, in the convent. He's been torn to pieces; his mind is gone. What are you up to? What game are you playing?"

Lenny could think of nothing to say. It occurred to him to remove his Tokarev and put a bullet through Glasanov's forehead, but the others were closing too quickly in the courtyard and he could feel his driver, reacting to the intensity of the moment, beginning to separate himself from the car and its connection to himself.

Glasanov pointed.

"Arrest the traitor Bolodin," he howled. "He's a state criminal."

39

DETECTIVES

NOBODY HAD BEEN INTERESTED IN THEM AND NOW THEY sat in a kind of numbed silence in the first-class coach, alone and silent. The train smelled of tobacco and use. Now and then, people moved down the corridor outside the open compartment, occasionally an Asalto. Once, one of them peeped in.

"*Es inglés, ¿verdad señor?*" he said.

"*Sí, señor,*" said Florry.

"Passport, *¿por favor?*"

"Ah. *Sí,*" said Florry, handing it over.

"*Muy bien,*" said the man, after a brief examination.

"*Gracias,*" said Florry.

"*Buenos días, señor,*" said the man, ducking out.

"It was so *easy,*" said Sylvia.

"The Asaltos don't matter," said Florry. "In Red Spain, only the NKVD matters."

He sat back. He felt exhausted. Could it all be done, all of it, Spain, the whole bloody thing? He looked out the window of the carriage and could only see steam, the tops of heads passing by under the level of the window, and, across the via, another train. He looked at his watch.

"We're late," he said after a time.

"Does it matter?" she said. "We *are* on board."

"I suppose you're right. Yet I'll feel a good deal better once the

bloody thing gets going. It was supposed to leave five minutes ago."

"Robert, the Spanish haven't done anything on time for several centuries."

Florry agreed and closed his eyes, trying to quell his uneasiness. But he could not get it out of his head. Why are we not moving?

By now they had almost completely encircled him, guns drawn. Lenny stood in the courtyard, not ten feet from his car, feeling his automatic heavy in the shoulder holster. He had no real image of the doom closing in on him, but he knew he was in big trouble. They'd found the old man. They'd search his case, find the passports and the money. He was a dead man. The impulse came to go out in smoke and flame, the way Dutch Schultz went out: he could feel the hunger for the pistol build in his fingers. He wanted to grab it and start shooting. You always know, when you go into the rackets, you always know something like this may happen: a bigger gang catches you in the open, unexpected, and it's over. He'd put the lights out on enough guys himself.

"You American scum," said Glasanov, "I've been watching you for some time. I've seen your ambition, your deals, the hungry way you look. You profess to be a Communist and are nothing but gangster scum. Now there's proof you're pulling something. We'll get the truth. Take him."

The men closed to Lenny and Glasanov, led by the two big new Russians.

"Commissar Glasanov—"

"Take the American trash!" screamed Glasanov, close enough to spray up into Lenny's face. Lenny could see the hairs in the man's nostrils and the moles on his chin.

"Comrade Glasanov," said one of the new Russians, "it's you who are under arrest."

They surrounded Glasanov.

"You are charged with wrecking and oppositionism. You are in

league with the Jew traitor Levitsky whom you let escape and the puppet master Trotsky. You will be returned to Moscow immediately."

"But I—"

"Take him away!" shouted Lenny. "I can't stand to look at the traitorous pig."

The officers lead Glasanov off.

"Comrade Bolodin?" the arresting officer said. It was some new kid Lenny knew was named Romanov. He was a real hotshot, this Romanov. Straight from the big boss himself.

"Yes, comrade."

"I just wanted you to know Moscow knows you've been attending your duties. They are very pleased in Moscow with the big Amerikanski."

"I'm pleased to serve the Party and can only wait to spread the struggle to my own land."

"Good work, Bolodin," said Comrade Romanov.

Lenny turned and walked swiftly to his car.

"The station," he commanded.

His driver sped along, siren screaming. He ran through the crowd, racing past Ugarte without a word of recognition. They were locking the gate at Via 7, but he got by them and could see it ahead in the bellowing steam as it moved away. He didn't think he would make it, but from somewhere there came a burst of energy and he leaped and felt his hands close about the metal grip hung in the last door, and he pulled himself aboard.

"Thank God," said Florry. "Well, I hope that's the last delay."

"I'm sure it will be," said Sylvia.

The train pushed its slow way up the coast toward Port Bou, flanked on one side by the Mediterranean and on the other by the hulking Pyrenees, and after a time, Florry and Sylvia went to dine. They sat in the first-class dining car over a bad paella of dry rice with leathery little chunks that had once been sea creatures and

drank bitter young wine and attempted in their game of disguise to make clever Noël Coward repartee for anyone in earshot.

Sylvia seemed quiet, typically distant; some color had returned to her face. Hard to believe two days ago they'd been standing next to their own graves in front of the firing squad. She appeared to have forgotten about it, or to have dispensed with it. It was something about her he liked a great deal: this gift for living only in the absolute present, this wonderful gift for practicality.

Florry looked away, out the window. He tried not to think of the dead he'd left in Red Spain. He tried to think of the bright, beautiful future, he and Sylvia perhaps together at last. He knew if he tried hard enough he could earn his way back. He knew there wouldn't be the problem over Julian any more; he felt he could control his jealousy and his sense of possessiveness that had mussed things up over Julian. The future would be theirs and wonderful. They had survived. They would be the inheritors.

"Robert." There was urgency in her voice. "Detectives."

He looked and could see them.

"Start chatting," he said.

They must have come aboard at the last stop. They were heavyset men in raincoats with that sleepy, unimpressible look to their eyes that any copper masters in the first few days of the job.

They came down the coach aisle slowly, fighting the lurch of it upon the rails, choosing whom to examine and whom not to on the basis of some strange, silent code or protocol between them. Florry stared straight into Sylvia's lovely face without seeing it, keeping the men in soft, peripheral focus nevertheless. Perhaps they'd arrest someone else before they got to him, perhaps that big fellow in the raincoat sitting there, or the—

But no. With their unerring instinct for such matters, the two policemen came straight to him. He could feel their eyes on him and could hear them thinking _inglés_ and knew how their minds would work: a deserter from the International Brigades or a political prisoner having fled some Barcelona _checa_.

"I do hope it's a rainy summer," he said, trying to think of the most English thing he could say. "The roses, darling. The rain is absolutely *topping* for the roses."

"Señor?"

"—and we must go to Wimbledon for the championships, I hear there's a dreadfully good Yank fellow who—"

"Señor?"

He felt a rough hand on his arm and looked up.

"Good heavens. Are you speaking to me, sir?"

"*Sí. ¿Es inglés, ¿verdad señor?*"

"*Sí.* Rather, yes. English, quite."

"*¿Era soldado en la revolución?*"

"Soldier? Me? Good heavens, you must be joking."

"George, what do they want?"

"I have no idea, darling."

The man took his right hand and turned it over to look at the palm.

"Now, see here," said Florry.

"*¿Puedo ver su pasaporte, por favor?*" said the man.

"This is most irritating," said Florry. He pulled his passport out and watched as the man rifled it, examined it carefully.

At last he handed it back.

"You like España, Señor Trent?" he asked.

"Yes, very. The missus and I come each year for the beach. Except *last* year, of course. It's nice things have settled down. You have the best sunlight in Europe after the Riviera, and we can't afford the Riviera."

"*¿No era fascista?*"

"Good heavens, of course not. Do I look like one?"

The man's pale eyes beheld him for just a second and then he conferred briefly with his partner.

"*Espero que se divirtiera en su viaje.*"

"Eh?"

"To hope you have enjoyed your trip, Señor Trent," he finally said and passed on.

Florry took another sip of the wine, pretending to be cool. He could see the little rills on its placid surface from the trembling in his hand. The stuff was impossibly bitter.

He reached for a cigarette, lit it.

"That's the last of the Spanish crew," he said. "We ought to be very close to the frontier."

"Why did he check your hand?"

"The Mosin-Nagent has a sharp bolt handle. If you've done a lot of firing, you'll almost certainly have a scab or a callous in the fleshy part of your palm."

"Thank God you didn't."

"Thank God the scab dropped off in the bath last night."

"I think," she said, "I think our troubles are finally over."

Yes, you're right, he thought. But he wondered why it was he had the odd, unsettling feeling of _being watched_.

"Are you cold?"

"Of course not," he said.

"You just shivered."

40

PAVEL

THE RIGHT EYE WAS GONE. SMASHED, SHATTERED, crushed when one of the brutes had kicked him as he lay on the floor of the pen. The surgeon had simply removed it, while wiring up the fractured zygoma, as the bone surrounding it was called. The left eye remained, though its lens had been dislocated in the same terrible blow. The old man could detect a moving hand but he could not count fingers.

The shoulders, of course, were broken from his long session on the rope; and the wrists, too. Additionally, he was bruised, cut, scraped, battered in a hundred places about his old body.

But the significant damage was psychological. His memories were jangled and intense. He was extremely nervous, unable to concentrate. He knew no peace. He had nightmares. He wept for no reason at all. His moods altered radically.

And he no longer talked.

Now he lay incarcerated in plaster and bandages in a private room in the Hospital of the People's Triumph, formerly the Hospital Santa Creu i Sant Pau, on the Avenida Stalin. The room seemed to be high and bright; it opened to a balcony that had an unrestricted view of—of something. The sea, perhaps. Levitsky could only recognize the illumination and smell the breeze.

He lay alone—or, it could be said, alone with history—on a sweet, cool, late afternoon. The doctor came in, as usual, at four, only this time—most *unusual*—he was accompanied by another man. Levitsky, of course, could see none of this, but he could hear

the second, unfamiliar snap of footsteps, and inferred from their speed and precision a certain energy, perhaps even eagerness, as opposed to the grimly proficient rhythm of the doctor's shoes.

"Well, Comrade Levitsky," said the doctor in Russian, "it appears you are a tough old bird." Levitsky could sense the doctor over him and could see just enough movement as the fellow bent. "A man your age, a mangling such as this, so long among the horses. My goodness, nineteen out of twenty would have died on the operating theater table." Levitsky knew what would occur next —the flash of pain as the light hit his surviving eye—and, indeed, a second later, the doctor's torch snapped on. It went off like a concussive boom in his head.

"He's stable?" The second voice was harder and younger.

"Yes, commissar. At last."

"How long before he can be moved?"

"Two weeks. A month, to be safe."

"You're sure, comrade doctor?"

"In these times, it wouldn't do to make a mistake."

"Indeed. A month, then."

"Yes."

"All right. Leave us."

"He's still fragile, commissar."

"I won't excite him."

Levitsky heard the doctor walking out. Then there was nearly a full minute of silence. Listening carefully, Levitsky could hear the other breathing. He stared through the milky incandescence of his single eye at the ceiling.

At last, the young man spoke.

"Well, old Emmanuel Ivanovich, your comrades at Znamensky Street send their greetings. You've become quite an important fellow. This man is to be protected at all expense, they insist. But I forget myself. Pavel Valentinovich Romanov, of the Glavnoe Razvedyvatelnoe Upravlenie. Lieutenant commander, actually, at a rather young age, you might say."

He paused, waiting for a response. Levitsky had none, and so the young man responded himself.

"My pride, you would tell me if you could, will be my downfall. Well, perhaps you are right." He laughed. "It certainly was yours."

Levitsky said nothing.

"Now, I know all about you, but you know so little about me. Well, I'll spare you a list of my accomplishments. But let me just say," said the young man, with a certain hard edge to his voice, "that if you are the past of our party, one could argue that I am its future."

The young man went proudly to the window. Levitsky followed his shape with his one good eye. He was a soft, dark blur against the whiter purity of the opening.

"Lovely view! That mountain. Magnificent! Not as beautiful as the Caucasus, of course, but beautiful, nevertheless. Sends shudders up one's spine, Emmanuel Ivanovich. So, how do you like the room? It's nice, isn't it? Indeed, yes, the very best. Do you know that doctor? He's the best also. London-trained. No shitty Russian medicine for dear old Emmanuel Ivanovich Levitsky. No! Can't have it! Only the best Western medicine!"

The fellow laughed.

"Well, Ivanch," he said, allowing himself the intimacy of the romantic diminutive form of address, something permitted under normal etiquette only between family members, "I must be off, but I'll be back tomorrow and every day until you're strong enough to travel. I shall guard you like a baby and tend you like a mother."

Levitsky stared up at him furiously.

"Why?" said Pavel, with a smile. "Because the boss himself has ordered it. Your old revolutionary comrade Koba has taken a personal interest in this. I am, one might say, his personal representative here. Koba wants you back, healthy and sound and chipper in Mother Russia."

He bent over the old man to complete the thought before walking out.

". . . for your execution."

41

NIGHT TRAIN TO PARIS

JUST BEFORE NIGHTFALL, FLORRY LEANED AGAINST THE glass and made out the approach of a small station house that sat above what appeared, in the fading light, to be a seedy beach town spilling away in chalky white desolation down a slope to the water's edge. The station wore a sign that said, in rusted-out letters, PORT BOU.

"Christ, we've made it," said Florry, feeling a sudden surge of exaltation. "Look, Sylvia, has anything so scabby ever looked so bloody lovely to you?"

The train halted at last and Florry removed Sylvia's grip from the overhead. It was only a few seconds until they had left the train, edging out among the crowd. Stepping down, Florry smelled the salt air and heard the cries of the birds that must have been circling overhead. Up ahead, he could see that the tracks ended up against a concrete barrier; beyond that, there was a fence; and beyond that, France.

"Do you see? There's a train," he said, pointing beyond the wire to the continuation of the track. "It must be the overnight to Paris."

"You should try to get us a compartment," said Sylvia. "We are traveling as man and wife; to do otherwise would appear ridiculous."

"I say, you've thought awfully hard about this."

"I rather want to survive, that's all."

"You know, it's probably not necessary. We're out. We could stay in separate—"

"Let's play the fiction out to London."

He could not help but laugh. "You seem to know more about this business than *I* do."

They followed the drift of the passengers toward the guard post, a smallish brick building nestled near the barbed wire by a crude pedestrian gate—the whole affair had a rough, improvised look to it—and a line had already formed into which they slipped. It seemed to be a dream play set under the calm Mediterranean moon, the line of passengers filing listlessly into the little shack under the scrutiny of sleeping *carabineros*—no revolutionary Asaltos here—for a cursory examination. If you had the passport you were all right.

Florry handed his and Sylvia's over to the man, an old-time civil servant, who didn't give them a second look, except to run mechanically their names off against his list.

"*¿Arma de fuego?*"

"Eh?"

"Firearms, Señor Trent?"

"Oh, of course not," said Florry, remembering his vanished Webley and the automatic he'd tossed away.

The man nodded.

"Go on to French customs," he said.

"That's it?" said Florry.

"*Sí, señor.* That's it."

They stepped out of the building and through the gate and into another little shed, which turned out to contain two little booths, each with its policeman. Florry got into one line and Sylvia the next and in time they arrived at the tables. The officer game him a quick, lazy glance.

"*¿No tiene equipaje a portar de España?*"

"Er, sorry?"

"Do you have bags?" the man said in French.

"Oh. My wife has it."

"You take no bags from Spain?"

"We believe in traveling light."

The man nodded him on and he emerged to find that Sylvia had already made it through and was waiting with her grip.

"Hullo," she said.

"Hullo. No problems?"

"No. The fellow opened the bag and began to go through it, but your awful raincoat was in the way and the woman behind made a scene about missing the Paris train. He was a decent chap. Rather, a lazy one. He just waved me on."

It then occurrred to them that they were standing at the gate into France. They stood in line to present their passports to the frontier gendarme, who made a disinterested examination, and ultimately issued the proper stamp.

"*Bien,*" he said.

"*Merci,*" said Florry.

It was that simple: they stepped outside the shed, and they were in France.

"One should *feel* something," Florry said. "Relief, or some such. What I feel like is a smoke."

"I feel like brushing my teeth," Sylvia said.

The French train up ahead hooted. Near it, a temporary French station had been built, the mirror image of the Spanish installation on the other side of the frontier.

"We must hurry," she said.

"I'll get tickets. Darling, see if there's a tobacconist's about, will you, and get cigarettes. American, if they've got them. Pay anything. And get some chocolate. I love chocolate."

He raced for the ticket window.

"Do you have a first-class compartment left open for Paris?" he asked in French.

"Yes. Several, in fact; there's not many first-class travelers who leave Spain, monsieur. Not since July."

"I only have pesetas. Can you make the exchange for me?"

"I will only charge a small percentage."

"It's only fair."

He pushed the money across to the man and waited while the fellow figured it out and paid him back with the tickets.

"I only took a little extra."

"Fine, fine," said Florry, grabbing them and trying to quell his exuberance.

"You must hurry; this train leaves in a few minutes."

"Believe me, this is one train I won't miss."

He turned and ran toward it, to find Sylvia waiting at the door to the sleeping car.

"I've got it," he said. "God, look at that!"

"It's only English tobacco, darling," she said, holding up a pack of Ovals.

"This must be heaven," Florry said. He could not stop himself from smiling.

"I'm sorry they didn't have American. The tobacconist had just sold all his American cigarettes to some hulking Yank."

"It doesn't matter, Sylvia. We're safe at last."

The train whistled.

"Come on, it's time to get aboard," he said.

They ate in the first-class dining car, and whatever one could say against the French, the French knew how to cook. The meal was— or perhaps this was merely an expression of their parched tastes after so many months in Red Spain—extraordinary. Afterward, they went to the parlor car and had a drink and sat smoking as the train hurled through the darkened countryside of southern France.

"Paris by morning," said Florry. "I know a little hotel in the Fourteenth Arrondissement. Sylvia, let's go there. We've earned a holiday, don't you think? There's enough money, isn't there? We haven't to face the future quite yet, do we?"

Sylvia looked at him: her gray green eyes beheld him curiously, and after a bit, a smile came to her face.

"It really is over, isn't it? Spain, I mean," she said.

Florry nodded.

"Well," she said. "Let me think about it will you, Robert?"

"Of course."

She hadn't said no—quite. And it sounded wonderful: a fortnight of luxury in a small, elegant hotel in the most civilized
country in Europe after what had been the least civilized. Florry sat
back against the comfortable chair, smoking an Oval. Maybe the
woman would be his after all. He felt he owed it to himself to
begin to feel rather good.

But of course exactly the opposite occurred. A curious melancholy began to seep through him. He seemed to still smell Spain
somehow, or still dream it, even when wakeful. He remembered
Julian in the dust, begging for death. He remembered the bridge
exploding. The blast, for all its fury, had meant nothing after all it
had cost them. He remembered the POUM rifles leveled at them,
and the comical idiocy of the trial, and the Communist Asaltos
heading up the mountain with their Hotchkiss gun. He remembered Harry Uckley's empty holster. He remembered the night
attack on Huesca and firing his revolver into the boy's face. He
remembered the abrupt cold numbness when the bullet struck him.
He remembered the ship digging beneath the surface and the flames
on the water.

"Robert, what on earth is wrong?"

"Julian," he said. "I wish I had not let Julian down at the end.
I know he meant so much to you."

"Julian always got what he wanted," said Sylvia with odd coldness. "And never what he deserved."

She touched his arm. "Forget the war. Forget politics. Forget it
all. Forget Julian."

"Of course you're right. Absolutely. One mustn't let oneself get
to brooding on things one is helpless to alter. And I swear I won't."

But it was a lie. Even as he saw her pretty face he remembered
Julian. Hold my hand. I'm so frightened. Kill me.

"Yes," she said. "I could not get the American cigarettes, and so
I should not feel as if I've failed, eh?"

"I say, shall we have another drink?" he said cheerfully.

"Pardon me, folks."

They turned, and looked up into the eyes of a rather large, almost handsome man in a suit standing in the aisle.

"I hate to interrupt," he said, "the name's Fenney, Ed Fenney. I saw you on the train out of Barcelona. I just heard the lady say she's sorry she missed the American cigarettes. I bought them all. Look, here, take these."

It was a pack of American Camels.

"Mr. Fenney, it's really not necessary," said Sylvia.

"No, I know how you get, missing your best smokes. I just got a little greedy at the border. My apologies, miss. Please, take these. You Brits and us Americans, we ought to stick together. It's going to be us against the world one of these days, you just wait."

He smiled. There was something peculiarly intense about him and remotely familiar, but he seemed so eager to please that Florry found himself accepting the cigarettes.

"Well, thanks awfully," he said. "Would you care to join us?"

"No, listen, after a long day like this, I really want to turn in. I've calls to make in Paris tomorrow, have to be sharp. Nice seeing you." He left.

"Robert, I'm awfully tired, too," said Sylvia.

"Well, then. That seems to be that. Shall we go?"

It was nearly midnight: they walked through the dark, rocking corridor from car to car until at last they found their compartment. They entered; the porter had opened the bed and turned it back.

"Not much room in here, is there?" he said.

"The French are so romantic," Sylvia said. She held up a single red rose that had been placed in a vase by the tiny night table that had been folded out of the wall.

Florry pulled the door shut behind him, snapping it locked. When he turned, Sylvia had undressed to her slip and washed her hands and face in the small basin. He went to her bag and opened it. Julian's ring had fallen out of the pocket of his coat and worked its way into the corner of the case. He picked it up, looked at it.

This is all there is of my friend Julian Raines, he thought. There was little enough to it: a simple gold band, much tarnished, much

nicked, as well it should be. The inscription inside it read, "From this day forth, Love, Cecilia." It was dated 6-15-04.

For luck, Florry thought, and gave it a little secret kiss.

There was a knock at the door.

"Who on earth could that be?" he said.

"It's Ed Fenney, Mr. Florry," came the voice through the door.

"Oh. Well, what on earth—"

"Listen, I have an extra carton of Camels here. I might not see you in the morning. I'd like to give them to you."

"Well, it's not necessary but—"

"It'd be my pleasure."

Florry turned, gave Sylvia a quizzical look, and turned to the door.

"Robert, don't. We don't know—"

"Oh, he's just a big, friendly American. Just a moment," he called, getting the door unlocked, even as he wondered how this Fenney knew his name, "You know, this is awfully damned kind—"

The man hit him in the stomach and he felt the pain like an explosion; he hit him twice again, driving him back, filling his mind with astonishment and, by the power of the blows, his heart with fear.

Yet even as he fell, Florry was trying to rise, for the man had just smashed Sylvia across the face with the back of his hand.

The big man hit Sylvia a second time, killing the scream in her throat, and she dropped bleeding on the bed when Florry, having somehow accumulated a bit of strength, assaulted him with a desperate rugby tackle, but it hurt Florry worse than the other and as Florry slid off, a brute knee rose and met him cruelly flush beneath the eye with a sick ugly sound that filled his head with sparks and scattered his will. He began to crawl away to collect himself, but the man dropped onto his back, pinned him with a knee as one pins the butterfly through the thorax to the board, and had his thick hands under his throat. He pulled his head back. Florry felt

the strength and the force. He knew the man could snap his neck in an instant. He could hardly breathe. He was gagging.

"Pleased to meet you, *yentzer*," the man hissed. "I'm your new pal."

Florry was instantly released and felt the man rise off him. Then a powerful kick slammed against his ribs, lifting him against the wall in the tiny room, flipping him. He tried to scream when a short sharp blow delivered with a boxer's grace and cunning nailed the exact center of his body and the sound was frozen forever in his lungs. He lay back, his eyes closed, sucking desperately at the air.

The man leaned across the bed and pulled Sylvia up by the hair. He slapped her face hard twice to bring her awake to scream, and as her throat constricted in the effort, he rapped her there lightly to trap it. He pulled her over and her head down.

Florry knew he had to help her. He had to get air, and help Sylvia.

"Please," Florry begged. "Don't hurt her. I'll do anything. Just tell me. I'll do it."

Please him, he thought.

The man dropped Sylvia unconscious to the bed and turned to Florry. Florry seized Sylvia's suitcase from the corner and desperately hurled it, but it was open and the clothes falling from it crippled the velocity of the thrust. The man elbowed it aside contemptuously. He walked over the litter of clothing now spread about the floor and smashed Florry in the face and Florry wasn't fast enough to slip the blow. Instead, head a mess of confusion and lights, he went down to the floor. The man sat atop him. Florry could feel the hot, excited breath and the heaving heart and the strength and the totality of him, the overwhelming force of him.

"I know it all," said the man. "The old Jew Levitsky. The guy at Cambridge. He told me. You're working for the reds."

"I- I-" Florry struggled with the idea.

"Yeah. He told me, Levitsky himself, your great buddy. And I got *this*, too, fucker."

He leaned back, reached into his pocket, and pulled something out. Florry recognized it immediately. It was the confession he'd signed for Steinbach.

"The gold," the man said. "Where's the gold?"

"What? I—"

"Don't fuck around. The gold! God damn it, the gold." He pulled something from his pocket, snapped it, and a knife blade popped out. He put the icy-sharp point of the blade into the soft skin under Florry's eye. "I'll cut you and cut you and cut you. Then I'll cut the girl. I'll cut everybody you ever knew. The gold. The gold!"

Florry knew now he was hopelessly insane, his ideas crazed and pitiful, his willingness to hurt absolute and unending.

"You've got it all wrong," Florry said. "It's—"

The man's eyes widened at this defiance and he hit Florry savagely in the face.

"No," said Florry, gasping and curling, seeking desperately for something to put between himself and the pain, "no. It's Julian. Take Julian, don't take me. He's the one. Leave us alone, please, I beg you."

But the man stood above him, looming like some titanic statue. Florry watched as the man's foot came forward until it covered his face with its black shadow and descended onto his face. He could feel the shoe on his nose and lips, flattening and spreading them, and he could taste the grit and filth on the sole, little flecks and curds of it, falling into his mouth.

Florry's fingers scrabbled desperately at the floor and the clothes littering it as a single thought filled his head: who will help me now?

Nobody, the answer came. You are alone.

"Lick it," the man commanded in a hoarse, mad whisper. "Lick it, you little fucker."

Florry's tongue caressed the sole of the filthy shoe exactly as his fingers, crawling through the clothes on the floor, touched something hard and recognized it before his mind did.

"The gold," the man said. "Tell me where the gold is, God damn you or—"

Florry raised Julian's little automatic, thumbing back the nubby hammer, and fired into the crotch above him and felt the boot come off his face and saw the blood spurt. Florry fired again into the lower belly and into the chest, the gun cracking in his hand. The blood spurted and sprayed everywhere and the man seemed to sink back stunned and disappointed, holding his red fingers before him, and Florry shot him in the throat, opening a hideous wound, the larynx blown to shreds even by a small-caliber bullet at this range. He made grotesque mewling noises. He was spitting blood and it was coming out his nose and spilling down his chest. Florry rose, cupping the pistol with both hands, and fired carefully into the face; a black crater erupted in the crack and flash of the pistol under the eye while brain tissue and red fog rose from somewhere and he fired into the eye, shattering it. The slide on the pistol locked back. It was empty.

In the corridor, somebody was shouting. Florry looked down at the little pistol. It had lain in the pocket of the Burberry all those days since the bridge, packed away in Sylvia's absurd case, a shell in its chamber, because when he needed to, he could not use it to help Julian.

But Julian had helped him.

42

THE GREEN

HOLLY-BROWNING STUDIED THE PROBLEM. IT WAS A QUESTION of angle of approach and at the same time of impending obstacles—a classic, in other words. It called for a peculiar combination of delicacy and power, the perfect equipoise. It called also for firmness of decision. It was not a time for equivocation, for appeasement, for lack of will. The situation demanded his utmost.

"Five iron, I think, Davis."

"Yessir. Excellent selection, sir. I'd watch the elms on the left. There's not much air among their leaves."

"Thank you, Davis," said Holly-Browning, taking the club. He laced his fingers together about the grip and let the natural weight of the club head pull the shaft down; it fell, with unerring accuracy, to its absolute perfect placement behind the ball.

Holly-Browning paused, concentrating. He let a wave of power build and build in his blood until it almost sang in his veins and he felt the muscles ache and tremble and hunger for release. Yet still he held it, feeling himself—this was quite odd—*sink* utterly into the ball until at last there was nothing, nothing at all in the universe but the white dimpled sphere and the green concave of grass embracing it and his own will, and in a sudden, fluid, Godlike whip of power and—odd again—terror, almost, he coiled and unleashed a blow that mashed it to smithereens. The contact was solid and shivered up his arms as the stroke followed its own inclinations through and came to rest all the way around his body.

At last he lifted his head to follow the straight, clean white flight of the ball as it rushed to the green with just the right kiss of loft and just the right pitch of power; it bounced on the fairway, bounced again, and struck the green, rolling slower and slower, its energy decreasing until at last it came to a halt about six feet from the flag.

"Pretty shot, sir," said Davis.

"Thank you, Davis," said Holly-Browning, handing back the club.

"Sir, may I say, it's an honor to see a man who knows how to play the game."

"Thank you, Davis," said Holly-Browning.

It was a bonny bright day full of elms and summer under a lilac English sky. Major Holly-Browning's spikes gripped the moist turf as he walked.

"I say, Holly-Browning, well-struck," C called out, not without some bitterness, for his own second shot had come to rest a good twenty-five feet below the green. But that was as it had been and should be.

"Thank you, sir," said the major.

In the past, Holly-Browning, an excellent golfer, had held back when playing with his service chief, out of respect for the protocols of rank. It was how one rose, or so many believed. But not today.

"Well, Holly-Browning, I daresay you're playing well," said C, falling into step beside him.

"I seem to be, for some reason, sir."

"Good to get you out on the links after all that time hibernating in the office. Now that awful business in Spain is finished and we are well quit of our bad apple."

They reached C's ball. The old man took an eight iron from his boy and, with a great, grunting effort, chopped a shot too high; it rolled way beyond the cup, coming to rest on the apron at the far side of the green, easily (given C's gracelessness) three putts' distance off.

"Damned bad luck, sir."

"Ah, bloody gone. Sometimes it's there, sometime's it's not."

"You're out, sir."

"Yes, I am."

C took the putter and went to his ball. After what seemed an interminable period bent over studying a trajectory whose subtleties he could never hope to master, he rose, addressed the ball, and, with a show of concentration, patted at it weakly. The ball rose over a hump in the green, picked up speed, and began to veer crazily off, finally petering out still a good ten feet from the cup.

"Blast!" said C. "It's certainly not my day! Go on, putt out, Holly-Browning."

Holly-Browning moved to his ball and crouched to study his own course to the cup. Then, having swiftly settled on a strategy, he climbed back up and faced the little white thing, crisp and immaculate as a carnation before him. He tucked his elbows and locked his wrists and willed his chin to sink, almost submerge, into his chest, and with the barest, most imperceptible of motions, he tapped the ball toward the cup. It hugged the contours of the green, seemed to roll and glide of its own volition, and once almost died, but then picked up a final spurt on the downward side of the green's last little bulge and dropped in with the sound of a wooden spoon falling onto a wooden floor.

"God heavens, you're playing well today, Holly-Browning. Been taking lessons?"

"Actually, I haven't touched a club since July of last year," said Holly-Browning.

If C caught the reference to the beginning of the Spanish War and the defector Lemontov's flight to the Americans, he didn't show it. He bent and patted out another dud of a putt, which still left him a solid three feet shy.

"Damn. My chap keeps telling me to keep my head locked but I always seem to look *up*. What do you recommend, Holly-Browning? What's your secret?"

"Just hard work, sir. Practice, all that."

"Yes, indeed. By the way, James, I thought I ought to tell you. It seems there may be a bit of a stink."

"Oh?"

"Oh, nothing really. It's that MI-5 bunch. They seem to have found out all about it. I thought I was done with them."

"I thought in principle they agreed with our handling of the case, sir."

"It's not a question of *that*, old man. It's just that their interrogators never got a crack at the inside part of Julian's head. Now bloody Sir Vernon has his dander up. A terrible bother."

Holly-Browning didn't say anything.

"They've put it out that it was a *personal* thing between you and Raines, with poor Florry just the errand boy in the middle."

"That quite simplifies things, sir," said Holly-Browning, stung at the injustice of it all.

"I know that, Holly-Browning. But that's what these damned security people *are*: simplifiers. Everything's black and white to them."

"Yessir."

"And, I should tell you, there are those in our own house who think Section V ought to leave the red lads alone and concentrate on the gray lads. Jerry's the next big show, eh?"

"Yessir, I suppose Jerry is."

They had reached the next tee. Birds sang, tulips bloomed, still ponds reflected the sun's gold touch, and vivid butterflies hung in the light. The sky was cobalt blue, of a purity the bizarre English clime permits rarely enough. Ahead, several argyle-clad figures in plus-fours and caps putted out on a par three, 108 yards out.

"Damn this fellow Hitler. He really has confused the world, hasn't he?"

"Yessir, he has."

C planted his ball on the tee, took his three wood, and addressed the thing with a waggle of his rear end, knotting his fingers into a confusion of sausages about the club.

"And that's why I'm placing you in charge of a key operation, James. It's a big move, James."

Holly-Browning showed nothing on his face. He simply nodded.

"It's a big job, James. Take your wife and daughters out if it suits. It'll get you away from Broadway. Most bracing change, I say. You shall have Jamaica station. Damn, I must say, I *envy* you. Jamaica!"

The bloody colonies! An island full of niggers and flowers!

C swung. The ball popped off the tee, bending oddly in the air, its flight weirdly *crippled,* and sank itself in a trap with a puff of sand.

"Damn! Damn!" said C. "I simply wasn't *meant* to play this bloody game. In any event, I suppose I'll have to boost your fellow Vane up to Section V head. He's the right chap, don't you think?"

Holly-Browning shuddered at the idea of Vane as V (a).

"A splendid idea," he said.

"And I'll bring this young Sampson in to help him. He'll be V (b), eh? He's a bright chap; he can handle London, don't you think?"

"Yessir," said Holly-Browning, addressing his ball. "Yes. Very good, sir." He drew back and seemed to lose himself in the rush of the stroke, and felt his four iron meet the ball with the authority of an edict from Stalin. It rose, a pill, white and nearly invisible against the bright sky, and then fell as if dropped from the Almighty Himself. It landed square on the green perhaps two feet above the pin and began to describe a spin-crazed curlicue over the short grass in the general vicinity of the . . .

"Good Christ," said C, "it went *in*! Holly-Browning, it went *in* the bloody hole."

"Yes, yes, it did, didn't it, sir?" said Holly-Browning, handing his club to Davis.

43

THE HANGAR

THE OLD MAN GREW STRONGER WITH REMARKABLE SWIFT-ness and was well enough to travel within seven days. The speed of the recovery stunned the British-educated doctor. Pavel Romanov, however, something of a scholar of the lives and times of Emmanuel Ivanovich Levitsky, was not particularly amazed; he knew the old agent to be a man of rare resilience and will.

Yet Levitsky still did not talk.

One evening, they drove him by ambulance to the Barcelona airport well after midnight and took him to a special, isolated hangar on the far outskirts of the place, hundreds of meters from the terminal. He was amazed at the activity at the obscure locality; there were armed guards everywhere, Soviet Black Sea Marines with German machine pistols.

Inside the building, he sat ramrod stiff in a wheelchair, a blanket drawn about him, a pair of sunglasses shielding his damaged eye from the harsh light. He could hardly move, what with his shoulders locked in the plaster, but he could still make out the airplane. It was a giant Tupolev TB-3, a four-engine bomber whose fuselage had the odd appearance of having been mounted on its sturdy wings upside down and whose landing gear was so primitive it looked like gigantic bicycle tires.

"A big aircraft," said Romanov, laughing. "To accommodate both our egos."

Romanov felt loquacious.

"It's a shame you can't talk, old man. We could have had some wonderful conversations. I shall have to do the talking for both of us. Did you know this airplane has been specially modified, with fuel tanks added under the wings and through the fuselage. It's our only bird that can make the straight flight from Barcelona to Sebastopol without refueling. It's taken us a long time to get it ready for tonight."

He looked into the old man's eye for a hint of curiosity, and convinced himself that he found it.

"You're wondering if you are so important a cargo?" he asked. "Well, it's not quite all for you, old man."

Listening exhausted Levitsky. He sat back and settled into his perpetual semidarkness and his silence. With an act of will, he restrained himself from his memories, which sometimes threatened to consume him these dark days. He had ordered himself not to think. To think was to yield to regret, to the infinite allure of what might have been, in another world. Be strong, old one, he told himself. It is almost over.

They seemed to be taking their time on the plane. One would think they could handle these arrangements with a good deal more precision. He was growing impatient. Perhaps the ground staff were all Spaniards, taken to moving slowly and without—

It then occurred to him that the mechanics whose vague shapes he had been able to discern scurrying over the vaster shape of the grotesque airplane had vanished. It was strangely silent. Then he heard the arrival of a car, some far-off mutter, and with that, Pavel Romanov dipped behind him, pivoted him, and began to push him across the bumpy tarmac. He could smell petrol and oil as they moved through the hangar, but in time they arrived in a kind of smaller room off the larger one. Pavel opened the door, dropped back, and pushed him through. It was a small place, tight as a coffin, and pitch dark. Levitsky could sense the close press of the tin walls. Pavel did not turn on the light.

"You have fifteen minutes," Pavel said. "And then we leave."

Levitsky listened to his jaunty footsteps snapping away; the door

closed, somehow damping down the air. Levitsky waited and after a bit made out the sound of breathing.

"Old man." The whisper reached him from across the room and across the years. "God, what have they done to you? They've treated you so terribly."

Levitsky could say nothing.

"I had to come. I *had* to see you. Once more . . . before—"

He let it lapse into silence, and just stared in wonder at the old man.

"You appear disappointed in me, old man. You sense my doubt." He stared intently at the old mute. "I know what you're thinking. I must remember I'm working for the future. I've been blessed enough, with that chance. It's enough to live for. And to die for. One should not look twice at an offer of enrollment in an elite force. One should not hesitate."

Levitsky could feel the young man's gaze and adoration upon him: his ardor and his willingness to learn. He remembered him at Cambridge: young, bright, callow, but incredibly eager.

He felt the young man rise and come over in the darkness. He felt the warmth of his body, his closeness. The young man bent and touched his hand. "The sacrifices you made. For me."

He swallowed.

"When they were so close . . . I knew you'd save me. You foresaw that one day they'd be close. You knew that rumors, suggestions, hints, leaks, always get out, even from Moscow, and there would come a time when even the British would begin to see through their illusions and begin to suspect an agent in their midst.

"And so you recruited *two* agents. Deep and shallow. Or no. No, I see it now." He spoke more quickly, with the excitement of a mathematician suddenly understanding some subtlety of calculus that had been beyond him for years. "Julian was not your agent. He was your lover but never your agent. As I am your agent but never your lover. Because you knew that anyone who investigated

Cambridge in the year 1931 would uncover you. And so you would have to lead them to Julian and not me."

Levitsky stared passionately at the boy with his good eye.

The boy did not seem to be able to stop talking because he would never talk of it again: it was the pleasure of explaining that he had denied himself and would go on denying himself for years.

"And when you learned that Lemontov had gone and the British and the Americans knew, it was essential that you confirm for them their suspicion that Julian was the man you had recruited."

"And they sent poor Florry. And you crossed hell to reach Julian in Florry's presence. And Florry informed them of his guilt. Florry validated their own illusions for them. And then you made certain that Julian would die, forever sealed off from their interrogations, forever beyond their reach. The case is closed. Forever. The British have their spy and I have my future."

The young man paused, as if to breathe.

"They are pleased now," he said. "I'm due back in London shortly. I'm going into their service full time. It's good, I think, to enter before the war with Hitler. The service will swell, and the ones on the inside will rise."

The door opened.

"Almost time," called Pavel Romanov.

The young man came closer and spoke in a whisper.

"I've been reporting to them from Spain. Through a special GRU link via Amsterdam. For the Suppression, the Arrests. It was _my_ information that enabled them to—" But he halted, as if coming at last to the thing that troubled him most.

"It's not only that. Do you know what else they've had me do? Do you know why I'm here in Spain? For gold, Ivanch. For simple gold."

Levitsky stared at him.

"They had me rent a villa and one night a truck came by with a hundred crates. And then another one and another one. I've been

the richest man in the world. Romanov said they were afraid to move it by sea with the submarines and afraid to guard it because the Spaniards might change their mind and want it back. So they hid it. In my villa. All these months, my real job has been to babysit gold, until an airplane could be modified. Now they can fly it out, nonstop, over a few nights."

Levitksy said nothing.

"It's just like the West, Ivanch. It's for treasure, for loot. There's no difference. I *hate* it."

"Shhh!" Levitsky hissed, grabbing his hand tightly.

"I *hate* it," the boy said. And then David Harold Allen Sampson began to weep.

"You must control yourself," said Levitsky hoarsely. "You must pay the price. You must sacrifice. It is not enough to be willing to die for your beliefs. That's a fool's sacrifice. You must be willing to kill for them, too. To free the world of its Cossacks, you must be willing to spill blood now, do you understand? I sacrificed my brother. I sacrificed my lover. I sacrificed the man who saved my life. I sacrificed myself. It's the process of history, comrade."

He grabbed the boy and pulled his head close and kissed him on the lips.

"Time," called Pavel Romanov.

"You must reach the back rank," said Levitsky, "and give the innocent dead their due."

The door opened and he could hear Pavel approach.

The boy whispered a last statement.

"I no longer believe in it, Emmanuel Ivanovich Levitsky, in any of it, revolutions, politics, history. It's all just murder and theft. But I have found a new faith to sustain me over the years. I believe in *you*. I love you."

The boy slipped away into the darkness.

Pavel rolled the wheelchair across the hangar toward the aircraft, chatting idiotically.

"I hope that wasn't too hard on you, old man. He quite insisted.

What a hero that one is. You recruited well, old fox. You recruited quality. GRU understands, even if Koba and NKVD do not," said Pavel. "We will sacrifice anything to save him, even you, old hero. For that young man is the future."

And I am the past, thought the Devil Himself, as they passed under the shadow of the great wing.

44

A WALK IN THE PARK

I N THE END, THE GENDARMERIE CARED LESS FOR THE BODY
than the pistol. Florry explained—endlessly—that it had been
his assailant's, that he had never seen it before he was set upon
and it was just the sheerest luck that he'd managed to get hold
of it in the scuffle. He was detained three nights in Limoges, the
next city along the line after the incident, while they tried to figure
out what to do with him and while Sylvia recovered in hospital. He
was ultimately levied a stiff fine by a skeptical prefecture and ad-
monished to leave the province swiftly, which he proposed to do as
soon as Sylvia could travel.

As for the body of the mysterious assailant, its papers proved
false and nobody would claim it and nobody could explain it. Florry
offered no precise opinions as to who this person had been: a crazed
thief, perhaps, clearly someone with dreadful mental difficulties.
The body was disposed of in a pauper's field without ceremony by
an undertaker and his teenage assistant. Its effects—including the
grip, which, unknown to them all, contained a good deal of money
as well as further false papers—simply disappeared in the uncaring
clumsiness of the French rail system.

Sylvia kept telling Florry to go on and that she would catch up
to him in Paris, but he insisted on staying. When her swelling had
finally gone down, and she was released from the hospital, he
suggested they go for a walk in the park. He had a question, he
said, and he had to ask it, he had to know the answer.

It was by this time July, a gloriously beautiful day, not as hot as

the French Julys can be but sunny and bold. No country seems more alive in the sunlight than France, and they spent that afternoon walking around in a beautiful park until at last they came to a bench hard by a pond in a glade of poplars. The air was full of dust and light and the birds were singing.

"God, it's lovely here," said Sylvia.

"Sylvia, there's something I have to ask you."

Sylvia sighed.

"I must say, I knew this was coming. I'm afraid I know what you're going to say, Robert. That you love me. That you want to marry me. That—"

She turned to him. "Robert," she said, "you're an awfully fine fellow. You saved my life. Twice, in fact. But—"

"Actually, Sylvia," he said, "the question I had was something else: how long have you been working for Major Holly-Browning?"

She missed a beat, then smiled.

"Robert, I'm afraid I haven't—"

He interrupted her. "You really are a little slut, aren't you, darling? The major's whore, sent to make sure poor Florry does his dirty deed. You never cared for me, except as a tool, as someone to be used. Give the old bastard credit, he saw my weaknesses. He knew how vulnerable I'd be to a sweet-faced tart who kept telling me what an impressive chap I was, who'd give me a bloody toss between the sheets. It was quite a performance, darling, especially the way you suddenly veered toward Julian and made me crazy with jealousy and made the job everybody so wanted done seem feasible. God, you deserve some kind of award."

"Robert, I—"

"You must have thought it quite comical when I confessed I was a 'British agent.' You must have felt the contempt a professional feels for a feckless, hapless amateur with delusions of grandeur. But it finally penetrated, Sylvia. Do you know where you went wrong, old girl? The bloody apartment. Sampson had a villa, for some damned reason. I recall him telling me. That wasn't *his* place we went to, it was yours. The major had it set up to get *you* out, not

me. That's how they had your picture for the passport. Yes, you were the major's little secret weapon, eh?"

"Robert, stop. You're all wrong, it's—"

"You pathetic little quim. It must have been hard, Sylvia, hanging around that dangerous city that week, waiting. But you weren't waiting for me, were you? You were waiting for word on Julian's death. You had to know. That was the last part of your job, to make certain the poor bastard was dead."

She stared stonily out across the pond. The terrible thing was that even now she looked beautiful to him. He wished he could hold her to him and make real his last illusion: that a better world could be theirs.

"Then you were too bloody good on the way out! You had it all figured. You'd gone over the route, you knew how to handle everything. You are something, Sylvia, I must say, you are a piece of work."

She turned back, eyes gray green, face tight and beautiful. She smelled so wonderful.

"I don't work for your major, Robert," she said. "I swear to God to you I don't." She took a deep breath. "It's what's called MI-5, actually," she said. "Security Service. We go after traitors, Robert. That's our job. Yes, I spied on you, because I thought you were my country's enemy. That is the truth. Without illusions and, damn you, without apologies."

"Poor Julian. He thought we were both his friends. With friends like us, the poor sot hardly needed enemies."

"He was a traitor, Robert. You reported so yourself in *Tristram Shandy*."

"I was wrong. I leaped to a conclusion. I made a mistake."

"No, you weren't wrong. No matter how brave he was at that bridge and how he chummed up to you, he was a Russian agent. No matter what he told you, the truth was, he was working for the Russians. He was a spy, Robert. He was the enemy. And you wouldn't have had the guts to deal with him if I hadn't played my little game. Yes, Robert, I made you a killer. You killed Julian

because I made you. Because it was the right thing. You couldn't see your duty, but I saw mine."

"You and all the rest of the voodoo boys, you're wrong. About Julian. About everything. Julian was the only one that was right. He knew. In the end, it was just a game."

"Stop it, Robert. You're still an innocent."

"Sylvia," he said. "You are my last illusion, and my most painful one. God, you're a cold bitch."

"Somebody has to be, darling," she said, turning back to the water, "so that the silly fools like you can write your silly books and feel as if you've done something for your country. It's the Sylvia Lillifords and the Vernon Kells and the MI-5s that make the world safe for the fools like you, Robert. You really are the most perfect ass I've ever met."

But he could see that she was crying.

"Good-bye, darling."

"No, don't you leave, you bastard," she spat at him. "I'll tell it all. I went to Spain to get them. To get them all, all those clever, bright, pretty young people in the Hotel Falcon who think revolution is so beautiful and communism is a new religion. Yes, I got them all, by name and by number, and it all goes back to the MI-5 files. They're dead in England, and they don't know it. And I'll get you, Robert, I will. You think you're going to write a book about all this, Robert? Well, we'll stop you. With Official Secrets, we'll close you down. You'll never publish anything, Robert. You're done, before you've even begun, God damn you, you're just like them. Soft, a dreamer, ready to piss on your inheritance."

Florry looked at her, and realized how full of hate she was, how she was nothing, in the end, except a kind of terrible hate.

"You've made me a clever boy, Sylvia. You've taught me some very interesting lessons about the future. And I don't think you'll stop me writing what I know. The funny thing is, darling, I still love you."

He smiled, then stood up and walked away, wondering if it would ever stop hurting.

✦ ✦ ✦

Florry went back to England and presented Julian's mother with the ring. The old lady was still beautiful and she lived in a glorious town house all hung with pictures of the Raines men down through the ages, but the thing did not seem to mean much to her. She simply put it on the table and did not look at it again. She did not appear to have been crying much, but then weeks had passed since the news.

"Did my son die well, Mr. Florry?" she asked.

"Yes," said Florry.

"I thought he might have. It's a gift the Raines men all seem to have," she said. "They are perfect rotters in life, but they die well. It was true of his father. Would you care for some tea?"

"No ma'am. I'd best be going."

"Do you know, they're saying awful things about my son. That he was a traitor. Have you heard these stories?"

"Yes, I've heard the stories. They're untrue. No man knows that better than I."

"Good. Well, if you know that, it's a start, one supposes. Are you sure you won't stay?"

"No, thank you."

"Good-bye, Mr. Florry."

"Good-bye, Lady Cecilia."

And then she added, "Tell the truth, won't you?"

"I shall try," he said.

"You do know what the truth is, don't you, Mr. Florry?"

"I think I do, yes," Florry said.

"Incidentally, they sent me something from Spain. It was some poetry that Julian was working on before he died. I can't think why. I always hated Julian's poetry, and this last I can't begin to understand. I believe the work was called 'Pons.' I'd like you to have it."

"Well, I really—"

"Please, Mr. Florry. I insist. You gave me the silly ring, now let me give you his last verse, all right?"

Florry waited patiently until the old lady returned, and took the foolscap. Yes, come to think of it, he'd seen Julian scribbling away in their little bunker in the trenches.

He thanked her, took it, and left.

Only later, in his little bed-sitting room, did he look at it.

> *To the trenches outside Huesca,*
> *We came as comrades but stayed as lovers.*
> *Our fingers froze, our rifles jammed,*
> *And when we died, were doubly damned,*
> *for History had passed to others.*
>
> *It had no lesson, or only one:*
> *that the test was ours and had begun.*

ACKNOWLEDGMENTS

The author would like to thank those who gave so generously of their time and their imaginations. First, thanks to Ernie Erber, who actually spent part of 1936 in Barcelona. Thanks to Mike Hill and Joe Fanzone for valuable early consultations; they see their ideas reflected on every page of the book. Thanks to Fred Rasmussen, of *The Sun* library, for digging out the Spanish Civil War photos that were of so much help; Antero Pietila of *The Sun*'s Moscow bureau, for unearthing the location, size, and architecture of the Hotel Lux; to another colleague, Matt Sieden, for his kind words and good suggestions. Thanks to my old college roommate, Lenne Miller, for his enthusiasms for the book. Thanks to my mother, Virginia Hunter, and my brother, Tim Hunter, for their comments and patience; and to my brother-in-law, medical consultant, and good friend, John D. Bullock, M.D. Thanks to David Petzal for his reading. Thanks to the night-shift concierge at the Hotel Colón in Barcelona for numerous courtesies and unfailing good humor. Thanks to Jeff Bass, for suggesting the epigram from the Mason book. And to Susan Carnochan and Zita Dabars, for assistance with my Spanish. Thanks especially to my courageous and stubborn agent, Victoria Gould Pryor, who believed in this book from the very start and fought for it as if it were her own; and to my brilliant editor, Barbara Grossman, of Crown, for her quotient of belief and her refusal to accept anything less than my best. And thanks—special thanks—to my wife, Lucy Hageman Hunter, for her glamourless, thankless, and yet heroic efforts on behalf of this book. Needless to say, errors are entirely my own.